PRENTICE HALL

SCIENCE EXPLORER

GET READY FOR A CONTENT-RICH, HANDS-ON EXPLORATION!

Teacher's Edition

PRENTICE HALL

SCIENCE EXPLORER

Cells and Heredity

PRENTICE HALL
Needham, Massachusetts
Upper Saddle River, New Jersey

ISBN 0-13-429192-1
2 3 4 5 6 7 8 9 10   03 02 01 00 99

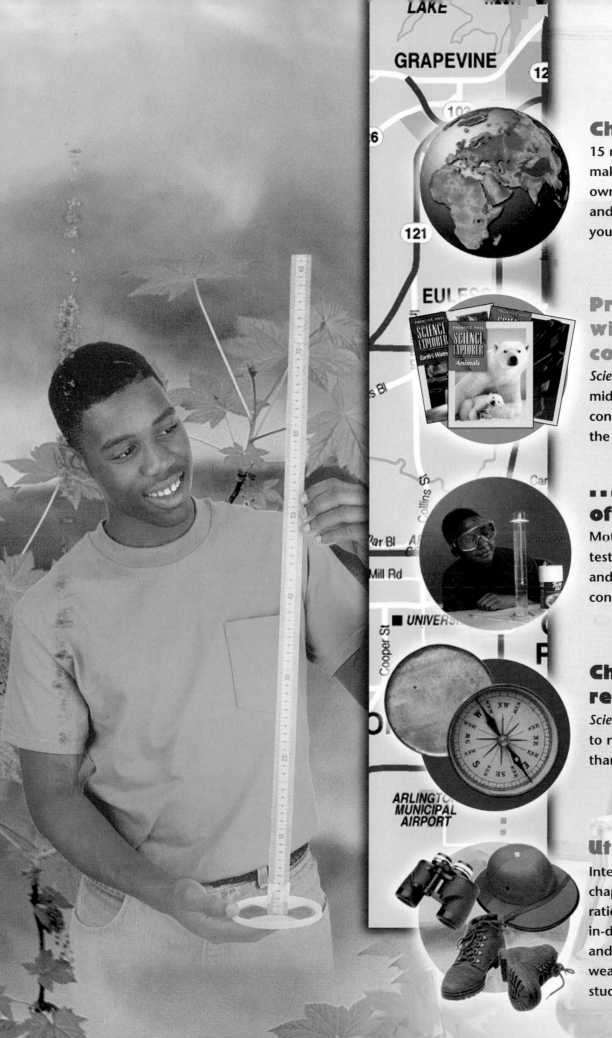

Chart your own course.

15 motivational hardcover books make it easy for you to create your own curriculum; meet local, state, and national guidelines; and teach your favorite topics in depth.

Prepare your students with rich, motivating content...

Science Explorer is crafted for today's middle grades student, with accessible content and in-depth coverage of all the important concepts.

...and a wide variety of inquiry activities.

Motivational student- and teacher-tested activities reinforce key concepts and allow students to explore science concepts for themselves.

Check your compass regularly.

Science Explorer gives you more ways to regularly check student performance than any other program available.

Utilize a variety of tools.

Integrated science sections in every chapter and Interdisciplinary Explorations in every book allow you to make in-depth connections to other sciences and disciplines. Plus, you will find a wealth of additional tools to set your students on a successful course.

h rt th   ours ou   t ith
15 motivating books that
easily match your curriculum.

Each book in the series contains:

- Integrated Science sections in every chapter
- Interdisciplinary Explorations for team teaching at the end of each book
- Comprehensive skills practice and application—assuring that you meet the National Science Education Standards and your local and state standards

For custom binding options, see your local sales representative.

EXPLORATION TOOLS: BASIC PROCESS SKILLS

Observing

Measuring

Calculating

Classifying

Predicting

Inferring

Graphing

Creating data tables

Communicating

LIFE SCIENCE TITLES

From Bacteria to Plants
1 Living Things
2 Viruses and Bacteria
3 Protists and Fungi
4 Introduction to Plants
5 Seed Plants

Animals
1 Sponges, Cnidarians, and Worms
2 Mollusks, Arthropods, and Echinoderms
3 Fishes, Amphibians, and Reptiles
4 Birds and Mammals
5 Animal Behavior

Cells and Heredity
1 Cell Structure and Function
2 Cell Processes and Energy
3 Genetics: The Science of Heredity
4 Modern Genetics
5 Changes Over Time

Human Biology and Health
1 Healthy Body Systems
2 Bones, Muscles, and Skin
3 Food and Digestion
4 Circulation
5 Respiration and Excretion
6 Fighting Disease
7 The Nervous System
8 The Endocrine System and Reproduction

Environmental Science
1 Populations and Communities
2 Ecosystems and Biomes
3 Living Resources
4 Land and Soil Resources
5 Air and Water Resources
6 Energy Resources

Integrated Science sections in every chapter

Posing questions

Forming operational definitions

Developing hypotheses

Controlling variables

Interpreting data

Interpreting graphs

Making models

Drawing conclusions

Designing experiments

 Integrated Science sections in every chapter

Place your students in the role of science explorer through a variety of inquiry activities.

Motivational student- and teacher-tested activities reinforce key concepts and allow students to explore science concepts for themselves. More than 350 activities are provided for each book in the Student Edition, Teacher's Edition, Teaching Resources, Integrated Science Lab Manual, Inquiry Skills Activity Book, Interactive Student Tutorial CD-ROM, and *Science Explorer* Web Site.

STUDENT EDITION ACTIVITIES

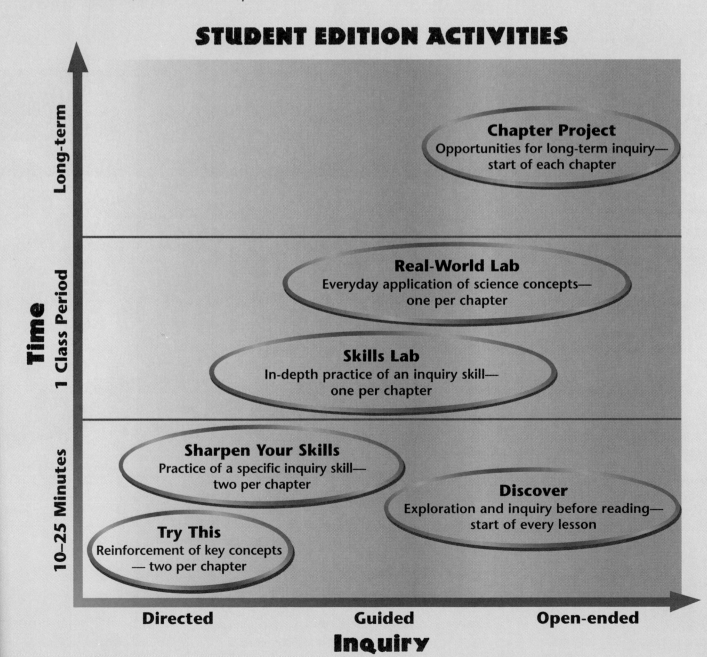

Time

Long-term

1 Class Period

10–25 Minutes

Chapter Project
Opportunities for long-term inquiry—
start of each chapter

Real-World Lab
Everyday application of science concepts—
one per chapter

Skills Lab
In-depth practice of an inquiry skill—
one per chapter

Sharpen Your Skills
Practice of a specific inquiry skill—
two per chapter

Discover
Exploration and inquiry before reading—
start of every lesson

Try This
Reinforcement of key concepts
— two per chapter

Directed   Guided   Open-ended

Inquiry

...c...ur c—m..ss r...ul..rly with integrated assessment tools.

Prepare for state exams with traditional and performance-based assessment.

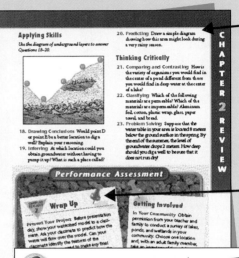

- **Comprehensive Chapter Reviews** include a wide range of question types that students will encounter on standardized tests. Types include multiple choice, enhanced true/false, concept mastery, visual thinking, skill application, and critical thinking. Also includes Chapter Project "Wrap Up."

- **Chapter Projects** contain rubrics that allow you to easily assess student progress.

- **Section Reviews** provide "Check your Progress" opportunities for the Chapter Project, as well as review questions for the section.

Additional Science Explorer assessment resources:

- **Assessment Resources with CD-ROM**
- **Resource Pro® with Planning Express® CD-ROM**
- **Standardized Test Practice Book**
- **On-line review activities** at www.phschool.com

See page T9 for complete product descriptions.

Self-assessment opportunities help students keep themselves on course.

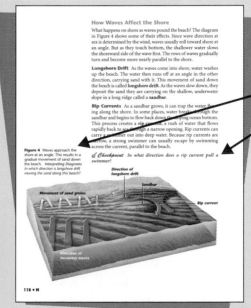

- **Caption Questions** throughout the text assess critical thinking skills.

- **Checkpoint Questions** give students an immediate content check as new concepts are presented.

- **Interactive Student Tutorial CD-ROM** provides students with electronic self-tests, review activities, and Exploration activities.

- **Got It! Video Quizzes** motivate and challenge students with engaging animations and interactive questions.

- **www.science-explorer.phschool.com** provides additional support and on-line test prep.

Utiliz___ wi__e v__ri__t_ of tools.

Easy-to-manage, book-specific teaching resources

15 Teaching Resource Packages, each containing a Student Edition, Teacher's Edition, Teaching Resources with Color Transparencies, Guided Reading Audiotape, Materials Kit Order form, and Correlation to the National Science Education Standards.

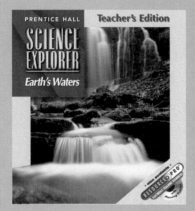

15 Teacher's Editions with a three-step lesson plan—*Engage/Explore, Facilitate,* and *Assess*—that is ideal for reaching all students. Chapter planning charts make it easy to find resources, as well as to plan for block scheduling and team teaching.

15 Teaching Resource Books with Color Transparencies offer complete support organized by chapter to make it easy for you to find what you need—when you need it.

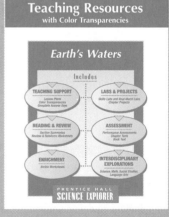

15 Guided Reading Audiotapes (English and Spanish) provide section summaries for students who need additional support.

15 Explorer Videotapes allow students to explore concepts through spectacular short videos containing computer animations. Available in Spanish.

1. **Materials Kits**—Prentice Hall and Science Kit, Inc. have collaborated to develop a Consumable Kit and Nonconsumable Kit for each book. Ordering software makes it easy to customize!

2&3. **Integrated Science Laboratory Manual with Teacher's Edition**—74 in-depth labs covering the entire curriculum, with complete teaching support.

4. **Inquiry Skills Activity Book**—additional activities to teach, practice, and assess a wide range of inquiry skills.

5. **Student-Centered Science Activities**—five activity books for the Northeast, Southeast, Midwest, Southwest, and West.

6. **Program Planning Guide**—course outlines, block scheduling pacing charts, correlations, and more.

7. **Product Testing Activities by *Consumer Reports***—19 student-oriented testing activities turn students into real-world explorers.

Additional print resources...
8. **Reading in the Content Area**—with Literature Connections
9. **Standardized Test Practice**—review and self-tests to prepare for statewide exams.
10. **15 Prentice Hall Interdisciplinary Explorations**
11. **How to Assess Student Work**
12. **How to Manage Instruction in the Block**
13. ***Cobblestone, Odyssey, Calliope,* and *Faces* Magazines**

Program-wide technology resources

1. **Resource Pro® CD-ROM**—the ultimate management tool with easy access to blackline masters and lab activities for all 15 books. Planning Express® software lets you customize lesson plans by day, week, month, and year. Also includes Computer Test Bank software.

2. **Assessment Resources with CD-ROM**—*Computer Test Bank* software with Dial-A-Test® provides you with unparalleled flexibility in creating tests.

3. *Science Explorer* **Web Site**—activities and teaching resources for every chapter at www.science-explorer.phschool.com

4. **Interactive Student Tutorial CD-ROMs**—provide students with self-tests, helpful hints, and Explorations. Tests are scored instantly and provide complete explanations to all answers.

5. **An Odyssey of Discovery CD-ROMs**—interactive labs encourage students to hypothesize and experiment. (Life and Earth Science).

6. **Interactive Earth CD-ROM**—explore global trends, search the media library, and zoom in on a 3-D globe.

7. **Mindscape CD-ROMs**—*The Animals!™, Oceans Below,* and *How Your Body Works* bring science alive with compelling videoclips, 3-D animations, and interactive databases.

8. **A.D.A.M. The Inside Story**—take an entertaining tour of each body system, designed for middle grades students.

9. **Interactive Physics**—explore physics concepts with computer simulations that encourage what-if questions.

10. **Explorer Videotapes and Videodiscs**—explore and visualize concepts through spectacular short documentaries containing computer animations (Spanish audio track).

11. **Got It! Video Quizzes**—make in-class review fun and prepare students for book tests and state assessments.

12. **Event-Based Science**—series of NSF-funded modules that engage students with inquiry-based projects. Includes video.

Options for Pacing *Cells and Heredity*

The Pacing Chart below suggests one way to schedule your instructional time. The *Science Explorer* program offers many other aids to help you plan your instructional time, whether regular class periods or **block scheduling**. Refer to the Chapter Planning Guide before each chapter to view all program resources with suggested times for Student Edition activities.

Pacing Chart

	Days	Blocks		Days	Blocks
Nature of Science: Unlocking the Secrets of Cells	1	$\frac{1}{2}$	**4** The DNA Connection	2–3	$1–1\frac{1}{2}$
Chapter 1 Cell Structure and Function			Chapter 3 Review and Assessment	1	$\frac{1}{2}$
Chapter 1 Project Egg-speriment With a Cell	Ongoing	Ongoing	**Chapter 4 Modern Genetics**		
1 Discovering Cells	2–3	$1–1\frac{1}{2}$	Chapter 4 Project A Family Portrait	Ongoing	Ongoing
2 Looking Inside Cells	4–5	$2–2\frac{1}{2}$	**1** Human Inheritance	2–3	$1–1\frac{1}{2}$
3 Integrating Chemistry: Chemical Compounds in Cells	2–3	$1–1\frac{1}{2}$	**2** Human Genetic Disorders	3–4	$1\frac{1}{2}–2$
4 The Cell in Its Environment	2	1	**3** Integrating Technology: Advances in Genetics	3–4	$1\frac{1}{2}–2$
Chapter 1 Review and Assessment	1	$\frac{1}{2}$	Chapter 4 Review and Assessment	1	$\frac{1}{2}$
Chapter 2 Cell Processes and Energy			**Chapter 5 Changes Over Time**		
Chapter 2 Project Shine On!	Ongoing	Ongoing	Chapter 5 Project Life's Long Calendar	Ongoing	Ongoing
1 Photosynthesis	2–3	$1–1\frac{1}{2}$	**1** Darwin's Voyage	4–5	$2–2\frac{1}{2}$
2 Respiration	3–4	$1\frac{1}{2}–2$	**2** Integrating Earth Science: The Fossil Record	2–3	$1–1\frac{1}{2}$
3 Cell Division	4–5	$2–2\frac{1}{2}$	**3** Other Evidence for Evolution	2–3	$1–1\frac{1}{2}$
4 Integrating Health: Cancer	2–3	$1–1\frac{1}{2}$	Chapter 5 Review and Assessment	1	$\frac{1}{2}$
Chapter 2 Review and Assessment	1	$\frac{1}{2}$	Interdisciplinary Exploration: Dogs—Loyal Companions	2–3	1–2
Chapter 3 Genetics: The Science of Heredity					
Chapter 3 Project All In The Family	Ongoing	Ongoing			
1 Mendel's Work	3–4	$1\frac{1}{2}–2$			
2 Integrating Mathematics: Probability and Genetics	3–4	$1\frac{1}{2}–2$			
3 The Cell and Inheritance	2–3	$1–1\frac{1}{2}$			

RESOURCE PRO®

The Resource Pro® CD-ROM is the ultimate scheduling and lesson planning tool. Resource Pro® allows you to preview all the resources in the *Science Explorer* program, organize your chosen materials, and print out any teaching resource. You can follow the suggested lessons or create your own, using resources from anywhere in the program.

Thematic Overview of *Cells and Heredity*

The chart below lists the major themes of *Cells and Heredity*. For each theme, the chart supplies a big idea, or concept statement, describing how a particular theme is taught in a chapter.

	Chapter 1	Chapter 2	Chapter 3	Chapter 4	Chapter 5
Patterns of Change		During photosynthesis, carbon dioxide and water are converted into oxygen and sugars. The regular sequence of growth and division that cells undergo is called the cell cycle.	Individual alleles control the inheritance of traits. During meiosis, a cell undergoes two divisions to produce sex cells with half the number of chromosomes.	The effects of genes are often altered by the environment. Genetic disorders are caused by mutations.	A new species can form when a group of individuals is isolated from the rest of the species. Most fossils form when organisms that die are buried in sediments.
Scale and Structure	Cells are the basic unit of structure and function in living things. Cells have different structures that perform different functions. The cell membrane is selectively permeable.	Photosynthesis occurs inside chloroplasts in the cells of plants and some other organisms. Respiration takes place in the cytoplasm and mitochondria of an organism's cells.	Genes are located on chromosomes. Sex cells have half the normal number of chromosomes. DNA and RNA are made up of nitrogen bases.	The 23 pairs of chromosomes that make up the human genome contain about 60,000 to 80,000 chromosomes.	Homologous structures are similar structures that related species have inherited from a common ancestor.
Unity and Diversity	All living things are composed of cells. Plant cells have cell walls and chloroplasts, while animal cells do not. Organic compounds contain carbon, while most inorganic compounds do not.			Human traits can be controlled by single genes, multiple alleles, or many genes. A genetic disorder is an abnormal condition that a person inherits through genes or chromosomes.	A species is a group of similar organisms that can mate and produce fertile offspring. Two theories of how quickly evolution occurs are gradualism and punctuated equilibria.
Systems and Interactions	Cell organelles produce energy, build and transport materials, and store and recycle wastes. Substances move into and out of a cell by diffusion, osmosis, and active transport.	Through photosynthesis and respiration, the sun's energy is converted into energy that living organisms can use.		Doctors use tools such as amniocentesis and karyotypes to help detect genetic disorders.	Overproduction, competition, and variations affect the process of natural selection.
Evolution			Genes are the basic units of heredity. Genes are carried from parents to offspring on chromosomes. Mutations can be a source of genetic variety.	People have used selective breeding, cloning, and genetic engineering to develop organisms with desirable traits.	Over a long period of time, natural selection can lead to evolution. The fossil record provides clues about how and when new groups of organisms evolved.
Energy	Mitochondria produce most of the energy a cell needs to carry out its functions. Chloroplasts capture energy from the sun and use it to produce food. Carbohydrates and lipids are energy-rich organic compounds.	During photosynthesis, plants and some other organisms use the sun's energy to make food. During respiration, cells break down food molecules and release the energy they contain.			
Stability		Photosynthesis and respiration form a cycle that keeps the levels of oxygen and carbon dioxide fairly constant in the atmosphere.	In the genetic code, a group of three bases codes for the production of a specific amino acid.	A clone is an organism that is genetically identical to the organism from which it was produced.	Natural selection is the survival and reproduction of those organisms best suited to their environment.

Inquiry Skills Chart

The Prentice Hall *Science Explorer* program provides comprehensive teaching, practice, and assessment of science skills, with an emphasis on the process skills necessary for inquiry. The chart lists the skills covered in the program and cites the page numbers where each skill is covered.

Basic Process SKILLS				
	Student Text: Projects and Labs	Student Text: Activities	Student Text: Caption and Review Questions	Teacher's Edition: Extensions
Observing	14–15, 32, 48–49, 69, 86–87, 134	16, 21, 30, 55, 126, 174	47, 160	30, 52, 81, 99, 142, 160, 174
Inferring	32, 124–125, 134	23, 35, 42, 50, 52, 56, 80, 96, 112, 119, 143, 145, 151, 153, 174	47, 77, 84, 100, 109, 137, 167	20, 24, 56, 62, 67, 102, 116, 158, 174
Predicting	14–15, 38–39, 94–95, 146–147, 164	44, 70, 88, 93, 148, 169, 174	28, 36, 41, 47, 68, 77, 103, 109, 137, 167	174
Classifying	69, 124–125	140, 159, 175	34, 67, 93, 100, 118	17, 92, 175
Making Models	78–79, 94–95, 110–111, 124–125, 134, 138–139, 146–147, 164	29, 63, 116, 175		53, 98, 105, 175
Communicating	138–139	19, 25, 47, 77, 109, 121, 131, 137, 148, 172, 175	46, 76, 108, 136, 166	56, 132, 144, 156, 175
Measuring	14–15, 48–49	22, 176–177		176–177
Calculating	69, 78–79, 110–111, 138–139, 146–147	89, 93, 154, 169	21, 89, 91, 109, 137, 167	19, 37, 63, 71, 90, 93, 114
Creating Data Tables	38–39, 94–95	184		184
Graphing	14–15, 48–49	184–185	77	184–185
Advanced Process SKILLS				
Posing Questions	48–49	178		178
Developing Hypotheses	86–87	40, 61, 178		178
Designing Experiments	14–15, 38–39, 48–49, 86–87, 146–147	114, 179		179
Controlling Variables	48–49, 60	179		179
Forming Operational Definitions		33, 101, 179		179

Advanced Process SKILLS (continued)

	Student Text: Projects and Labs	Student Text: Activities	Student Text: Caption and Review Questions	Teacher's Edition: Extensions
Interpreting Data	15, 60, 69, 79, 164	66, 91, 173, 179	77, 137	162, 179
Drawing Conclusions	38, 39, 49, 79, 86, 87, 134	160, 179	109, 137, 167	179

Critical Thinking SKILLS

Comparing and Contrasting	32, 60	31, 180	17, 47, 77, 137, 142, 158, 167	24, 36, 58, 121, 155, 180
Applying Concepts	146, 147	56, 117, 148, 180	22, 47, 51, 54, 58, 77, 81, 85, 97, 109, 137, 150, 167	84, 180
Interpreting Diagrams, Graphs Photographs, and Maps	134, 164	63, 115, 170–171, 173, 180	25, 43, 53, 58, 72, 83, 90, 98, 102, 113, 149, 152, 154, 163	155, 180
Relating Cause and Effect	14–15, 48–49, 60, 146–147	181	47, 71, 73, 106, 120, 167	43, 120, 181
Making Generalizations		181	47, 77, 127, 144	181
Making Judgments	134	74, 133, 181	36, 130, 132, 163	181
Problem Solving	124–125	93, 181	109, 123, 137	117, 153, 181

Information Organizing SKILLS

Concept Maps		182	46, 136	45, 67, 182
Compare/ Contrast Tables		182	108	57, 182
Venn Diagrams		183		43, 183
Flowcharts		183	166	53, 183
Cycle Diagrams		183	76	183

The *Science Explorer* program provides additional teaching, reinforcement, and assessment of skills in the Inquiry Skills Activities Book and the Integrated Science Laboratory Manual.

Throughout the *Science Explorer* program, every effort has been made to keep the materials and equipment *affordable, reusable,* and *easily accessible.*

The *Science Explorer* program offers an abundance of activity options so you can pick and choose those activities that suit your needs. To help you order supplies at the beginning of the year, the Master Materials List cross-references the materials by activity. If you prefer to create your list electronically, use the electronic order forms at:
www.science–explorer.phschool.com

There are two kits available for each book of the *Science Explorer* program, a Consumable Kit and a Nonconsumable Kit. These kits are produced by **Science Kit and Boreal Laboratories,** the leader in providing science kits to schools. Prentice Hall and Science Kit collaborated throughout the development of *Science Explorer* to ensure that the equipment and supplies in the kits precisely match the requirements of the program activities.

The kits provide an economical and convenient way to get all of the materials needed to teach each book. For each book, Science Kit also offers the opportunity to buy equipment and safety items individually. For a current listing of kit offerings or additional information about materials to accompany *Science Explorer*, please, contact Science Kit at:
1-800-828-7777
or at their Internet site at:
www.sciencekit.com

Master Materials List

Consumable Materials

*	Description	Quantity per class	Textbook Section(s)	*	Description	Quantity per class	Textbook Section(s)
SS	Air Freshener	1	1-4 (DIS)	C	Food Coloring, Dark Red, 30 mL, In Dropper Bottle	1	1-4 (TT)
C	Alcohol, Isopropyl (Rubbing), 500 mL	1	2-1 (SYS)	SS	Food Samples, Assortment	5	1-3 (Lab)
C	Bag, Paper, 10 × 20 × 7.5 cm	25	1-3 (Lab) 3-2 (Lab) 4-1 (TT)	SS	Fresh Fruit, Assortment	5	5-2 (TT)
				C	Gelatin, Box of 4 Packets	2	1-2 (TT)
C	Baking Soda, 454 g	1	1-3 (DIS)	SS	Graph Paper, Sheet	5	4-1 (DIS)
SS	Bird Seed, Pkg.	1	5-1 (TT)	C	Ink Pad, Washable (Black)	5	4-3 (DIS)
C	Bromothymol Blue Sodium Salt, Indicator Powder, 1 g	1	2-2 (Lab)	C	Iodine (Starch Test) Reagent, 100mL Solution	1	1-3 (Lab)
C	Cards, Index, Blank, 3" × 5", Pkg/100	1	4-2 (Lab)	C	Labels, Pressure Sensitive, Roll/100	1	1-3 (DIS)
C	Chalk, White, Pkg/12	1	1-3 (DIS)	SS	Leaf	5	2-1 (SYS)
C	Cornstarch, 500 g	1	1-3 (Lab)	SS	Marker	5	4-2 (Lab) 5-1 (Lab)
SS	Cracker, Unsalted	30	1-3 (TT)	C	Marking Pencil, Black Wax	5	2-2 (Lab) 3-2 (Lab)
C	Cup, Plastic, Clear, Cocktail, 9 oz	50	1-3 (DIS) 1-3 (Lab) 1-4 (TT) 2-1 (SYS) 5-1 (TT) 5-2 (TT)	SS	Materials that Resemble Cell Organelles, Set	5	1-2 (TT)
				C	Methylene Blue Chloride Stain, 100 mL, 1% Aqueous Solution	1	2-3 (DIS)
C	*Elodea* (12 Sprigs), Coupon	2	1-2 (Lab) 2-2 (Lab)	SS	Newspaper	1	1-1 (DIS)
C	Filters, Coffee, Box/100	1	2-1 (SYS)		Oil, Vegetable, 16 oz	1	1-3 (Lab)

KEY: **DIS**: Discover; **SYS**: Sharpen Your Skills; **TT**: Try This; **Lab**: Lab
Quantities based on 5 lab groups per class.
* Items designated **C** are in the Consumable Kit, **NC** are in the Nonconsumable Kit, and **SS** are School Supplied.

Master Materials List

Consumable Materials (cont.)

*	Description	Quantity per class	Textbook Section(s)
SS	Paper, Construction, Asst, Pkg/50	1	2-3 (TT) 5-1 (Lab)
SS	Paper, Sheet	60	1-2 (TT) 3-3 (DIS) 4-3 (DIS) 5-1 (SYS)
SS	Pencils, Colored, Pkg/12	5	1-2 (Lab) 2-3 (Lab)
SS	Pens, Variety	40	5-3 (DIS)
C	Pipe Cleaners, Assorted Colors, 6", Pkg/110	1	2-3 (TT)
C	Plates, Paper, 9", Pkg/50	1	5-1 (TT)
C	Pond Culture, Mixed, Coupon	1	1-1 (SYS)
C	PTC Taste Paper, Vial/100	1	3-1 (Lab)

*	Description	Quantity per class	Textbook Section(s)
SS	Raisins, Box	1	5-1 (TT)
C	Salt, Non-Iodized, 737 g	1	1-3 (DIS)
C	Seeds, Sunflower, 30 g (Approx. 200 seeds)	1	5-1 (DIS)
C	Sticks, Craft, Pkg/30	1	3-3 (DIS)
C	Stirrer Sticks, Pkg/50	1	1-3 (Lab)
C	Straws, Plastic (Wrapped), Pkg/50	1	2-2 (DIS) 2-2 (Lab)
C	Sugar, Granulated, 454 g	1	2-2 (DIS)
SS	Sunblock	1	1-3 (DIS)
SS	Tape, Masking, 3/4" × 60 yd	1	2-4 (DIS) 3-2 (TT)
SS	Yeast, Pkg.		2-2 (DIS) 2-3 (DIS)

Nonconsumable Materials

*	Description	Quantity per class	Textbook Section(s)
SS	Bar Codes, Set	5	4-3 (Lab)
NC	Beads, Plastic, 3/8", Pkg/144 (Assorted colors)	1	3-2 (Lab) 4-1 (TT)
NC	Chips, Black, Pkg/50	2	5-1 (SYS)
NC	Chips, White, Pkg/350	1	5-1 (SYS)
SS	Clock or Watch	1	5-1 (TT) 5-1 (SYS)
NC	Clothespin, Spring Type	5	5-1 (TT)
SS	Coin	10	3-2 (DIS) 3-2 (TT)
NC	Cylinder, Graduated, Polypropylene, 10 × 0.2 mL	5	1-3 (Lab) 2-2 (DIS)
NC	Cylinder, Graduated, Polypropylene, 100 mL	5	2-2 (Lab)
SS	Dime	5	2-1 (SYS)

*	Description	Quantity per class	Textbook Section(s)
NC	Dropper, Plastic	5	1-1 (SYS) 1-2 (Lab) 1-3 (Lab) 1-4 (TT) 2-3 (DIS)
NC	Dropping Bottle, Barnes, 30 mL	5	1-3 (Lab)
NC	Flask, Erlenmeyer, Pyrex, 250 mL	15	2-2 (Lab)
NC	Forceps, Tweezers, Fine Tip, 115 mm	5	1-2 (Lab) 5-1 (TT)
SS	Hair Clips	5	5-1 (TT)
SS	Light Source	1	2-2 (Lab)
NC	Magnifying Glass, 3x, 6x	5	1-1 (DIS) 5-1 (DIS)
NC	Meter Stick, Half (50 cm in length)	5	2-4 (DIS) 4-1 (DIS)

KEY: **DIS**: Discover; **SYS**: Sharpen Your Skills; **TT**: Try This; **Lab**: Lab
* Items designated **C** are in the Consumable Kit, **NC** are in the Nonconsumable Kit, and **SS** are School Supplied.

Nonconsumable Materials (cont.)

*	Description	Quantity per class	Textbook Section(s)	*	Description	Quantity per class	Textbook Section(s)
NC	Mirror, Plastic, 7.5 × 12.5 cm, (With Beveled Edges and ground corners)	5	3-1 (Lab)	NC	Stopper, Rubber, Size 6, Solid, Lb.	1	2-2 (Lab)
NC	Pan, Aluminum Foil, 11 × 21 × 6 cm (bread pan)	5	1-2 (TT)	NC	Test Tube Support, Wood, Holds six, 21mm tubes, w/6 drying pins	5	2-2 (DIS)
NC	Pan, Aluminum Foil, 22.5 cm Diam (pie pan)	5	1-2 (TT)	NC	Test Tube, 18 × 150 mm, 27 mL	10	2-2 (DIS)
NC	Pins, Bobby, Card/60	1	5-1 (TT)				

Equipment

*	Description	Quantity per class	Textbook Section(s)

*	Description	Quantity per class	Textbook Section(s)
SS	Ruler, Plastic, 12"/30 cm	5	1-2 (DIS) 5-1 (DIS)
SS	Scissors	5	1-1 (DIS) 2-1 (SYS) 4-2 (Lab) 5-1 (Lab)
NC	Slide, Allium (Onion root tip)	5	2-3 (Lab)
NC	Slide, Animal Cell, General Type	5	1-2 (Lab)
NC	Slide, Cork Section	5	1-1 (SYS)
NC	Slides, Plastic & Coverglass Set (Includes 72 plastic slides & 100 coverglasses)	1	1-1 (SYS) 1-2 (Lab) 2-3 (DIS)
NC	Stopper, Rubber, Size 2, Solid	10	2-2 (DIS)

*	Description	Quantity per class	Textbook Section(s)
SS	Apron, Vinyl	30	1-3 (Lab) 2-2 (Lab)
SS	Balance, Triple Beam	5	1-3 (Lab)
SS	Calculator, Light-Powered	5	2-1 (DIS) 2-3 (Lab)
SS	Goggles, Chemical Splash—Class Set	1	1-3 (Lab) 2-2 (DIS) 2-2 (Lab)
SS	Microscope	5	1-1 (DIS) 1-1 (SYS) 1-2 (Lab) 2-3 (DIS) 2-3 (Lab)

KEY: **DIS**: Discover; **SYS**: Sharpen Your Skills; **TT**: Try This; **Lab**: Lab
* Items designated **C** are in the Consumable Kit, **NC** are in the Nonconsumable Kit, and **SS** are School Supplied.

PRENTICE HALL SCIENCE EXPLORER

Cells and Heredity

Program Resources

Student Edition
Annotated Teacher's Edition
Teaching Resources Book with Color Transparencies
Cells and Heredity Materials Kits

Program Components

Integrated Science Laboratory Manual
Integrated Science Laboratory Manual, Teacher's Edition
Inquiry Skills Activity Book
Student-Centered Science Activity Books
Program Planning Guide
Guided Reading English Audiotapes
Guided Reading Spanish Audiotapes and Summaries
Product Testing Activities by Consumer Reports™
Event-Based Science Series (NSF funded)
Prentice Hall Interdisciplinary Explorations
Cobblestone, Odyssey, Calliope, and *Faces* Magazines

Media/Technology

Science Explorer Interactive Student Tutorial CD-ROMs
Odyssey of Discovery CD-ROMs
Resource Pro® (Teaching Resources on CD-ROM)
Assessment Resources CD-ROM with Dial-A-Test®
Internet site at www.science-explorer.phschool.com
Life, Earth, and Physical Science Videodiscs
Life, Earth, and Physical Science Videotapes
Got It! Video Quizzes

Science Explorer Student Editions

From Bacteria to Plants

Animals

Cells and Heredity

Human Biology and Health

Environmental Science

Inside Earth

Earth's Changing Surface

Earth's Waters

Weather and Climate

Astronomy

Chemical Building Blocks

Chemical Interactions

Motion, Forces, and Energy

Electricity and Magnetism

Sound and Light

Staff Credits

The people who made up the *Science Explorer* team—representing editorial, editorial services, design services, field marketing, market research, marketing services, on-line services/multimedia development, product marketing, production services, and publishing processes—are listed below. Bold type denotes core team members.

Kristen E. Ball, **Barbara A. Bertell,** Peter W. Brooks, **Christopher R. Brown, Greg Cantone,** Jonathan Cheney, **Patrick Finbarr Connolly,** Loree Franz, Donald P. Gagnon, Jr., **Paul J. Gagnon, Joel Gendler,** Elizabeth Good, Kerri Hoar, **Linda D. Johnson,** Katherine M. Kotik, Russ Lappa, Marilyn Leitao, David Lippman, **Eve Melnechuk, Natania Mlawer,** Paul W. Murphy, **Cindy A. Noftle,** Julia F. Osborne, Caroline M. Power, Suzanne J. Schineller, **Susan W. Tafler,** Kira Thaler-Marbit, Robin L. Santel, Ronald Schachter, **Mark Tricca,** Diane Walsh, Pearl B. Weinstein, Beth Norman Winickoff

Acknowledgment for page 172: Excerpt from *James Herriot's Dog Stories.* Copyright ©1986 by James Herriot. Published by St. Martin's Press.

ISBN 0-13-434479-0
2 3 4 5 6 7 8 9 10   02 01 00 99

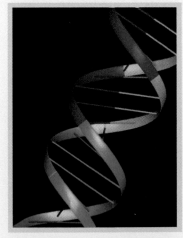

Cover: This computer image shows the structure of a DNA molecule.

Teacher's Edition ISBN 0-13-429192-1

Program Authors

Michael J. Padilla, Ph.D.
Professor
Department of Science Education
University of Georgia
Athens, Georgia

Michael Padilla is a leader in middle school science education. He has served as an editor and elected officer for the National Science Teachers Association. He has been principal investigator of several National Science Foundation and Eisenhower grants and served as a writer of the National Science Education Standards.

As lead author of *Science Explorer,* Mike has inspired the team in developing a program that meets the needs of middle grades students, promotes science inquiry, and is aligned with the National Science Education Standards.

Ioannis Miaoulis, Ph.D.
Dean of Engineering
College of Engineering
Tufts University
Medford, Massachusetts

Martha Cyr, Ph.D.
Director, Engineering
    Educational Outreach
College of Engineering
Tufts University
Medford, Massachusetts

Science Explorer was created in collaboration with the College of Engineering at Tufts University. Tufts has an extensive engineering outreach program that uses engineering design and construction to excite and motivate students and teachers in science and technology education.

Faculty from Tufts University participated in the development of *Science Explorer* chapter projects, reviewed the student books for content accuracy, and helped coordinate field testing.

CHAPTER PROJECT

Book Author

Donald Cronkite, Ph.D.
Professor of Biology
Hope College
Holland, Michigan

Contributing Writers

Susan Offner
Biology Teacher
Milton High School
Milton, Massachusetts

Warren Phillips
Science Teacher
Plymouth Community Intermediate School
Plymouth, Massachusetts

Thomas R. Wellnitz
Science Teacher
The Paideia School
Atlanta, Georgia

Reading Consultant

Bonnie B. Armbruster, Ph.D.
Department of Curriculum
    and Instruction
University of Illinois
Champaign, Illinois

Interdisciplinary Consultant

Heidi Hayes Jacobs, Ed.D.
Teacher's College
Columbia University
New York City, New York

Safety Consultants

W. H. Breazeale, Ph.D.
Department of Chemistry
College of Charleston
Charleston, South Carolina

Ruth Hathaway, Ph.D.
Hathaway Consulting
Cape Girardeau, Missouri

Teacher Reviewers

Stephanie Anderson
Sierra Vista Junior
   High School
Canyon Country, California

John W. Anson
Mesa Intermediate School
Palmdale, California

Pamela Arline
Lake Taylor Middle School
Norfolk, Virginia

Lynn Beason
College Station Jr. High School
College Station, Texas

Richard Bothmer
Hollis School District
Hollis, New Hampshire

Jeffrey C. Callister
Newburgh Free Academy
Newburgh, New York

Judy D'Albert
Harvard Day School
Corona Del Mar, California

Betty Scott Dean
Guilford County Schools
McLeansville, North Carolina

Sarah C. Duff
Baltimore City Public Schools
Baltimore, Maryland

Melody Law Ewey
Holmes Junior High School
Davis, California

Sherry L. Fisher
Lake Zurich Middle
   School North
Lake Zurich, Illinois

Melissa Gibbons
Fort Worth ISD
Fort Worth, Texas

Debra J. Goodding
Kraemer Middle School
Placentia, California

Jack Grande
Weber Middle School
Port Washington, New York

Steve Hills
Riverside Middle School
Grand Rapids, Michigan

Carol Ann Lionello
Kraemer Middle School
Placentia, California

Jaime A. Morales
Henry T. Gage Middle School
Huntington Park, California

Patsy Partin
Cameron Middle School
Nashville, Tennessee

Deedra H. Robinson
Newport News Public Schools
Newport News, Virginia

Bonnie Scott
Clack Middle School
Abilene, Texas

Charles M. Sears
Belzer Middle School
Indianapolis, Indiana

Barbara M. Strange
Ferndale Middle School
High Point, North Carolina

Jackie Louise Ulfig
Ford Middle School
Allen, Texas

Kathy Usina
Belzer Middle School
Indianapolis, Indiana

Heidi M. von Oetinger
L'Anse Creuse Public School
Harrison Township, Michigan

Pam Watson
Hill Country Middle School
Austin, Texas

Activity Field Testers

Nicki Bibbo
Russell Street School
Littleton, Massachusetts

Connie Boone
Fletcher Middle School
Jacksonville Beach, Florida

Rose-Marie Botting
Broward County
   School District
Fort Lauderdale, Florida

Colleen Campos
Laredo Middle School
Aurora, Colorado

Elizabeth Chait
W. L. Chenery Middle School
Belmont, Massachusetts

Holly Estes
Hale Middle School
Stow, Massachusetts

Laura Hapgood
Plymouth Community
   Intermediate School
Plymouth, Massachusetts

Sandra M. Harris
Winman Junior High School
Warwick, Rhode Island

Jason Ho
Walter Reed Middle School
Los Angeles, California

Joanne Jackson
Winman Junior High School
Warwick, Rhode Island

Mary F. Lavin
Plymouth Community
   Intermediate School
Plymouth, Massachusetts

James MacNeil, Ph.D.
Concord Public Schools
Concord, Massachusetts

Lauren Magruder
St. Michael's Country
   Day School
Newport, Rhode Island

Jeanne Maurand
Glen Urquhart School
Beverly Farms, Massachusetts

Warren Phillips
Plymouth Community
   Intermediate School
Plymouth, Massachusetts

Carol Pirtle
Hale Middle School
Stow, Massachusetts

Kathleen M. Poe
Kirby-Smith Middle School
Jacksonville, Florida

Cynthia B. Pope
Ruffner Middle School
Norfolk, Virginia

Anne Scammell
Geneva Middle School
Geneva, New York

Karen Riley Sievers
Callanan Middle School
Des Moines, Iowa

David M. Smith
Howard A. Eyer Middle School
Macungie, Pennsylvania

Derek Strohschneider
Plymouth Community
   Intermediate School
Plymouth, Massachusetts

Sallie Teames
Rosemont Middle School
Fort Worth, Texas

Gene Vitale
Parkland Middle School
McHenry, Illinois

Zenovia Young
Meyer Levin Junior
   High School (IS 285)
Brooklyn, New York

PRENTICE HALL
SCIENCE
EXPLORER

Contents

Cells and Heredity

Prepare your students with rich, motivating content

Science Explorer is crafted for today's middle grades student, with accessible content and in-depth coverage. **Integrated Science Sections** support every chapter and the **Interdisciplinary Exploration** provides an engaging final unit.

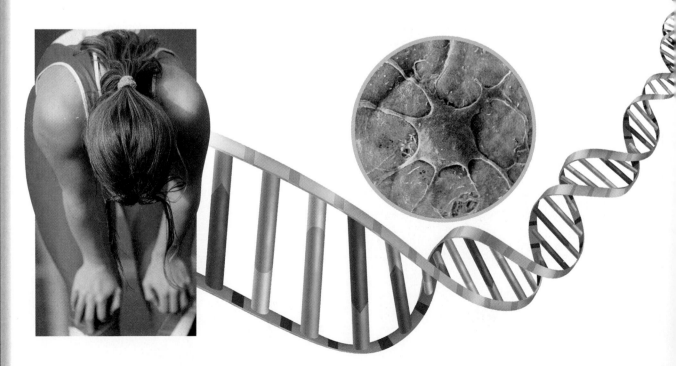

Check your compass— regularly assess student progress.

Self-assessment tools are built right into the student text and **on-going assessment** is woven throughout the Teacher's Edition. You'll find a wealth of **assessment technology** in the Resource Pro®, Interactive Student Tutorial, and Assessment Resources CD-ROMs.

Guide your students to become science explorers.

A wide range of student-tested activities, **from guided to open-ended,** with options for short- and long-term inquiry.

Inquiry Activities

CHAPTER PROJECT

Opportunities for long-term inquiry

DISCOVER

Exploration and inquiry before reading

Sharpen your Skills

Practice of specific science inquiry skills

TRY THIS

Reinforcement of key concepts

Draw upon the world around you.

Interdisciplinary Activities connect to every discipline and give science a meaningful, real-world context.

Skills Lab

In-depth practice of inquiry skills

Real-World Lab

Everyday application of science concepts

Interdisciplinary Activities

Science and History

Science and Society

Connection

EXPLORING

Visual exploration of concepts

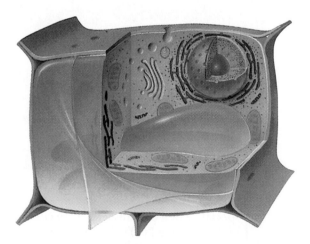

Unlocking the Secrets of Cells

Focus on Molecular Biology

This four-page feature presents an interview with a working scientist, molecular biologist Lydia Villa-Komaroff. Using Dr. Villa-Komaroff's work in developing a technique to produce human insulin, this interview focuses on scientific problem solving as a key element of scientific inquiry.

The DNA molecule is described in Chapter 2 of this book. The cellular processes by which proteins are synthesized following the genetic code in DNA are presented in Chapter 3. Human genetic diseases and the use of genetic engineering to produce medicines is presented in Chapter 4. However, students need not have any previous knowledge of the content of these chapters to understand and appreciate this feature.

Scientific Inquiry

Before students read the interview, encourage them to read the title and the captions and examine the pictures. Then ask: **What is the focus of this scientist's work?** *(To use genetic engineering to produce human proteins, such as insulin)* **What is diabetes?** *(Some students may know that diabetes is a disorder in which the body cannot control levels of sugar in the blood.)* Explain that the bodies of people with diabetes do not produce enough insulin.

UNLOCKING THE
Secrets of Cells

It takes courage and dedication to follow your dreams. Lydia Villa-Komaroff learned that early in her career. She comes from a family of courageous Mexican American women. Her mother and both grandmothers were strong role models for her. Their support, as well as her father's, encouraged her to pursue a career in science. As a molecular biologist, Dr. Villa-Komaroff studies the role of proteins in the growth and development of living things.

In 1976, Lydia was part of a team conducting genetic engineering, a technique by which scientists transfer genes from one organism into another. Today, scientists use this technique to produce medicines, to treat diseases, and to improve crops. In the 1970s, genetic engineering was a new idea. It was feared by many people who thought it might have harmful results. In fact, the city where Lydia worked banned genetic engineering.

To continue her research, Lydia was forced to move her lab to another state. She spent a year away from many of her colleagues and friends. "It was a frustrating and lonely time," she recalls.

Lydia Villa-Komaroff is Vice President for Research at Northwestern University in Chicago, Illinois. She earned her Ph.D. in cell biology at the Massachusetts Institute of Technology. An avid skier and photographer, Lydia also loves to read, particularly mysteries and biographies.

10 ◆ C

Background

Biology is the study of living things. It is a very broad area of study, and most biologists specialize in a certain field. Molecular biologists, like Lydia Villa-Komaroff, study the molecules that direct cellular processes in organisms. Molecular biology developed from the study of genetics and incorporates principles of biochemistry and physics as they apply to biology. Research in molecular biology has begun to explain why certain genes are expressed in some cells, but not in others. Molecular biologists often manipulate DNA or RNA to help them understand the functions of particular proteins. Knowledge about how genes are regulated and how their proteins function has direct applications to medicine and agriculture.

But her hard work paid off. The ban was lifted, and soon after, Lydia helped discover a method for making insulin. Insulin is used to treat people who suffer from diabetes. Discovering a way to make insulin launched a new industry—biotechnology. It marked a personal triumph for Lydia. "Scientifically, that was the most exciting time of my life," she says. "There were any number of reasons to think we couldn't make insulin. But we planned it, we tried it, and no experiment before or since has worked so smoothly."

Many secrets of the human cell remain to be unlocked. Lydia hopes to provide some of the keys.

Talking With Dr. Lydia Villa-Komaroff

Q *How did you become interested in science?*

A My Mexican grandmother was very interested in natural history—plants in particular. She had books we used to look at with beautiful color pictures of plants. What really sparked my interest was just following her around, learning about the plants in our garden, and going out collecting wild spinach with her.

Q *What made you choose a career in biology?*

A I had an incredibly exciting developmental biology course in college. One time we camped out in the lab for 36 hours so we could watch frogs develop. Normally you study that in pictures in textbooks. But we were seeing it happen in real life. It was very exciting.

Q *What does a molecular biologist do?*

A We study development at the most basic level: what goes on within a cell. Think of the cell as a house, with many different parts—the foundation, the walls, the roof, and lots of bricks and wood and wiring. I'm interested in finding out how that structure gets built.

Dr. Villa-Komaroff explains her work to a group of students.

C ◆ 11

Background

Insulin is a hormone produced by the pancreas. Insulin functions to regulate the level of glucose, a sugar used by cells for energy, in the bloodstream. Specifically, insulin controls the absorption of glucose by the cells. If the level of insulin in the blood is too low, then the concentration of glucose in the blood increases. This condition is called diabetes. Symptoms of diabetes include excessive thirst and increased urination. If left untreated, diabetes can result in blindness, kidney failure, or the degeneration of blood vessels. Some forms of diabetes are treated with injections of insulin into the bloodstream.

- After students have read the feature, discuss the accomplishment that was most exciting to Dr. Villa-Komaroff. *(Discovering a way to make insulin)* Then ask: **What choices did Dr. Villa-Komaroff have to make in order to continue working on a method to produce insulin?** *(She had to choose between leaving her home and her friends and colleagues to continue her work, or stop working on her project.)* **Why did the city ban genetic engineering research?** *(People were afraid it might have harmful results.)* **Do you think the decision by the city to ban genetic engineering was a good one?** *(Accept all answers, but encourage students to explain their opinions.)* Use this as an opportunity to discuss the importance of science knowledge in everyday life. Explain that many issues in science are discussed on nightly news programs, in newspapers, and in government chambers ranging from city halls to the United States Senate. In order to make informed decisions about these issues, people must have knowledge about science.
- Point out to students that scientists' work is usually involved in solving problems. Ask: **What problems has Dr. Villa-Komaroff tried to solve?** *(She has tried to learn how cells get "built," especially when and how cells use information from DNA. Then she wanted to learn how to genetically engineer bacteria to produce human insulin.)*
- Ask students: **What analogy does Dr. Villa-Komaroff use to describe her work?** *(She compares the functions of certain molecules in a cell to the process of building a house.)* **Why is this analogy useful?** *(It makes a complex concept easier to understand and visualize.)* **Would you have understood what Dr. Villa-Komaroff was talking about if she didn't use an analogy?** *(Accept all answers without comment.)*

◆ Help students sort the information about cells and relate it to the house analogy by listing on the board the terms used in the interview. You might wish to diagram both a house and a cell and label them with the terms. Also record each molecule's role in the cell. *(DNA: blueprints, hereditary information that determines the traits of an organism; RNA: copy of blueprints that goes to the construction site; proteins: bricks and mortar and hammers and drills, make up cell structure and read DNA and RNA to build other proteins)* Students will probably not know the meanings of all the terms at this time. However, you can remind students of the house-building analogy when they study protein synthesis in Chapter 3.

◆ Have students study the diagram that illustrates Dr. Villa-Komaroff's technique to produce insulin. Relate the house-building analogy to this diagram by pointing out the parts of the cell that are used to make human insulin. The human insulin gene, the bacterial chromosome, and the plasmid are all DNA. Dr. Villa-Komaroff used certain proteins as "saws" to cut the human insulin gene out of human DNA. She used other proteins as "bolts" to connect the human insulin gene to the plasmid. Once the bacteria took up the plasmid, the bacteria's machinery made the human insulin as if it were its own protein.

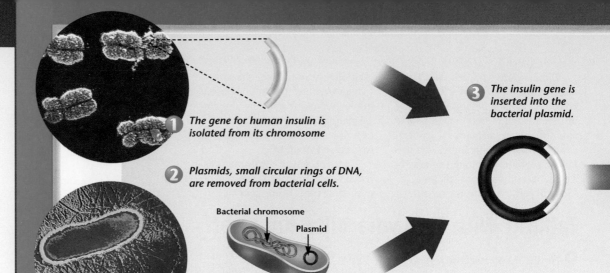

1 *The gene for human insulin is isolated from its chromosome*

2 *Plasmids, small circular rings of DNA, are removed from bacterial cells.*

Bacterial chromosome

Plasmid

3 *The insulin gene is inserted into the bacterial plasmid.*

Dr. Villa-Komaroff pioneered the use of genetic engineering to produce human proteins, such as insulin.

Q *Is there a plan or blueprint for building a cell?*

A All the instructions are in the DNA. That is the material in the nucleus of a cell that carries the hereditary information that determines traits, such as your skin and hair color. The machinery, which is made up of proteins, comes in and reads bits of that information, which are called genes. Then DNA is copied into RNA, a message that travels out to the part of the cell where all the building activity goes on. Other proteins read it and start to produce the materials that the cell needs to work.

Q *Are proteins the tools or the structure of a cell?*

A Actually, they're both. Proteins are the building blocks of cells, like the bricks and mortar in a house. But they're also the machinery that builds cells, like hammers and drills. Proteins make up the cell, and build the cell.

Q *What other information does DNA contain?*

A It contains coding instructions to make sure the right information gets used at the right time. If you were building a house, you couldn't put up the roof before you had walls. In building a human, a certain amount of the head needs to be in place, for example, before you can make eyes. So it's very important for a cell to know what information to use, and when to use it.

Q *How do cells know when to start and stop building?*

A It's still not clear how that process is coordinated. There are certain genes that we understand very well. We know what signals they send the cell to say it's time to become a heart or a liver. But how does the cell know when to use that information, and when to stop? Those are some of the big questions that we're trying to answer.

Background

Plasmids are small, circular molecules of DNA found in some bacterial cells. They are separate from the chromosomal DNA of bacteria, and they carry genes that are not essential to the basic functions of the bacterial cell. Plasmids require the bacterial chromosome's machinery for replication and for making their proteins. Plasmids commonly carry genes for resistance to specific antibiotics. Bacterial cells that contain these plasmids are resistant to those antibiotics.

4 Plasmids with the insulin gene are taken up by the bacterial cells. The gene directs the cell to produce insulin.

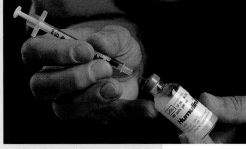

5 The insulin is collected and used to treat people with diabetes.

Q *What was the significance of the technique you developed to produce insulin?*

A People with diabetes used to be treated with pig insulin. But pig insulin is in short supply and therefore expensive. The work we did showed how to make a lot of insulin very cheaply, by growing it in bacteria. And it's human insulin.

Q *How did you trick the cell into making insulin?*

A We were able to isolate the gene with instructions for making insulin. We then inserted it into bacteria. Basically, we tricked the bacteria into thinking the gene was one of its own pieces of DNA. The bacteria then made the appropriate RNA, which was translated into insulin.

Q *Why didn't you give up when your research was banned?*

A We were doing very important work. To quit would have been to admit that the ban was right. We knew that others were doing the same research. You can't win a race if you quit.

Q *Were you ever discouraged?*

A There were times when I was discouraged, but I think that is true of anyone doing something where there is no guarantee of success. I think I've always approached a project with the idea that I have to give it my best shot.

Q *What advice would you give a person planning a science career?*

A You can't be entirely sure what you'll be able to do. The world is changing too fast. The important thing is to find something you like, and learn it very well. If you follow what you like, it may be different in 10 years, but it will be a logical extension of your own interests.

In Your Journal

As a young scientist, Lydia continued her research in genetic engineering in spite of obstacles that blocked her work. What does her action tell you about her as a person? Describe some character traits that you think would help a scientist to be successful. Why would those traits be important?

C ◆ 13

◆ Discuss Dr. Villa-Komaroff's success in her work. Ask: **What can you learn from Dr. Villa-Komaroff's success?** *(Accept all answers, encouraging students to explain their answers. If necessary, focus students on Villa-Komaroff's character traits.)* Help students realize that they can also be successful in whatever they choose to do in their lives by following the example of Dr. Villa-Komaroff.

In Your Journal Students should identify Dr. Villa-Komaroff as being persistent and confident about the importance of her work. Students might use these same character traits to describe a successful scientist. Successful scientists are also creative thinkers, good problem solvers, good communicators, focused on details, careful observers, cooperative, and hard workers. Students should also describe how these character traits would help a scientist in his or her work. In the process, they should identify the different aspects or duties of a scientist. You might allow class time to discuss these character traits. Invite students to describe the traits they wrote about in their journals. Help students realize that these character traits are useful in many other careers in addition to careers in the sciences.

Introducing Cells and Heredity

Have students look through the book to find the parts that relate most closely to this feature. *(Chapter 4, Modern Genetics, particularly Section 4.3 in which advances in genetics are discussed.)* Ask: **What will you be learning about in this book?** *(Cell structure and function, cell processes, the inheritance of traits, human genetics, and evolution)*

Cell Structure and Function

Sections	Time	Student Edition Activities	Other Activities
CHAPTER PROJECT 1 **Egg-speriment With a Cell** p. 15	Ongoing (2–3 weeks)	Check Your Progress, p. 22 Check Your Progress, p. 31 Check Your Progress, p. 44 Wrap Up, p. 47	
1 Discovering Cells pp. 16–22 <ul><li>Explain how the invention of the microscope contributed to scientists' understanding of living things.</li><li>State the three points of the cell theory.</li><li>Describe how a light microscope works, including how a lens magnifies an object.</li></ul>	2–3 periods/ 1–1½ blocks	**Discover** Is Seeing Believing?, p. 16 **Sharpen Your Skills** Observing, p. 21	TE Building Inquiry Skills: Classifying, p. 17 TE Building Inquiry Skills: Calculating, p. 19 TE Including All Students, p. 19 TE Integrating Physics, p. 21
2 Looking Inside Cells pp. 23–32 <ul><li>Identify the role of the cell membrane and nucleus in the cell.</li><li>Describe the functions performed by other organelles in the cell.</li><li>Compare bacterial cells with plant and animal cells.</li><li>Describe the role of specialized cells in many-celled organisms.</li></ul>	4–5 periods/ 2–2½ blocks	**Discover** How Large Are Cells?, p. 23 **Try This** Gelatin Cell, p. 29 **Skills Lab: Observing** A Magnified View of Life, p. 32	TE Building Inquiry Skills: Comparing and Contrasting, p. 25 TE Including All Students, p. 27 TE Demonstration, p. 27 TE Inquiry Challenge, p. 28 TE Demonstration, p. 30 TE Building Inquiry Skills: Observing, p. 30 ISLM C-1, "Cell Membranes and Permeability"
3 *INTEGRATING CHEMISTRY* **Chemical Compounds in Cells** pp. 33–39 <ul><li>Describe the four main kinds of organic molecules in living things.</li><li>Explain how water is essential to the functioning of cells.</li></ul>	2–3 periods/ 1–1½ blocks	**Discover** What Is a Compound?, p. 33 **Try This** What's That Taste?, p. 35 **Science at Home,** p. 37 **Real-World Lab: Careers in Science** What's in Your Lunch, pp. 38–39	TE Demonstration, p. 35
4 The Cell in Its Environment pp. 40–44 <ul><li>Describe the three methods by which materials move into and out of cells.</li><li>Compare passive transport to active transport.</li></ul>	2 periods/ 1 block	**Discover** How Do Molecules Move?, p. 40 **Try This** Diffusion in Action, p. 42	TE Including All Students, p. 41 TE Integrating Chemistry, p. 41 TE Demonstration, p. 42 TE Inquiry Challenge, p. 43 TE Demonstration, p. 44
Study Guide/Chapter Review pp. 45–47	1 period/ ½ block		ISAB Provides teaching and review of all inquiry skills

For Standard or Block Schedule The Resource Pro® CD-ROM gives you maximum flexibility for planning your instruction for any type of schedule. Resource Pro® contains Planning Express®, an advanced scheduling program, as well as the entire contents of the Teaching Resources and the Computer Test Bank.

CHAPTER PLANNING GUIDE

Program Resources	Assessment Strategies	Media and Technology
TR Chapter 1 Project Teacher Notes, pp. 8–9 **TR** Chapter 1 Project Overview and Worksheets, pp. 10–13 **TR** Chapter 1 Project Scoring Rubric, p. 14	**SE** Performance Assessment: Chapter 1 Project Wrap Up, p. 47 **TE** Check Your Progress, pp. 22, 31, 44 **TE** Performance Assessment: Chapter 1 Project Wrap Up, p. 47 **TR** Chapter 1 Project Scoring Rubric, p. 14	Science Explorer Internet Site
TR 1-1 Lesson Plan, p. 15 **TR** 1-1 Section Summary, p. 16 **TR** 1-1 Review and Reinforce, p. 17 **TR** 1-1 Enrich, p. 18 **SES** Book O, *Sound and Light,* Chapter 4	**SE** Section 1 Review, p. 22 **TE** Ongoing Assessment, pp. 17, 19, 21 **TE** Performance Assessment, p. 22 **TR** 1-1 Review and Reinforce, p. 17	Audiotapes: English-Spanish Summary 1-1 Transparency 1, "The Compound Microscope" Interactive Student Tutorial CD-ROM, C-1
TR 1-2 Lesson Plan, p. 19 **TR** 1-2 Section Summary, p. 20 **TR** 1-2 Review and Reinforce, p. 21 **TR** 1-2 Enrich, p. 22 **TR** Chapter 1 Skills Lab, pp. 31–32 **SES** Book A, *From Bacteria to Plants,* Chapter 2	**SE** Section 2 Review, p. 31 **SE** Analyze and Conclude, p. 32 **TE** Ongoing Assessment, pp. 25, 27, 29 **TE** Performance Assessment, p. 31 **TR** 1-2 Review and Reinforce, p. 21	Exploring Life Science Videodisc, Unit 1 Side 2, "What's in a Cell?" Exploring Life Science Videodisc, Unit 1 Side 2, "Evolution of Cells" Audiotapes: English-Spanish Summary 1-2 Transparencies 2, "Exploring a Plant Cell"; 3, "Exploring an Animal Cell" Interactive Student Tutorial CD-ROM, C-1
TR 1-3 Lesson Plan, p. 23 **TR** 1-3 Section Summary, p. 24 **TR** 1-3 Review and Reinforce, p. 25 **TR** 1-3 Enrich, p. 26 **TR** Chapter 1 Real-World Lab, pp. 33–35 **SES** Book K, *Chemical Building Blocks,* Chapter 4 **SES** Book D, *Human Biology and Health,* Chapter 3	**SE** Section 3 Review, p. 37 **SE** Analyze and Conclude, p. 39 **TE** Ongoing Assessment, p. 35 **TE** Performance Assessment, p. 37 **TR** 1-3 Review and Reinforce, p. 25	Audiotapes: English-Spanish Summary 1-3 Interactive Student Tutorial CD-ROM, C-1
TR 1-4 Lesson Plan, p. 27 **TR** 1-4 Section Summary, p. 28 **TR** 1-4 Review and Reinforce, p. 29 **TR** 1-4 Enrich, p. 30 **SES** Book K, *Chemical Building Blocks,* Chapter 2	**SE** Section 4 Review, p. 44 **TE** Ongoing Assessment, pp. 41, 43 **TE** Performance Assessment, p. 44 **TR** 4-4 Review and Reinforce, p. 29	Exploring Life Science Videodisc, Unit 1 Side 2, "How Does It Get in There?" Audiotapes: English-Spanish Summary 1-4 Transparency 4, "Passive and Active Transport" Interactive Student Tutorial CD-ROM, C-1
TR Chapter 1 Performance Assessment, pp. 152–154 **TR** Chapter 1 Test, pp. 155–158	**SE** Chapter 1 Review, pp. 45–47 **TR** Chapter 1 Performance Assessment, pp. 152–154 **TR** Chapter 1 Test, pp. 155–158 **CTB** Test C-1	Interactive Student Tutorial CD-ROM, C-1 Computer Test Bank, Test C-1 Got It! Video Quizzes

Key: **SE** Student Edition   **TE** Teacher's Edition   **TR** Teaching Resources
      CTB Computer Test Bank   **SES** Science Explorer Series Text   **ISLM** Integrated Science Laboratory Manual
      ISAB Inquiry Skills Activity Book   **PTA** Product Testing Activities by *Consumer Reports*   **IES** Interdisciplinary Explorations Series

Meeting the National Science Education Standards and AAAS Benchmarks

National Science Education Standards	Benchmarks for Science Literacy	Unifying Themes
Science As Inquiry (Content Standard A) ◆ **Use appropriate tools and techniques to gather, analyze, and interpret data** Students compare plant and animal cells. Students test foods for starches and lipids. *(Skills Lab; Real-World Lab)* ◆ **Think critically and logically to make the relationships between evidence and explanations** Students investigate how various materials enter or leave a cell, using an egg as a model of the cell. *(Chapter Project)* **Life Science** (Content Standard C) ◆ **Structure and function in living systems** All living things are composed of cells. Each of the various structures in a cell has a different function. The most important organic compounds found in living things are carbohydrates, lipids, proteins, and nucleic acids. *(Sections 1, 2, 3)* ◆ **Regulation and behavior** Substances can move into and out of a cell by diffusion, osmosis, or active transport. *(Section 4)* **Science and Technology** (Content Standard E) ◆ **Understandings about science and technology** The invention of the microscope made it possible for people to discover and learn about cells. *(Section 1; Science & History)*	**1B Scientific Inquiry** Students investigate how various materials enter or leave a cell, using an egg as a model of the cell. Students compare plant and animal cells. Students test foods for starches and lipids. *(Chapter Project; Skills Lab; Real-World Lab)* **1C The Scientific Enterprise** The observations and conclusions of many scientists led to the development of the cell theory. *(Section 1)* **3A Technology and Science** The invention of the microscope made it possible for people to discover and learn about cells. Microscopes have improved in many ways over the last 400 years. *(Section 1; Science & History)* **5C Cells** All living things are composed of cells. Each of the various structures in a cell has a different function. The most important groups of organic compounds found in living things are carbohydrates, lipids, proteins, and nucleic acids. Substances can move into and out of a cell by diffusion, osmosis, or active transport. *(Sections 1, 2, 3, 4; Skills Lab)*	◆ **Energy** Mitochondria produce most of the energy a cell needs to carry out its functions. Chloroplasts capture energy from the sun and use it to produce food. Carbohydrates and lipids are energy-rich organic compounds. Active transport is the movement of materials through a cell membrane using energy. *(Sections 2, 3, 4)* ◆ **Modeling** Students investigate how various materials enter or leave a cell, using an egg as a model of the cell. *(Chapter Project)* ◆ **Scale and Structure** Cells are the basic unit of structure and function in living things. Cells have different structures that perform different functions. Students compare plant and animal cells. The cell membrane is selectively permeable. *(Sections 1, 2, 4; Skills Lab)* ◆ **Systems and Interactions** The invention of the microscope made it possible for people to discover and learn about cells. Cell organelles function to produce energy, build and transport needed materials, and store and recycle wastes. Without water, most chemical reactions within cells could not take place. Substances move into and out of a cell by diffusion, osmosis, or active transport. *(Sections 1, 2, 3, 4; Science & History)* ◆ **Unity and Diversity** All living things are made of cells. Plant cells have cell walls and chloroplasts, while animal cells do not. Organic compounds contain carbon, while most inorganic compounds do not. *(Sections 1, 2, 3; Skills Lab)*

Media and Technology

Exploring Life Science Videodiscs

◆ **Section 2** "What's in a Cell?" shows the parts of a cell and their functions. "Evolution of Cells" models the symbiotic theory of modern cell development.

◆ **Section 4** "How Does It Get in There?" models the processes of diffusion, osmosis, and active transport.

Interactive Student Tutorial CD-ROM

◆ **Chapter Review** Interactive questions help students self-assess their mastery of key chapter concepts.

Student Edition Connection Strategies

◆ **Section 1 Integrating Physics,** p. 21

◆ **Section 2 Language Arts Connection,** p. 25

◆ **Section 3 Integrating Chemistry,** pp. 33–39
  Integrating Health, p. 36

◆ **Section 4 Integrating Chemistry,** p. 41

USING THE INTERNET

www.science-explorer.phschool.com

Visit the Science Explorer Internet site to find an up-to-date activity for Chapter 1 of *Cells and Heredity*.

Student Edition Activities Planner

ACTIVITY	Time (minutes)	Materials — Quantities for one work group	Skills
Section 1			
Discover, p. 16	10	**Consumable** black and white newspaper photograph **Nonconsumable** scissors, hand lens, microscope	**Observing**
Sharpen Your Skills, p. 21	15	**Consumable** pond water **Nonconsumable** prepared slide of cork, microscope, plastic dropper, slide, coverslip	**Observing**
Section 2			
Discover, p. 23	10	**Nonconsumable** calculator, metric ruler	**Inferring**
Try This, p. 29	10/10	**Consumable** packet of colorless gelatin, warm water, other miscellaneous materials to represent cell structures **Nonconsumable** rectangular or round pan	**Making Models**
Skills Lab, p. 32	40	**Consumable** water, *Elodea* leaf **Nonconsumable** plastic dropper, microscope slide, microscope, prepared slide of animal cells, colored pencils, forceps, coverslip	**Observing, Comparing and Contrasting**
Section 3			
Discover, p. 33	10	**Consumable** labeled containers of various chemical compounds such as salt, zinc oxide sun block, baking soda, and chalk	**Forming Operational Definitions**
Try This, p. 35	5	**Consumable** unsalted soda cracker	**Inferring**
Science at Home, p. 37	home	**Nonconsumable** food packages with "Nutrition Facts" labels	**Interpreting Data, Communicating**
Real-World Lab, pp. 38–39	40	**Consumable** 1 g cornstarch, food samples, plastic stirrers, 5 ml vegetable oil, iodine solution in dropper bottle, 5-cm squares of brown paper, water **Nonconsumable** plastic graduated cylinder, plastic cups, plastic dropper	**Predicting, Drawing Conclusions**
Section 4			
Discover, p. 40	10	**Consumable** air freshener spray	**Developing Hypotheses**
Try This, p. 42	10	**Consumable** cold water, food coloring **Nonconsumable** small clear plastic cup, plastic dropper	**Inferring**

A list of all materials required for the Student Edition activities can be found on pages T14–T15. You can order Materials Kits by calling 1-800-828-7777 or by accessing the Science Explorer Internet site at **www.science-explorer.phschool.com.**

Egg-speriment With a Cell

In the Chapter 1 Project, students will learn about an essential structure found in all cells—the cell membrane. During the course of the project, students will carry out experiments, make observations, and draw conclusions about how the cell membrane functions.

Purpose In the Chapter 1 Project, students will observe how fluids pass back and forth across the semi-permeable membrane surrounding a raw egg. Doing the project will help students understand the process of osmosis. It also will help them appreciate the important role played by the cell membrane.

Skills Focus After completing the Chapter 1 Project, students will be able to
◆ predict how various liquids will affect an egg;
◆ observe how the liquids affect the egg;
◆ measure and record changes in the egg;
◆ graph data of the egg's circumference;
◆ draw conclusions about what processes occurred during the experiment.

Project Time Line The entire project will require at least two weeks. It will take longer if students break their eggs and have to start over. On the first day, have students read about the Chapter 1 Project in their text, and ask if they have any questions. Then hand out the Chapter 1 Project Overview and Student Worksheets, pages 10–13 in Teaching Resources. You might also wish to give students a copy of the Chapter 1 Project Scoring Rubric, page 14 in Teaching Resources, so they know what will be expected of them. Encourage students to read the Overview and do the Worksheets early in the project so they will measure and record their data correctly and understand the changes taking place in their eggs.

If students will be working in groups, divide the class into groups at this time and give group members a chance to meet to plan the project. Also set aside some class time during the course of the project for group members to work on the project. If students are doing the

WHAT'S AHEAD

SECTION 1 Discovering Cells

Discover **Is Seeing Believing?**
Sharpen Your Skills **Observing**

SECTION 2 Looking Inside Cells

Discover **How Large Are Cells?**
Try This **Gelatin Cell**
Skills Lab **A Magnified View of Life**

SECTION 3 *Integrating Chemistry* **Chemical Compounds in Cells**

Discover **What Is a Compound?**
Try This **What's That Taste?**
Real-World Lab **What's in Your Lunch?**

14 ◆ C

project individually, allow a few minutes of class time each day for students to share their observations and ask questions. Students might also need class time at the end of the project to prepare their presentations and share their results with the class.

For more detailed information on planning and supervising the Chapter 1 Project, see Chapter 1 Project Teacher Notes, pages 8–9 in Teaching Resources.

Suggested Shortcuts To speed up the project, you can have each student soak his or her egg in a different liquid, after first soaking the eggs in vinegar for two days. One student should use water, one student water with food coloring, and one student salt water, but the other students could soak their eggs in a liquid of their choice. Then all students can pool their results.

You can limit the amount of student involvement in the project by doing it as a class project. First have students brainstorm

Egg-speriment With a Cell

Did you ever wonder how a baby chick can breathe when it's still inside the egg? The shell of the egg allows air through to reach the developing chick, while keeping out most other substances. Just as an egg needs to control which substances can enter, so too do all of the cells in your body.

In this chapter, you'll learn that all living things are made of cells—sometimes just one cell, sometimes trillions! You'll see the structures cells contain and how they work. You'll find out that important questions about life can be answered by understanding what happens in cells. You can start your discoveries right away by studying an everyday object that can serve as a model of a cell: an uncooked egg.

Your Goal To observe how various materials enter or leave a cell, using an egg as a model of the cell.

To complete this project, you will
◆ observe what happens when you soak an uncooked egg in vinegar, then in water, food coloring, salt water, and finally in a liquid of your choice
◆ measure the circumference of the egg every day, and graph your results
◆ explain the changes that your egg underwent
◆ follow the safety guidelines in Appendix A

Get Started Predict what might happen when you put an uncooked egg in vinegar for two days. How might other liquids affect an egg? Find a place where you can leave your egg undisturbed. Then begin your egg-speriment!

Check Your Progress You will be working on this project as you study this chapter. To keep your project on track, look for Check Your Progress boxes at the following points.
Section 1 Review, page 22: Make measurements and record data.
Section 2 Review, page 31: Experiment with different liquids.
Section 4 Review, page 44: Graph your data and draw conclusions.

Wrap Up At the end of the chapter (page 47), you will display your egg and share your results.

The thin shells of these eggs control what substances reach the developing chick inside.

C ◆ 15

Possible Materials Any clean plastic containers can be used to soak the eggs, as long as the containers are large enough for the eggs to be completely covered by liquid. Plastic is better than glass because eggs are less likely to break if they bump against plastic. Containers with tight-fitting lids may help avoid spills and broken eggs, but lids are not necessary.

Students can use either white or brown eggs. Large eggs will show a greater change in size, making it easier for students to observe the results of osmosis. Make sure that none of the eggs is cracked to begin with. Encourage students to use a wide variety of liquids for soaking their eggs, such as corn syrup, milk, orange juice, or shampoo. To measure their egg, students can use a flexible cloth or vinyl tape or a piece of string and a ruler.

Launching the Project Introduce the project by showing students a chicken egg. State that the egg is similar to a single large cell. Point out that in this project, students will study an egg to learn more about how cells function. Ask: **Why do you think you will be using an egg to study the cell instead of an actual cell, such as a human skin cell?** *(Because most cells are too small to be seen without a microscope. Also, unlike most cells mounted on microscope slides, eggs are still alive.)* Say that, although a chicken egg is larger than any of the cells in their own bodies, it has many of the same structures. Explain that the cell membrane is the structure they will focus on in this project.

Performance Assessment

To assess students' performance in this project, use the Chapter 1 Project Scoring Rubric on page 14 of Teaching Resources. Students will be assessed on
◆ how accurately and consistently they make measurements and record their data;
◆ the neatness and accuracy of their graphs and diagrams;
◆ how well their conclusions display an understanding of the functions of a cell membrane;
◆ their participation in a group, if they worked in groups.

---

predictions about what will happen to the egg when it is soaked in the various liquids, and record their predictions on the chalkboard. Then set up the experiment with the egg soaking in a container of vinegar, and every other day change the liquid in which the egg is soaking, according to the directions in the text. Assign a different student to measure and record changes in the size of the egg each day, and give all the students a chance to observe how the egg is changing. Have each student create a data table and graph.

Program Resources

◆ **Teaching Resources** Chapter 1 Project Teacher Notes, pp. 8–9; Chapter 1 Project Overview and Worksheets, pp. 10–13; Chapter 1 Project Scoring Rubric, p. 14

Objectives

After completing the lesson, students will be able to

◆ explain how the invention of the microscope contributed to scientists' understanding of living things;
◆ state the three points of the cell theory;
◆ describe how a light microscope works, including how a lens magnifies an object.

Key Terms cell, microscope, compound microscope, cell theory, magnification, convex lens, resolution

1 Engage/Explore

Activating Prior Knowledge

Help students appreciate the large number of cells that make up living things like themselves, by asking: **How many individual grains of sand do you think make up a beach?** (*Students probably will say millions or billions.*) Point out that humans and many other living things are composed of billions of tiny components as well. These components, called cells, are too small to be seen without a microscope.

········ DISCOVER ·········

Skills Focus observing
Materials *black and white newspaper photograph, scissors, hand lens, microscope*
Time 10 minutes
Tips Set up several microscopes around the room and, if necessary, review with students how to use them.
Expected Outcome With the hand lens and microscope, students should see the individual dots of ink that make up the newspaper photograph. This will help them appreciate how the hand lens and microscope allow them to see objects too small to be seen with the naked eye.
Think It Over Students may say that with the hand lens and microscope they can see that the black and grey shaded areas in the picture actually are made up of separate tiny dots of ink.

DISCOVER ···································· ACTIVITY

Is Seeing Believing?

1. Cut a black-and-white photograph out of a page in a newspaper. With your eyes alone, closely examine the photo. Record your observations.

2. Examine the same photo with a hand lens. Record your observations.

3. Place the photo on the stage of a microscope. Use the clips to hold the photo in place. Shine a light down on the photo. Focus the microscope on part of the photo. (See Appendix B for instructions on using the microscope.) Record your observations.

Think It Over

Observing What did you see in the photo with the hand lens and the microscope that you could not see with your eyes alone?

GUIDE FOR READING

◆ How did the invention of the microscope contribute to scientists' understanding of living things?
◆ What is the cell theory?
◆ How does a lens magnify an object?

Reading Tip As you read, make a flowchart showing how the contributions of several scientists led to the development of the cell theory.

A majestic oak tree shades you on a sunny day at the park. A lumbering rhinoceros wanders over to look at you at the zoo. After a rain storm, mushrooms sprout in the damp woods. What do you think an oak tree, a rhinoceros, and a mushroom have in common? You might say that they are all living things. What makes these living things—and all other living things—alike? If you say they are made of cells, you are correct.

Cells are the basic units of structure and function in living things. Just as bricks are the building blocks of a house or school, cells are the building blocks of life. Since you are alive, you are made of cells, too. Look closely at the skin on your arm. No

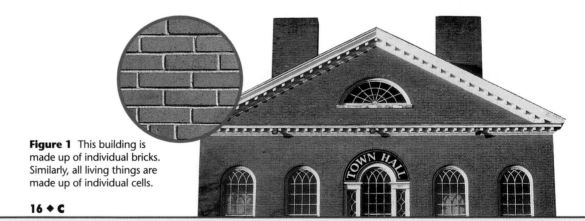

Figure 1 This building is made up of individual bricks. Similarly, all living things are made up of individual cells.

READING STRATEGIES

Reading Tip Students should include in their flowcharts contributions made by Janssen, Hooke, Leeuwenhoek, Schlieden, Schwann, and Virchow. Suggest that students illustrate their flowcharts and share them with the class. Also suggest that they save their flowcharts to use as study guides.

Study and Comprehension As students read about the microscope in this section, give visual and kinesthetic learners an opportunity to examine a microscope so they can see and touch the microscope as they read about it.

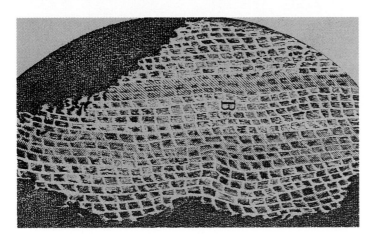

Figure 2 Robert Hooke made this drawing of dead cork cells that he saw through his microscope. Hooke called these structures *cells* because they reminded him of tiny rooms. *Comparing and Contrasting How are cells similar to the bricks in a building? How are they different?*

matter how hard you look with your eyes alone, you won't be able to see individual skin cells. The reason is that cells are very small. In fact, one square centimeter of your skin's surface contains over 100,000 cells.

First Sightings of Cells

Until the late 1500s there was no way to see cells. No one even knew that cells existed. Around 1590, the invention of the microscope enabled people to look at very small objects. **The invention of the microscope made it possible for people to discover and learn about cells.**

A **microscope** is an instrument that makes small objects look larger. Some microscopes do this by using lenses to focus light. The lenses used in light microscopes are similar to the clear curved pieces of glass used in eyeglasses. A simple microscope contains only one lens. A hand lens is an example of a simple microscope. A light microscope that has more than one lens is called a **compound microscope.**

Robert Hooke One of the first people to observe cells was the English scientist and inventor Robert Hooke. In 1663, Hooke observed the structure of a thin slice of cork using a compound microscope he had built himself. Cork, the bark of the cork oak tree, is made up of cells that are no longer alive. To Hooke, the cork looked like tiny rectangular rooms, which he called *cells.* Hooke described his observations this way: "These pores, or cells, were not very deep. . . ." You can see Hooke's drawings of cork cells in Figure 2. What most amazed Hooke was how many cells the cork contained. He calculated that in a cubic inch there were about twelve hundred million cells—a number he described as "most incredible."

Answers to Self-Assessment

Caption Question

Figure 2 Cells are the building blocks of organisms as bricks are the building blocks of buildings. However, bricks, unlike cells, are not alive.

2 Facilitate

First Sightings of Cells

Building Inquiry Skills: Classifying

Materials *a collection of several different small items that represent living or nonliving things, such as wood, rubber, cotton, silk, wool, hair, coral, bone, leaves, paper, sand, silt, pebbles, rocks, marbles, and plastic* **ACTIVITY**
Time 10 minutes

Give each student several different materials, such as the items listed above, and instruct them to divide the materials in two groups, living things and nonliving things. Tell students to classify as living any material that came from a living thing. Have students compare their groupings and resolve any differences. Ask: **In addition to being composed of cells, can you think of other ways that living things differ from nonliving things?** *(Possible answers are that living things take in energy, give off waste, grow and develop, respond to their environment, and reproduce.)* **learning modality: kinesthetic**

Using the Visuals: Figure 2

Help students appreciate how much Hooke's work contributed to the understanding of the nature of living things. Call their attention to the figure, and then point out that Hooke could not photograph what he saw under the microscope because there were no cameras then. Fortunately, Hooke was a gifted artist, and when he published his book, it became a bestseller. Ask: **Why do you think people were so interested in seeing Hooke's drawings?** *(Because they were drawings of things that up until that time had been invisible, so the book opened up a whole new world to people.)* **learning modality: visual**

Ongoing Assessment

Writing Have students explain how the invention of the microscope led to the discovery of the cell.

First Sightings of Cells, continued

Guide students who need more help in organizing and comprehending the technical information in the feature. First point out that, up until 1933, all microscopes operated under the same general principle: They used lenses to focus light on or through an object in order to magnify it enough to be seen by the human eye. Then ask: **How do electron microscopes differ from light microscopes?** *(Instead of using light, electron microscopes use electrons to "see" an object.)* **How does this difference make electron microscopes better?** *(They can magnify objects much more than light microscopes and provide different views of an object.)* **What are TEMs, SEMs, and STMs?** *(Transmission electron microscope, scanning electron microscope, and scanning tunneling microscope, respectively.)* **How are TEMs, SEMs, and STMs the same, and how are they different?** *(All three use electrons instead of light to view objects. A TEM sends electrons through objects, so it is good for seeing the insides of things. A SEM sends electrons over the surfaces of objects, so it can create three-dimensional images of them. A STM records electrons "leaking" from the surface of objects, so it can show individual molecules on the object's surface.)* **Which type of electron microscope has the greatest magnification?** *(STM, which can magnify an object up to 1,000,000 times its actual size)*

In Your Journal To stimulate ideas in visual learners, have students look at the many figures throughout the chapter that contain pictures of objects as seen through a microscope. Advise students to consider the time period they are writing about if they choose one of the earlier microscopes for their advertisement. Point out that, although Hooke's 1600s sketch of cork cells in Figure 2 looks crude compared with the 1900s electron microscope photo of the single-celled organism in Figure 10, to the people who lived at the same time as Hooke, his images were just as novel and exciting. **learning modality: verbal**

SCIENCE & History

Anton van Leeuwenhoek At about the same time that Robert Hooke made his discovery, Anton van Leeuwenhoek (LAY vun hook) also began to observe tiny objects with microscopes. Leeuwenhoek was a Dutch businessman and amateur scientist who made his own lenses. He then used the lenses to construct simple microscopes.

One of the things Leeuwenhoek looked at was water from a pond. He was surprised to see one-celled organisms, which he called *animalcules* (an uh MAL kyoolz), meaning "little animals."

The Microscope— Improvements Over Time

The discovery of cells would not have been possible without the microscope. Microscopes have been improved in many ways over the last 400 years.

1660
Hooke's Compound Microscope

Robert Hooke improved on the compound microscope. The stand at the right holds oil for a flame, which shines light on the specimen under the microscope.

1600	1750

1590
First Compound Microscope

Hans Janssen and his son Zacharias, Dutch eyeglass makers, made one of the first compound microscopes. Their microscope was simply a tube with a lens at each end.

1683
Leeuwenhoek's Simple Microscope

Although Leeuwenhoek's simple microscope used only one tiny lens, it could magnify a specimen up to 266 times. Leeuwenhoek was the first person to see many one-celled organisms, including bacteria.

Background

Facts and Figures To differentiate among particular cell structures under a microscope, scientists may stain the tissue to be examined. Different stains color different structures inside cells. For example, a stain called hematoxylin colors the cell's nucleus, the area where most nucleic acids in the cell are found.

After staining the tissue, a scientist shaves off extremely thin slices with a precision cutting instrument called a microtome. The microtome can cut slices so thin that they are less than one cell thick. This allows a clear view of even the tiniest cell structures.

Leeuwenhoek looked at many other specimens, including scrapings from teeth. When Leeuwenhoek looked at the scrapings, he became the first person to see the tiny single-celled organisms that are now called bacteria. Leeuwenhoek's many discoveries caught the attention of other researchers. Many other people began to use microscopes to see what secrets they could uncover about cells.

☑ **Checkpoint** *How does a simple microscope differ from a compound microscope?*

In Your Journal

Choose one of the microscopes. Write an advertisement for it that might appear in a popular science magazine. Be creative. Emphasize the microscope's usefulness or describe the wonders that can be seen with it.

1933
Transmission Electron Microscope (TEM)

The German physicist Ernst Ruska created the first electron microscope. TEMs make images by sending electrons through a very thinly sliced specimen. They can only examine dead specimens, but are very useful for viewing internal cell structures. TEMs can magnify a specimen up to 500,000 times.

1981
Scanning Tunneling Microscope (STM)

A STM measures electrons that leak, or "tunnel," from the surface of a specimen. With a STM, scientists can see individual molecules on the outer layer of a cell. STMs can magnify a specimen up to 1,000,000 times.

1900 ———————————————— **2050**

1886
Modern Compound Light Microscope

German scientists Ernst Abbé and Carl Zeiss made a compound light microscope similar to this one. The horseshoe stand keeps the microscope steady. The mirror at the bottom focuses light up through the specimen. Modern compound light microscopes can magnify a specimen up to 1,000 times.

1965
Scanning Electron Microscope (SEM)

The first commercial SEM is produced. This microscope sends a beam of electrons over the surface of a specimen, rather than through it. The result is a detailed three-dimensional image of the specimen's surface. SEMs can magnify a specimen up to 150,000 times.

Answers to Self-Assessment

☑ *Checkpoint*

A simple microscope has just one lens, whereas a compound microscope has two or more lenses.

Materials *calculator*
Time 5 minutes

ACTIVITY

Help students appreciate how greatly electron microscopes increase magnification by having them calculate differences in magnification among microscopes.

First explain that a microscope with a magnification of 100 is 10 times stronger than a microscope with a magnification of 10 ($100 \div 10$). Then ask: **How much stronger is a modern light microscope than Leeuwenhoek's microscope?** *(1,000 ÷ 266, or about 3.8 times stronger)* **How much stronger is an STM electron microscope than a modern light microscope?** *(1,000,000 ÷ 1,000, or 1,000 times stronger)* **learning modality: logical/mathematical**

Including All Students

Materials *microscope, slide, coverslip*
ACTIVITY
Time 15 minutes

🧪 Let students actually experience the difference that the degree of magnification can make in how objects appear under a microscope. Have students choose a suitable object, such as a strand of human hair, to place on a slide with a coverslip and view under the microscope, first at low and then at high power. For students whose movements are limited, you can use a microprojector to project the images on a screen. Have students draw a simple sketch of what they see under each magnification. Remind them to label their drawings with the magnification. Ask volunteers to share their drawings with the class and have other students try to identify each object from the drawings. **learning modality: visual**

Ongoing Assessment

Oral Presentation Call on students at random to state Leeuwenhoek's contributions to science. *(Leeuwenhoek made microscopes powerful enough to see single-celled organisms, and he was the first person to see bacteria.)*

The Cell Theory

Addressing Naive Conceptions

Students may think the cell theory is not well-established because it is called a theory. Explain that in everyday speech, people often use the word *theory* to mean speculation or conjecture. However, in science a theory is a well-tested concept that consistently explains a wide range of observations and predicts future events. Point out that a theory may be the best explanation to date, but no theory is beyond dispute. Ask: **Do you think the cell theory has been proven conclusively? Explain.** (*No, it is not possible for scientists to examine every single living thing to determine if it is composed of cells, and a single exception would disprove the theory.*) **learning modality: verbal**

Building Inquiry Skills: Inferring

Help students infer the nature of the scientific process by asking: **Why do you think it took almost 200 years after cells were discovered for scientists to conclude that all living things consist of cells?** (*Students may say that there were far fewer scientists and microscopes than today, yet scientists had to examine thousands of samples of living things before they could reasonably conclude that all living things are made of cells.*) **learning modality: logical/mathematical**

Using the Visuals: Figure 3

Call students' attention to the figure and point out the small drawings of plant and animal cells. Help students identify the similarities and differences between the drawings by asking: **How would you describe the animal cells shown here?** (*They are round in shape, appear to be enclosed, and contain a single spot.*) **How would you describe the plant cells?** (*They are rectangular in shape, appear to be enclosed, and contain many spots.*) **How are the plant and animal cells similar?** (*Both appear to be enclosed by walls or membranes and have at least one large interior spot.*) Identify these structures as the cell wall or membrane and the nucleus. **learning modality: visual**

Plant cells

Animal cells

Figure 3 The cell theory states that all living things, including this giraffe and the leaf it is eating, are composed of cells.

20 ◆ C

The Cell Theory

Over the years, scientists have continued to use and improve the microscope. They have discovered that all kinds of living things were made up of cells. In 1838 a German scientist named Matthais Schleiden (SHLY dun) concluded that all plants are made of cells. He based this conclusion on his own research and on the research of others before him. The next year, another German scientist, Theodor Schwann, concluded that all animals are also made up of cells. Thus, stated Schwann, all living things are made up of cells.

Schleiden and Schwann had made an important discovery about living things. However, they didn't understand where cells came from. Until their time, most people thought that living things could come from nonliving matter. In 1855, a German doctor, Rudolf Virchow (FUR koh) proposed that new cells are formed only from existing cells. "All cells come from cells," wrote Virchow.

The observations and conclusions of Hooke, Leeuwenhoek, Schleiden, Schwann, Virchow, and others led to the development of the **cell theory**. The cell theory is a widely accepted explanation of the relationship between cells and living things. **The cell theory states:**

◆ **All living things are composed of cells.**

◆ **Cells are the basic unit of structure and function in living things.**

◆ **All cells are produced from other cells.**

The cell theory holds true for all living things, no matter how big or how small. Since cells are common to all living things, they can provide information about all life. Because all cells come from other cells, scientists can study cells to learn about growth, reproduction, and all other functions that living things perform.

✓ *Checkpoint* *What did Schleiden and Schwann conclude about cells?*

Background

History of Science Until about the mid-1800s, many people thought that new life could arise by a process called spontaneous generation. In other words, new life could arise from nonliving things. This mistaken idea originated to explain what people saw, such as the apparently spontaneous appearance of maggots and flies on decaying meat.

Today, people know that life arises only from other living things. For example, adult flies land on decaying meat and lay eggs, which develop into maggots, which in turn develop into adult flies. The idea that all life comes from preexisting, similar life is called biogenesis.

How a Light Microscope Works

 INTEGRATING PHYSICS Microscopes use lenses to make small objects look larger. But simply enlarging a small object is not useful unless you can see the details clearly. For a microscope to be useful to a scientist, it must combine two important properties—magnification and resolution.

Magnification The first property, **magnification,** is the ability to make things look larger than they are. **The lens or lenses in a light microscope magnify an object by bending the light that passes through them.** If you examine a hand lens, you will see that the glass lens is curved, not flat. The center of the lens is thicker than the edges. A lens with this curved shape is called a **convex lens.** Look at Figure 4 to see how light is bent by a convex lens. The light passing through the sides of the lens bends inward. When this light hits the eye, the eye sees the object as larger than it really is.

Because a compound microscope uses more than one lens, it can magnify an object even more. Light passes through a specimen and then through two lenses. Figure 4 also shows the path that light takes through a compound microscope. The first lens near the specimen magnifies the object. Then a second lens near the eye further magnifies the enlarged image. The total magnification of the microscope is equal to the magnifications of the two lenses multiplied together. For example, if the first lens has a magnification of 10 and the second lens has a magnification of 40, then the total magnification of the microscope is 400.

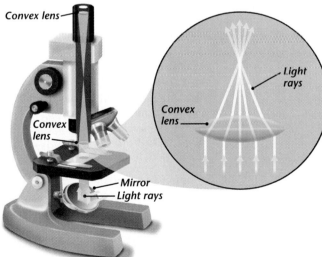

Convex lens

Convex lens

Light rays

Convex lens

Mirror
Light rays

Figure 4 Microscopes use lenses to make objects look larger. A compound microscope has two convex lenses. Each convex lens bends light, making the image larger. *Calculating If one lens has a magnification of 10 and the other lens has a magnification of 50, what would the total magnification be?*

Chapter 1 **C ◆ 21**

 **Sharpen your Skills**

Observing ACTIVITY

1. Place a prepared slide of a thin slice of cork on the stage of a microscope.
2. Observe the slide under low power. Draw what you see.
3. Place a few drops of pond water on another slide and cover it with a coverslip.
4. Observe the slide under low power. Draw what you see. Wash your hands after handling pond water.

Observing How does your drawing in Step 2 compare to Hooke's drawing in Figure 2? Based on your observations in Step 4, why did Leeuwenhoek called the organisms he saw "little animals"?

Program Resources

 Science Explorer Series *Sound and Light,* Chapter 4, has more information about lenses.

Media and Technology

Transparencies "The Compound Microscope," Transparency 1

Answers to Self-Assessment

✓ Checkpoint

Schleiden concluded that all plants are made of cells. Schwann concluded that all animals are also made of cells.

Caption Question

Figure 4 The total magnification would be 10 × 50, or 500.

How a Light Microscope Works

Integrating Physics

Materials *convex lens (hand lens)*  ACTIVITY
Time 10 minutes

Group students in pairs, and instruct one student to hold a hand lens steady at about 10 cm above a page. Tell the other student to move closer to or farther from the lens until the letters on the page come into focus. At this point, have both students note the relative positions of the eye, lens, and page and compare them with their positions in Figure 4. Ask: **At what position is your eye?** (*At the focal point*) By moving their eye farther back from the lens, students can see the difference between magnification and resolution. Ask: **How does the object appear now?** (*Even larger but blurry, or out of focus*) Have students switch positions and repeat the activity. **learning modality: kinesthetic**

Sharpen your Skills

Observing

Materials *prepared slide of cork, microscope, pond water, plastic dropper, slide, coverslip* ACTIVITY
Time 15 minutes
Tips Make sure students have focused the microscope and can see the cells clearly before they start their drawings.
Expected Outcome Students' drawings of cork cells should resemble Hooke's drawing on page 17. Students' drawings of pond water should show various microorganisms. Leeuwenhoek called the organisms he saw "little animals" because they moved as animals move.
Extend Ask: **What do you think a drop of tap water would look like under the microscope?** (*It would contain few if any microorganisms.*) **learning modality: visual**

Ongoing Assessment

Oral Presentation Randomly call on students to name a part of a compound microscope and explain its function.

C ◆ 21

Electron Microscopes

Including All Students

Urge students who need extra challenges to work together to prepare a presentation on electron microscopes, which may be difficult for some students to understand. The presentation should explain in simple terms how electron microscopes work and why electron microscopes can magnify so greatly.
cooperative learning

3 Assess

Section 1 Review Answers

1. The invention of the microscope made it possible for people to discover and learn about cells.

2. According to the cell theory, all living things are made of cells, cells are the basic building blocks of life, and they are the only source of new cells.

3. Light passing through the first lens magnifies the object; then light passing through the second lens magnifies the image of the object even more.

4. Both magnification and resolution are important because magnification makes an object larger whereas resolution sharpens the image so you can see details.

5. Each time the microscope is improved, scientists can see structures in cells more clearly.

Check Your Progress
CHAPTER PROJECT 1

Make sure students have started soaking their eggs in vinegar and are measuring and recording their circumferences every day. Also check that they are measuring the eggs in the same way each time.

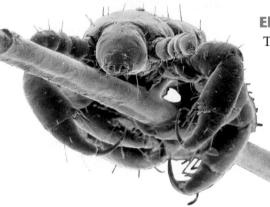

Figure 5 This head louse, shown clinging to a human hair, was photographed through a scanning electron microscope. It has been magnified to about 80 times its actual size.

Resolution To create a useful image, a microscope must also help you see individual parts clearly. The ability to clearly distinguish the individual parts of an object is called **resolution**. Resolution is another term for the sharpness of an image.

For example, when you use your eyes to look at a photo printed in a newspaper, it looks like a complete picture from one side to the other. That picture, however, is really made up of a collection of small dots. To the unaided eye, two tiny dots close together appear as one. If you put the photo under a microscope, however, you can see the dots. You see the dots not only because they are magnified but also because the microscope improves resolution. Good resolution—being able to see fine detail—is not needed when you are reading the newspaper. But it is just what you need when you study cells.

Electron Microscopes

The microscopes used by Hooke, Leeuwenhoek, and other early researchers were all light microscopes. Since the 1930s, scientists have developed different types of electron microscopes. Electron microscopes use a beam of electrons instead of light to examine a specimen. Electrons are tiny particles that are smaller than atoms. Because they use tiny electrons to produce images, the resolution of electron microscopes is much better than the resolution of light microscopes. As the technology of microscopes keeps improving, scientists will continue to learn more about the structure and function of cells.

Section 1 Review

1. How did the invention of the microscope affect scientists' understanding of living things?
2. Explain the three main ideas of the cell theory.
3. How does a compound microscope use lenses to magnify an object?
4. Explain why both magnification and resolution are important when viewing a small object with a microscope.
5. **Thinking Critically Applying Concepts** Why do scientists learn more about cells each time the microscope is improved?

Check Your Progress
CHAPTER PROJECT 1

By now you should have started your egg-speriment by soaking an uncooked egg in vinegar. Leave your egg in the vinegar for at least two days. Each day, rinse your egg in water and measure its circumference. Record all of your observations. (*Hint:* Handle the egg gently. If your egg breaks, don't give up or throw away your data. Simply start again with another egg and keep investigating.)

SECTION
2 Looking Inside Cells

DISCOVER ••••••••••••••••••••••••••• ACTIVITY ••••

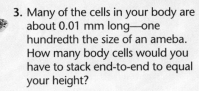

How Large Are Cells?

1. Look at the organism in the photo. The organism is an ameba, a large single-celled organism. This type of ameba is about 1 millimeter (mm) long.

2. Multiply your height in meters by 1,000 to get your height in millimeters. How many amebas would you have to stack end-to-end to equal your height?

3. Many of the cells in your body are about 0.01 mm long—one hundredth the size of an ameba. How many body cells would you have to stack end-to-end to equal your height?

Think It Over

Inferring Look at a metric ruler to see how small 1 mm is. Now imagine a distance one-hundredth as long, or 0.01 mm. Why can't you see your body's cells without the aid of a microscope?

Imagine you're in California standing next to a giant redwood tree. You have to bend your head way back to see the top of the tree. Some of these trees are over 75 meters tall and more than 10 meters in circumference! How do redwoods grow so large? How do they carry out all the functions necessary to stay alive?

To answer these questions, and to learn many other things about living things, you are about to take an imaginary journey. It will be quite an unusual trip. You will be traveling inside a living redwood tree, visiting its tiny cells. On your trip you will observe some of the structures found in plant cells. You will also learn about some of the differences between plant and animal cells.

GUIDE FOR READING

◆ What role do the cell membrane and nucleus play in the cell?

◆ What functions do other organelles in the cell perform?

◆ How do bacterial cells differ from plant and animal cells?

Reading Tip Before you read, preview *Exploring Plant and Animal Cells* on pages 26–27. Make a list of any unfamiliar terms. As you read, write a definition for each term.

◀ A giant redwood tree

Program Resources

◆ **Teaching Resources** 1-2 Lesson Plan, p. 19; 1-2 Section Summary, p. 20

Media and Technology

 Audiotapes English-Spanish Summary 1-2

READING STRATEGIES

Vocabulary Help students learn the many technical words in this section by having them construct crossword puzzles using the boldfaced terms. Urge students to exchange puzzles and try to solve them.

Study and Comprehension Before students read the section, suggest that they use the heads and subheads to make an outline.

Objectives

After completing the lesson, students will be able to
◆ identify the role of the cell membrane and nucleus in the cell;
◆ describe the functions performed by other organelles in the cell;
◆ compare bacterial cells with plant and animal cells;
◆ describe the role of specialized cells in many-celled organisms.

Key Terms organelle, cell wall, cell membrane, nucleus, chromatin, cytoplasm, mitochondrion, endoplasmic reticulum, ribosome, Golgi body, chloroplast, vacuole, lysosome

1 Engage/Explore

Activating Prior Knowledge

Introduce students to the division of labor among structures in cells by relating it to the division of labor in a community. Ask: **How are the various jobs in a town divided up among people?** *(Possible answers might include: shopkeepers supply food, police officers enforce laws, and the mayor and city council members make decisions.)* **Why is it effective to divide the labor in this way?** *(By dividing the labor, people can become specialized at the work they do and do it more effectively.)* Point out that, like a town and its people, cells have a division of labor among their structures.

•••••••• DISCOVER ••••••••

Skills Focus inferring
Materials *calculator, metric ruler*
Time 10 minutes
Tips If students do not know their height in meters, have partners measure each other's height with a metric ruler.
Expected Outcome A student who is 1.5 m tall would be the same height as a stack of 1,500 amebas. The same student would be 150,000 body cells tall.
Think It Over Students should infer that they cannot see body cells without a microscope because they are too small.

C ◆ 23

2 Facilitate

Cell Wall

Building Inquiry Skills: Inferring

Extend the analogy in the text by first naming several different parts of the body, including the brain, skin, and blood vessels, and challenging students to identify their roles in the body. Point out that each cell, like the body as a whole, has structures that perform similar functions. Then ask: **What are the functions of some organelles you would expect to find in the cell?** *(Answers should include an organelle like the brain to control the rest of the cell, an organelle like the skin to enclose and protect the cell, and an organelle like the blood vessels to carry materials from one part of the cell to another.)* **learning modality: logical/mathematical**

Cell Membrane

Including All Students

Help students still mastering English build language skills and improve their understanding of the cell membrane. First, challenge students to find the origin of the word *membrane* in a dictionary. *(Membrane comes from the Latin word,* membrana, *which means "skin.")* Then ask: **Do you think the skin on your body is a good analogy for the cell membrane? Why or why not?** *(Most students probably will say that the skin is a good analogy for the cell membrane, because both the cell membrane and the skin enclose and protect what's inside.)* **limited English proficiency**

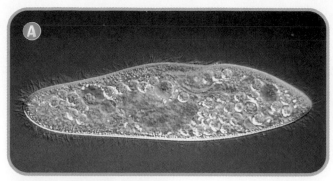

Figure 6 All cells have cell membranes, but not all cells have cell walls. **A.** The cell membrane of this single-celled paramecium controls what substances enter and leave the cell. **B.** The cell walls of these onion root cells have been stained green so you can see them clearly. Cell walls protect and support plant cells.

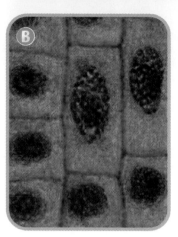

As you will discover on your journey, inside a cell are even smaller structures. These tiny cell structures, called **organelles,** carry out specific functions within the cell. Just as your stomach, lungs, and heart have different functions in your body, each organelle has a different function within the cell. You can see the organelles found in plant and animal cells in *Exploring Plant and Animal Cells* on pages 26 and 27. Now it's time to hop aboard your imaginary ship and prepare to enter a typical plant cell.

Cell Wall

Entering a plant's cell is a bit difficult. First you must pass through the cell wall. The **cell wall** is a rigid layer of nonliving material that surrounds plant cells. The cell wall is made of a tough, yet flexible, material called cellulose. If you think of a wooden desk, you will have a good idea of what cellulose is. Wood contains a lot of cellulose.

The cells of plants and some other organisms have cell walls. In contrast, the cells of animals and some other organisms lack cell walls. A plant's cell wall helps to protect and support the cell. In woody plants, the cell walls are very rigid. This is why giant redwood trees can stand so tall. Each cell wall in the tree adds strength to the tree. Although the cell wall is stiff, many materials, including water and oxygen, can pass through the cell wall quite easily. So sail on through the cell wall and enter the cell.

☑ *Checkpoint* *What is the function of the cell wall?*

Cell Membrane

As you pass through the cell wall, the next structure you encounter is the **cell membrane.** All cells have cell membranes. In cells with cell walls, the cell membrane is located just inside the cell wall. In other cells, the cell membrane forms the outside boundary that separates the cell from its environment.

Background

Facts and Figures Complex living things such as human beings are organized on several different levels, with the cell at the lowest level. The next level of organization is the tissue, which is composed of groups of similar cells. For example, muscle is a tissue made up of muscle cells. The next level of organization is the organ, which is composed of one or more types of tissue. For example, the heart is composed of muscle and other types of tissue. The next level of organization is the system, which is composed of different organs. The circulatory system is one example. It is composed of the heart and the blood vessels. The final level of organization is the individual organism, which is composed of different systems. A human being, for example, is composed of circulatory, digestive, and several other systems.

As your ship nears the edge of the cell membrane, you notice that there are tiny openings, or pores, in the cell membrane. You steer toward an opening. Suddenly, your ship narrowly misses being stuck by a chunk of waste material passing out of the cell. **You have discovered one of the cell membrane's main functions: the cell membrane controls what substances come into and out of a cell.**

Everything the cell needs—from food to oxygen—enters the cell through the cell membrane. Harmful waste products leave the cell through the cell membrane. For a cell to survive, the cell membrane must allow these materials to pass into and out of the cell. In a sense, the cell membrane is like a window screen. The screen keeps insects out of a room. But holes in the screen allow air to enter and leave the room.

Nucleus

As you sail inside the cell, a large, oval structure comes into view. This structure, called the **nucleus** (NOO klee us), acts as the "brain" of the cell. **You can think of the nucleus as the cell's control center, directing all of the cell's activities.**

Nuclear Membrane Notice in Figure 7 that the nucleus is surrounded by a nuclear membrane. Just as the cell membrane protects the cell, the nuclear membrane protects the nucleus. Materials pass in and out of the nucleus through small openings, or pores, in the nuclear membrane. So aim for that pore just ahead and carefully glide into the nucleus.

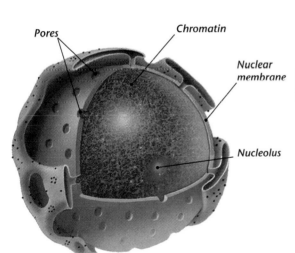

Pores

Chromatin

Nuclear membrane

Nucleolus

Figure 7 The nucleus is the cell's control center. The chromatin in the nucleus contains instructions for carrying out the cell's activities. *Interpreting Diagrams How do materials pass into and out of the nucleus?*

Language Arts
CONNECTION

Writers often use analogies to help readers understand unfamiliar ideas. In an analogy, a writer explains something by comparing it to something similar with which the reader is more familiar. For example, the author of this textbook describes the cell membrane by making an analogy to a window screen. This analogy helps the readers understand that the cell membrane is a boundary that separates the cell from the outside environment.

In Your Journal

Identify other analogies used by the author. Then choose two cell parts from this section. Write an analogy for each part that helps explain its structure or function.

Language Arts
CONNECTION

The analogy in the text, in which the cell membrane is compared with a window screen, is an extended analogy, because it is more than just a brief statement of comparison. Referring to the nucleus as the cell's "brain" is a simple analogy.

In Your Journal Examples of simple analogies in this section include referring to the mitochondria as the cell's "powerhouses" and the ribosomes as the cell's "factories." After students have finished writing in their journals, ask: **Why do analogies help you better understand the parts of a cell?** *(Because they compare them with things that are more familiar or easier to understand.)* **learning modality: verbal**

Nucleus

Building Inquiry Skills: Comparing and Contrasting

Time 5 minutes

ACTIVITY

Help students avoid confusing the cell membrane and nuclear membrane by having them form two concentric circles in the classroom and asking: **Which circle represents the nuclear membrane? Which circle represents the cell membrane?** *(The inner circle represents the nuclear membrane. The outer circle represents the cell membrane.)* **How is the nuclear membrane like the cell membrane? How is it different?** *(Both are thin films that enclose and protect what is inside the membrane. However, the nuclear membrane encloses and protects just the cell's nucleus, whereas the cell membrane encloses and protects the entire cell.)* **learning modality: kinesthetic**

Program Resources

◆ **Integrated Science Laboratory Manual** C-1, "Cell Membranes and Permeability"

Answers to Self-Assessment

Checkpoint

The function of the cell wall is to help protect and support the cell.

Caption Question

Figure 7 Materials pass into and out of the nucleus through small openings, or pores, in the nuclear membrane.

Ongoing Assessment

Oral Presentation Call on students at random to identify differences and similarities between cell walls and cell membranes.

EXPLORING
Plant and Animal Cells

Call students' attention to the feature, and ask if they have any questions. Point out that some cell structures, including Golgi bodies, ribosomes, and mitochondria, are defined on just one drawing or the other because they are much the same in both plant cells and animal cells. Help students organize the material in the feature by creating a table on the chalkboard titled "Comparison of Plant and Animal Cells." For headings use *Similarities* and *Differences,* and for rows use *Plants* and *Animals.* Encourage students to interpret the diagrams and other information in the feature to help fill in the cells of the table. Stimulate their thinking by asking: **Which organelles are found only in plant cells? Which are found in both plant and animal cells?** *(Except for cell walls and chloroplasts, most organelles are found in both plant and animal cells.)* Complete the table as students volunteer their ideas. When the table is finished, you may want to have students copy it in a notebook and refer to it as they study this section. **learning modality: verbal**

Addressing Naive Conceptions

Emphasize that the drawings of plant and animal cells shown in the feature are generalized representations of cells. In reality, cells can take on many different shapes and sizes. They also can vary in the specific organelles they contain. For comparison, show students drawings of other types of cells, such as leaf and root cells for plants and muscle and bone cells for animals. In each drawing, challenge students to locate the cell membrane and organelles if these are visible. Ask: **Why do you think different cells look so different from each other?** *(Because they play different roles in the organism.)* **learning modality: visual**

EXPLORING Plant and Animal Cells

On these pages, you can compare structures found in two kinds of cells: plant cells and animal cells. As you study these cells, remember that they are generalized cells. In living organisms, cells vary somewhat in shape and structure.

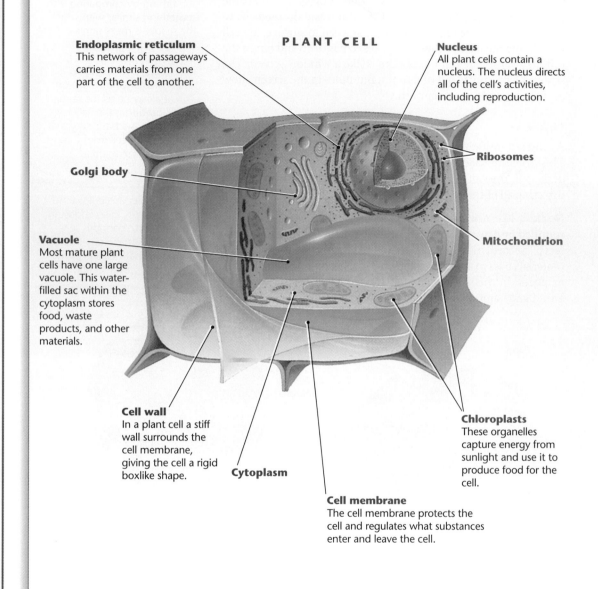

PLANT CELL

Endoplasmic reticulum This network of passageways carries materials from one part of the cell to another.

Nucleus All plant cells contain a nucleus. The nucleus directs all of the cell's activities, including reproduction.

Golgi body

Ribosomes

Mitochondrion

Vacuole Most mature plant cells have one large vacuole. This water-filled sac within the cytoplasm stores food, waste products, and other materials.

Cell wall In a plant cell a stiff wall surrounds the cell membrane, giving the cell a rigid boxlike shape.

Cytoplasm

Cell membrane The cell membrane protects the cell and regulates what substances enter and leave the cell.

Chloroplasts These organelles capture energy from sunlight and use it to produce food for the cell.

Background

Facts and Figures Many types of organisms are unicellular. Bacteria are single-celled organisms called prokaryotes. Prokaryotic cells do not contain nuclei and most other cell organelles. Many protists, such as paramecia and amebas, are unicellular organisms called eukaryotes. Eukaryotic cells contain nuclei and most cell organelles.

Paramecia have many hairlike projections

called cilia that beat rhythmically to propel the paramecia through water. Paramecia also use cilia to obtain food. Amebas move by forming pseudopods, or "false feet"—bulges in their cell membranes into which cytoplasm flows. To feed, amebas surround smaller organisms with their pseudopods, thereby entrapping their prey in vacuoles inside the cytoplasm of their cells.

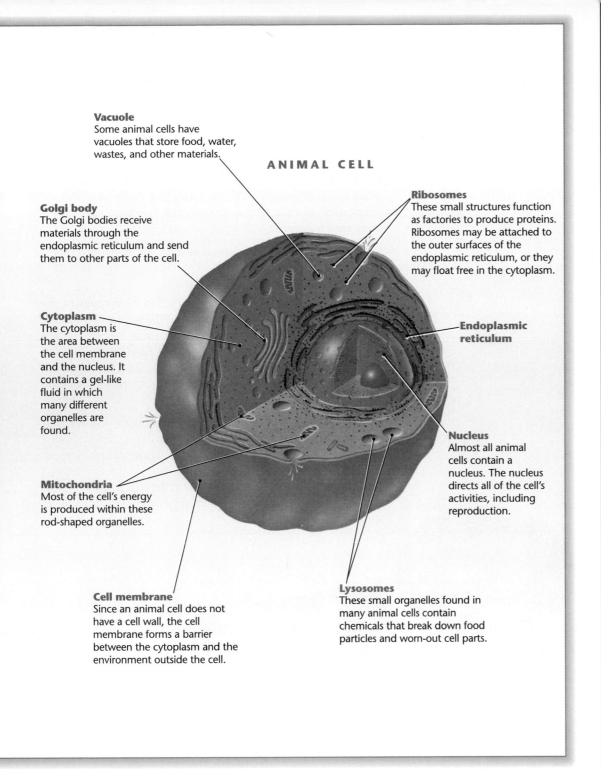

Vacuole
Some animal cells have vacuoles that store food, water, wastes, and other materials.

ANIMAL CELL

Golgi body
The Golgi bodies receive materials through the endoplasmic reticulum and send them to other parts of the cell.

Ribosomes
These small structures function as factories to produce proteins. Ribosomes may be attached to the outer surfaces of the endoplasmic reticulum, or they may float free in the cytoplasm.

Cytoplasm
The cytoplasm is the area between the cell membrane and the nucleus. It contains a gel-like fluid in which many different organelles are found.

Endoplasmic reticulum

Nucleus
Almost all animal cells contain a nucleus. The nucleus directs all of the cell's activities, including reproduction.

Mitochondria
Most of the cell's energy is produced within these rod-shaped organelles.

Cell membrane
Since an animal cell does not have a cell wall, the cell membrane forms a barrier between the cytoplasm and the environment outside the cell.

Lysosomes
These small organelles found in many animal cells contain chemicals that break down food particles and worn-out cell parts.

Media and Technology

Transparencies "Exploring a Plant Cell," Transparency 2; "Exploring an Animal Cell," Transparency 3

Including All Students

Materials *10 index cards*
Time 20 minutes

Students who are not native English speakers and any other students who are having difficulty with the material on the parts of the cell may benefit from creating and using flash cards. On one side of each flash card, students should write the name of a cell structure. On the other side, they should summarize in their own words the structure's function in the cell. When students have finished, check to make sure they have correctly identified each cell structure. For example, ask: **What does the cell membrane do?** *(It protects the cell and controls what enters and leaves it.)* **What does the nucleus do?** *(It directs all the cell's activities)* Then divide students into pairs and challenge them to use their flash cards to quiz each other. **limited English proficiency**

Demonstration

Materials *microprojector, prepared slide of plant cells, prepared slide of animal cells*
Time 10 minutes

Help students relate the generalized cells shown in *Exploring Plant and Animal Cells* to actual plant and animal cells. Use a microprojector to project first a prepared slide of plant cells and then a prepared slide of animal cells onto a screen. (If a microprojector is not available, use an opaque projector and photographs of plant and animal cells.) Challenge students to locate the cell wall or cell membrane, nucleus, and other organelles on the projected images. Encourage students to describe how the actual cells vary in shape and structure from the generalized cells in the text. **learning modality: visual**

Ongoing Assessment

Skills Check Have students write two lists, one summarizing the similarities between plant and animal cells, the other summarizing the differences. Students can save their lists in their portfolios.

Nucleus, continued

Addressing Naive Conceptions

Because cells can be so different, students may think that different types of cells within an organism must contain different genetic material. Point out to students that exactly the same genetic material is found in every cell of an organism. Explain that different cells in their bodies, such as skin cells and blood cells, look and function so differently because they respond to different genetic instructions. Ask: **Can you think of an analogy to different cells containing the same genetic material, yet looking and functioning differently because they are following different genetic instructions?** *(One possible analogy is the same cookbook being used by different cooks to make different recipes.)* **learning modality: verbal**

Organelles in the Cytoplasm

Inquiry Challenge

Materials *sheets of plain white paper, markers, cans of food, bottles of water, batteries, storage boxes, other miscellaneous items*
Time 15 minutes

After students have read about all of the organelles, challenge them to make a human model of a cell that shows how two or more organelles function. One possible way is for one student to represent each type of organelle and the rest of the class to represent the cell and nuclear membranes. Provide students with paper and markers for making signs and with props such as those listed above. Encourage students to use any other suitable props they wish. Give students enough time to plan and prepare their model. Then have them demonstrate the functioning of the organelles in the cell. *(For example, a sign labeled "protein" might be passed from a student representing a ribosome to a student representing an endoplasmic reticulum, who then carries the "protein" to the students representing the cell membrane, one of whom passes the sign out of the "cell.")* **cooperative learning**

Chromatin You might wonder how the nucleus "knows" how to direct the cell. The answer lies in those thin strands floating directly ahead in the nucleus. These strands, called **chromatin,** contain the genetic material, the instructions that direct the functions of a cell. For example, the instructions in the chromatin ensure that leaf cells grow and divide to form more leaf cells. The genetic material is passed on to each new cell when an existing cell divides. You'll learn more about how cells divide in Chapter 2.

Nucleolus As you prepare to leave the nucleus, you spot a small object floating by. This structure, the nucleolus, is where ribosomes are made. Ribosomes are the organelles where proteins are produced.

☑ *Checkpoint* *Where in the nucleus is genetic material found?*

Organelles in the Cytoplasm

As you leave the nucleus, you find yourself in the **cytoplasm,** the region between the cell membrane and the nucleus. Your ship floats in a clear, thick, gel-like fluid. The fluid in the cytoplasm is constantly moving, so your ship does not need to propel itself. Many cell organelles are found in the cytoplasm. **The organelles function to produce energy, build and transport needed materials, and store and recycle wastes.**

Mitochondria As you pass into the cytoplasm, you see rod-shaped structures looming ahead. These organelles are called **mitochondria** (my tuh KAHN dree uh) (singular *mitochondrion*). Mitochondria are called the "powerhouses" of the cell because they produce most of the energy the cell needs to carry out its functions. Muscle cells and other very active cells have large numbers of mitochondria.

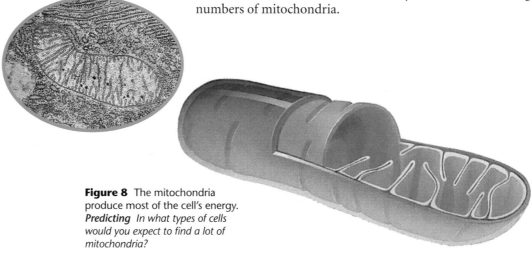

Figure 8 The mitochondria produce most of the cell's energy. *Predicting In what types of cells would you expect to find a lot of mitochondria?*

Background

Facts and Figures In both plant and animal cells, mitochondria have a smooth outer membrane and a folded inner membrane with a lot of surface area where chemical reactions take place. Because energy is released during these chemical reactions, mitochondria frequently are called the "powerhouses" of the cell.

Both mitochondria and chloroplasts have a double membrane and the ability to divide. In addition, both contain small amounts of DNA. These three features also characterize some bacteria, leading some biologists to think that mitochondria and chloroplasts are descendants of bacteria that lived as independent organisms long ago.

Figure 9 The endoplasmic reticulum is a passageway through which proteins and other materials move within the cell. The spots on the outside of the endoplasmic reticulum are ribosomes, structures that produce proteins.

Endoplasmic Reticulum As you sail farther into the cytoplasm, you find yourself in a maze of passageways called the **endoplasmic reticulum** (en duh PLAZ mik rih TIK yuh lum). These passageways carry proteins and other materials from one part of the cell to another. Now steer your ship into one of these passageways.

Ribosomes Attached to the outer surface of the endoplasmic reticulum are small grainlike bodies called **ribosomes.** Other ribosomes are found floating in the cytoplasm. Ribosomes function as factories to produce proteins. The ribosomes release some proteins through the wall of the endoplasmic reticulum. From the interior of the endoplasmic reticulum, the proteins will be transported to the Golgi bodies.

Golgi Bodies As you move through the endoplasmic reticulum, you see structures that look like a flattened collection of sacs and tubes. These structures, called **Golgi bodies,** can be thought of as the cell's mailroom. The Golgi bodies receive proteins and other newly formed materials from the endoplasmic reticulum, package them, and distribute them to other parts of the cell.

Chloroplasts Have you noticed the many large green structures floating in the cytoplasm? Only the cells of plants and some other organisms have these structures. These organelles, called **chloroplasts,** capture energy from sunlight and use it to produce food for the cell. It is the chloroplasts that give plants their green color. You will learn more about chloroplasts in Chapter 2.

Gelatin Cell

Make your own model of a cell.

1. Dissolve a packet of colorless gelatin in warm water. Pour the gelatin into a rectangular pan (for a plant cell) or a round pan (for an animal cell).

2. Choose different materials that resemble each of the cell structures found in the cell you are modeling. Insert these materials into the gelatin before it begins to solidify.

Making Models On a sheet of paper, develop a key that identifies each cell structure in your model. Describe the function of each structure.

Chapter 1 **C ◆ 29**

Answers to Self-Assessment

☑ *Checkpoint*

The genetic material in the nucleus is found in strands called chromatin.

Caption Question

Figure 8 You would expect to find a lot of mitochondria in muscle cells and other very active cells.

TRY THIS

Skills Focus making models

Materials *packet of colorless gelatin, warm water, other miscellaneous materials to represent cell structures, rectangular or round pan*

Time 10 minutes one day; 10 minutes later the same day

Tips Advise students to stir the gelatin until it dissolves completely in the warm water. Suggest that they leave the gelatin in the refrigerator for up to an hour until it starts to thicken before they add the "cell structures." Make sure the water is not too hot for students to work safely.

Expected Outcome Students should create a round gelatin mold to represent an animal cell or a rectangular gelatin mold to represent a plant cell. The gelatin should contain objects to represent each of the cell structures described on pages 26 or 27, and there should be a key identifying and describing each of the structures.

Extend Challenge hands-on learners to make a model of an animal cell with gelatin using a resealable plastic bag instead of a pan for a mold. Ask: **What does the bag represent in your model?** *(Students probably will say the cell membrane.)* Give students a chance to handle the plastic bag after the gelatin in it solidifies, then ask: **Why is the plastic-bag model a better representation of an animal cell than the pan model?** *(There is no "cell wall," as there is with the pan, to support the cell and make it rigid.)*
learning modality: kinesthetic

Ongoing Assessment

Skills Check Have each student create a table listing at least five organelles in the cell and summarizing their functions.

 Students can save their tables in their portfolios.

Organelles in the Cytoplasm, continued

Demonstration

Materials *wilted houseplant, water*

Time 5 minutes at the beginning of class, 5 minutes at the end of class

Call students' attention to the passage in the text that describes how plants look when their vacuoles are full of water and how they look when their vacuoles do not contain much water. Then show students a wilted coleus or impatiens that is in need of water. Water the plant thoroughly. By the end of class, the plant should no longer be drooping. Ask: **Why is the plant no longer wilted?** *(Its vacuoles have filled up with water.)*
learning modality: visual

Bacterial Cells

Using the Visuals: Figure 10

Call students' attention to the figure, and then read the following description from the text of a bacterial cell's genetic material: ". . . a thick, tangled string found in the cytoplasm." Ask: **Can you find this bacterium's genetic material?** *(Help students who cannot find the genetic material locate it in the figure.)* **Besides a nucleus, what organelles does this bacterium appear to be lacking?** *(Possible answers include mitochondria, chloroplasts, and endoplasmic reticulum.)*
learning modality: visual

Building Inquiry Skills: Observing

Materials *soil, water, plastic dropper, microscope slide, coverslip, microscope*

Time 15 minutes

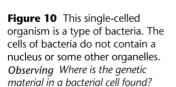 Have students observe bacterial cells under a microscope. Mix soil into water, and let the mixture sit out in an open, shallow container for several days. Then place drops of the water on microscope slides. Invite students to observe the water under high power and sketch any bacterial cells they find. Have them compare their sketches with photos of bacteria from either textbooks or encyclopedias. **learning modality: visual**

Vacuoles Steer past the chloroplasts and head for that large, round, water-filled sac floating in the cytoplasm. This sac, called a **vacuole** (VAK yoo ohl), is the storage area of the cell. Most plant cells have one large vacuole. Some animal cells do not have vacuoles; others do.

Vacuoles store food and other materials needed by the cell. Vacuoles can also store waste products. Most of the water in plant cells is stored in vacuoles. When the vacuoles are full of water, they make the cell plump and firm. Without much water in the vacuoles, the plant wilts.

Lysosomes Your journey through the cell is almost over. Before you leave, take another look around you. If you carefully swing your ship around the vacuole, you may be lucky enough to see a lysosome. **Lysosomes** (LY suh sohmz) are small round structures that contain chemicals that break down large food particles into smaller ones. Lysosomes also break down old cell parts and release the substances so they can be used again. In this sense, you can think of the lysosomes as the cell's cleanup crew. Lysosomes are more common in animal cells than in plant cells.

Although lysosomes contain powerful chemicals, you need not worry about your ship's safety. The membrane around a lysosome keeps these harsh chemicals from escaping and breaking down the rest of the cell.

Bacterial Cells

The plant and animal cells that you just learned about are very different from the bacterial cell you see in Figure 10. First, bacterial cells are usually smaller than plant or animal cells. A human skin cell, for example, is about 10 times as large as an average bacterial cell.

There are several other ways in which bacterial cells are different from plant and animal cells. **While a bacterial cell does have a cell wall and a cell membrane, it does not contain a nucleus.** The bacterial cell's genetic material, which looks like a thick, tangled string, is found in the cytoplasm. Bacterial cells contain ribosomes, but none of the other organelles found in plant or animal cells.

Figure 10 This single-celled organism is a type of bacteria. The cells of bacteria do not contain a nucleus or some other organelles. *Observing* Where is the genetic material in a bacterial cell found?

Background

Integrating Science Bacteria are found virtually everywhere, both inside and outside the human body. Some bacteria cause no harm—in fact, we need them to help break down food and eliminate waste. Other bacteria are harmful, and when they enter the body they may make us ill. Common examples of harmful bacteria include *Streptococcus* bacteria, which cause "strep" throat, and *Salmonella* bacteria, which cause food poisoning.

Bacteria are the most abundant life forms on Earth, and they have existed almost as long as the planet itself. In fact, some fossil bacteria have been found that are about 3.5 billion years old.

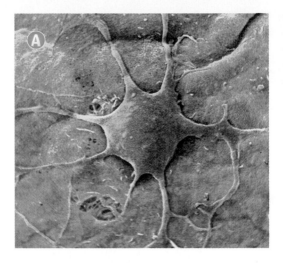

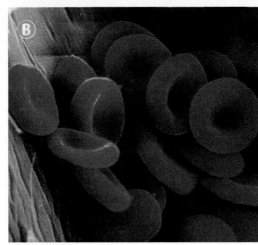

Figure 11 Your body contains a variety of different types of cells. **A.** Nerve cells have long projections through which messages are sent throughout the body. **B.** Red blood cells are thin and flexible, which allows them to fit through tiny blood vessels.

Specialized Cells

Unlike bacteria and other single-celled organisms, plants, animals (including yourself), and other organisms contain many cells. In a many-celled organism, the cells are often quite different from each other in size and structure. Think of the different parts of your body. You have skin, bones, muscles, blood, a brain, a liver, a stomach, and so on. Each of these body parts carries out a very different function. Yet all of these body parts are made up of cells. Figure 11 shows two examples of different kinds of cells in your body. The structure of each kind of cell is suited to the unique function it carries out within the organism.

Section 2 Review

1. What is the function of the cell membrane?
2. Why is the nucleus sometimes called the control center of the cell?
3. Name two plant cell parts that are not found in animal cells. What is the function of each part?
4. How do the cells of bacteria differ from those of other organisms?
5. **Thinking Critically Comparing and Contrasting** Compare the functions of the cell wall in a plant cell and the cell membrane in an animal cell. How are the functions of the two structures similar and different?

Check Your Progress

CHAPTER PROJECT 1

At this point, you should soak your egg for one or two days in water, then in water with food coloring, then in salt water, and finally in another liquid of your choice. Continue to rinse your egg and measure and record its circumference every day. Your egg should be going through some amazing changes in appearance.

Answers to Self-Assessment

Caption Question

Figure 10 The genetic material in a bacterial cell is found in the cytoplasm.

Specialized Cells

Using the Visuals: Figure 11

Help visual learners relate cell structure to function. First have students compare the nerve cell and the red blood cells shown in the figure with the model animal cell shown on page 27. Then ask: **In what ways do the real cells look different from the model?** *(The nerve cell looks like it has "arms," and the red blood cells look flattened or donut-shaped.)* **How do you think each cell's shape helps it do its job?** *(The "arms" on nerve cells help them reach out and send messages to other cells; the flatness of red blood cells helps them squeeze through tiny blood vessels.)* **learning modality: visual**

3 Assess

Section 2 Review Answers

1. It separates a cell from its environment and controls what substances go into and come out of the cell.
2. It holds the genetic material, which contains the instructions for the cell's functions.
3. The cell wall supports and stiffens the cell, and the chloroplasts make food.
4. The cells of bacteria are smaller and do not contain a nucleus or any organelles except ribosomes.
5. Both surround the cell and allow some materials to pass through. The cell wall is rigid, and it supports the cell; the cell membrane is flexible, and it regulates what goes into and comes out of the cell.

Check Your Progress

CHAPTER PROJECT 1

Make sure students are not having problems with the project. Call on volunteers to describe the changes they have noticed in their egg. *(After two days in vinegar, the shell should have dissolved and the egg should have increased in size and become rubbery in texture.)*

Performance Assessment

Drawing Have students draw a plant cell, animal cell, and bacterial cell and label their structures.

A Magnified View of Life

Preparing for Inquiry

Key Concept Plant and animals cells have both similarities and differences.
Skills Objectives Students will be able to
◆ observe and draw cells under the microscope;
◆ compare and contrast plant and animal cells.
Time 40 minutes
Advance Planning You can order prepared slides of animal cells from a biological supply company.
Alternative Materials You may wish to have students use prepared slides of plant cells instead of preparing their own slides.

Guiding Inquiry
Troubleshooting the Experiment

◆ Tell students to raise the lenses before going from low to high power so they do not damage the microscope or slide.
◆ Check to be sure students have focused their microscopes correctly.
◆ Remind students to label their diagrams with the magnification.

Expected Outcome

Students should observe individual plant and animal cells under the microscope and draw diagrams that show their similarities and differences.

Analyze and Conclude

1. Both kinds of cells have a cell membrane, nucleus, and such organelles as mitochondria and ribosomes.
2. Plant cells have a cell wall and chloroplasts, whereas animal cells do not.
3. The color is green; it comes from chloroplasts in the plant cells.
4. So you do not forget details

Extending the Inquiry

More to Explore Provide students with slides of animal cells that look very different, such as red blood cells and muscle cells, and check that students can identify differences among them.

A Magnified View of Life

In this lab, you will use your observation skills to compare plant and animal cells.

Problem

How are plant and animal cells alike and different?

Materials

plastic dropper
water
microscope slide
microscope
colored pencils
prepared slide of animal cells

Elodea leaf
forceps
coverslip

Procedure

1. Before you start this lab, read *Using the Microscope* (Appendix B) on pages 190–191. Be sure you know how to use a microscope correctly and safely.

Part 1 Observing Plant Cells

2. Use a plastic dropper to place a drop of water in the center of a slide. **CAUTION:** *Slides and coverslips are fragile. Handle them carefully. Do not touch broken glass.*
3. With forceps, remove a leaf from an *Elodea* plant. Place the leaf in the drop of water on the slide. Make sure that the leaf is flat. If it is folded, straighten it with the forceps.
4. Holding a coverslip by its edges, slowly lower it onto the drop of water and *Elodea* leaf. If any air bubbles form, tap the slide gently to get rid of them.

5. Use a microscope to examine the *Elodea* leaf under low power. Then, carefully switch to high power.
6. Observe the cells of the *Elodea* leaf. Draw and label what you see, including the colors of the cell parts. Record the magnification.
7. Discard the *Elodea* leaf as directed by your teacher. Carefully clean and dry your slide and coverslip. Wash your hands thoroughly.

Part 2 Observing Animals Cells

8. Obtain a prepared slide of animal cells. The cells on the slide have been stained with an artificial color.
9. Observe the animal cells with a microscope under both low and high power. Draw and label the cell parts that you see. Record the magnification.

Analyze and Conclude

1. How are plant and animal cells alike?
2. How are plant and animal cells different?
3. What natural color appeared in the plant cells? What structures give the plant cells this color?
4. **Think About It** Why is it important to record your observations while you are examining a specimen?

More to Explore

Observe other prepared slides of animal cells. Look for ways that animal cells differ from each other. Obtain your teacher's permission before carrying out these observations.

Program Resources

◆ **Teaching Resources** Chapter 1 Skills Lab, pp. 31–32

Safety

Remind students to handle glass slides and coverslips carefully. Review the safety guidelines in Appendix A.

SECTION 3 Chemical Compounds in Cells

DISCOVER •••••••••••••••••••••••••••••••• ACTIVITY •••••

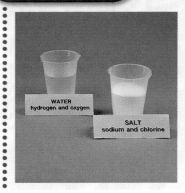

What Is a Compound?

1. Your teacher will provide you with containers filled with various substances. All of the substances are chemical compounds.

2. Examine each substance. Read the label on each container to learn what each substance is made of.

Think It Over

Forming Operational Definitions Write a definition of what you think a chemical compound is.

If cells are the basic building blocks of living things, then what substances are the basic building blocks of cells? In what ways are the basic building blocks of cells similar to those that make up other things around you? In this section you will explore how the substances that make up living cells differ from those that make up nonliving things.

Elements and Compounds

Think about the air around you. You probably know that air is a mixture of gases, including oxygen and nitrogen. Oxygen and nitrogen are examples of elements. An **element** is any substance that cannot be broken down into simpler substances. The smallest unit of an element is called an **atom.** An element is made up of only one kind of atom. The most common elements in living things, including you, are carbon, oxygen, hydrogen, and nitrogen.

When two or more elements combine chemically they form a **compound.** Water, for example, is a compound made up of the elements hydrogen and oxygen. The smallest unit of most compounds is called a **molecule.** Each water molecule is made up of two hydrogen atoms and one oxygen atom.

GUIDE FOR READING

◆ What are the four main kinds of organic molecules in living things?

◆ How is water important to the function of cells?

Reading Tip As you read, make a table of the main types of organic molecules and where in the cell each one is found.

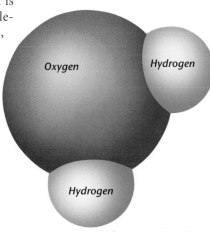

Oxygen
Hydrogen
Hydrogen

The structure of a water molecule ▶

Chapter 1   **C ◆ 33**

Program Resources

 Science Explorer Series *Chemical Building Blocks,* Chapter 4, has more information about chemical compounds.
◆ **Teaching Resources** 1-3 Lesson Plan, p. 23; 1-3 Section Summary, p. 24

Media and Technology

🎧 **Audiotapes** English-Spanish Summary 1-3

READING STRATEGIES

Reading Tip Students' tables should include carbohydrates, lipids, proteins, and nucleic acids and identify where each is found in the cell.

Vocabulary This section contains several terms, such as *amino acid, enzyme, lipid,* and *nucleic acid,* that may be unfamiliar to students. To help students better understand and retain the material, make sure they know how to spell and pronounce each term.

SECTION 3 Chemical Compounds in Cells

Objectives

After completing the lesson, students will be able to
◆ describe the four main kinds of organic molecules in living things;
◆ explain how water is essential to the functioning of cells.

Key Terms element, atom, compound, molecule, organic compound, inorganic compound, carbohydrate, protein, amino acid, enzyme, lipid, nucleic acid, DNA, RNA

1 Engage/Explore

Activating Prior Knowledge

Write this "recipe" for the human body on the board: 50 L of water (hydrogen, oxygen); 16 kg of coal (carbon); and about 5 kg total of fireworks (potassium, nitrogen, carbon, sulfur), chalk (calcium, carbon), matches (phosphorus), salt (sodium, chlorine), and several metals (including iron). Ask **What are the three chief chemical "ingredients" of the body?** (*Hydrogen, oxygen, and carbon*)

•••••••• DISCOVER ••••••••

Skills Focus forming operational definitions ACTIVITY
Materials *labeled containers of chemical compounds such as salt, zinc oxide sun block, baking soda, and chalk*
Time 10 minutes
Tips Label the compounds with their common and chemical names (sodium chloride for salt, zinc oxide for sun block, sodium bicarbonate for baking soda, and calcium carbonate for chalk).
Expected Outcome Students should discover that all the compounds consist of two or more different elements.
Think It Over Students may say that a chemical compound is something that is made up of more than one substance.

2 Facilitate

Elements and Compounds

Including All Students

For students who need more help, relate atoms to elements by showing them the periodic table of the elements and pointing out that the elements are arranged according to their atomic number. Explain that the atomic number is the number of protons, or positively charged particles, in each atom of the element. Add that elements have standard symbols, such as H for hydrogen, O for oxygen, and C for carbon. Ask: **What are the atomic numbers of the three elements that are most common in living things?** (*1 for hydrogen, 8 for oxygen, and 6 for carbon*) **learning modality: visual**

Organic and Inorganic Compounds

Including All Students

Help students understand the difference between the terms organic and inorganic by explaining that the combining form *organ-* means "having to do with life" and the prefix *in-* means "not." Then ask: **Based on these meanings, what does inorganic mean?** (*Not having to do with life.*) Ask: **Can you think of other words that start with** *organ-*? (*organism, organelle*) **Can you think of other words that contain the prefix** *in-* **meaning "not"?** (*indecent, incredible*) **limited English proficiency**

Carbohydrates

Real-Life Learning

Point out that carbohydrates are the most important source of energy for the body. Then challenge students to describe a healthful meal that is high in carbohydrates. (*One possible meal is spaghetti with tomato sauce, bread, peas, grape juice, and a banana.*) **learning modality: verbal**

Organic and Inorganic Compounds

Many of the compounds found in living things contain the element carbon, which is usually combined with other elements. Most compounds that contain carbon are called **organic compounds.**

The most important groups of organic compounds found in living things are carbohydrates, lipids, proteins, and nucleic acids. As you may know, many of these compounds are found in the foods you eat. This is not surprising, since the foods you eat come from living things.

Compounds that don't contain the element carbon are called **inorganic compounds.** One exception to this definition is carbon dioxide. Although carbon dioxide contains carbon, it is classified as an inorganic compound. Other inorganic compounds include water and sodium chloride, or table salt.

Carbohydrates

A **carbohydrate** is an energy-rich organic compound made of the elements carbon, hydrogen, and oxygen. Sugars and starches are examples of carbohydrates.

Sugars are produced during the food-making process that takes place in plants. Foods such as fruits and some vegetables are high in sugar content. Sugar molecules can combine, forming large molecules called starches. Plant cells store excess energy in molecules of starch. Many foods that come from plants contain starch. These foods include potatoes, noodles, rice, and bread. When you eat these foods, your body breaks down the starch into glucose, a sugar, which your cells can use to produce energy.

Carbohydrates are important components of some cell parts. The cellulose found in the cell walls of plants is a type of carbohydrate. Carbohydrates are also found in cell membranes.

Figure 12 These potatoes contain large amounts of starch, a type of carbohydrate. The blue grains you see in the closeup are starch granules in a potato. The grains have been colored blue to make them easier to see. *Classifying What types of carbohydrates combine to form starches?*

Background

History of Science In the 1920s, some scientists thought that life on Earth began to arise when a random series of chemical reactions in a primeval sea produced the first organic compounds. However it was not until 1953 that anyone presented experimental evidence to support this theory. In that year, the American scientist Stanley Miller modeled early conditions on Earth using a sealed chamber that contained gases thought to exist in Earth's early atmosphere and water that simulated the primeval sea. At intervals, he introduced an electric spark into the chamber as an energy source. After a week, Miller examined the contents of the sealed chamber and found organic compounds, including amino acids, which are the building blocks of proteins.

Figure 13 This bird's feathers are made up mainly of proteins. Proteins are important components of the cell membrane and many of the cell's organelles.

Proteins

What do a bird's feathers, a spider's web, and your fingernails have in common? All of these substances are made mainly of proteins. **Proteins** are large organic molecules made of carbon, hydrogen, oxygen, nitrogen, and, in some cases, sulfur. Foods that are high in protein include meat, eggs, fish, nuts, and beans.

Cells use proteins for many different things. For instance, proteins form parts of cell membranes. Proteins also make up many of the organelles within the cell. Certain cells in your body use proteins to build body parts such as hair.

Protein Structure Protein molecules are made up of smaller molecules called **amino acids.** Although there are only 20 common amino acids, cells can combine them in different ways to form thousands of different proteins. The kinds of amino acids and the order in which they link together determine the type of protein that forms. You can think of the 20 amino acids as being like the 26 letters of the alphabet. Those 26 letters can form thousands of words. The letters you use and their order determine the words you form. Even a change in one letter, for example, from *rice* to *mice*, creates a new word. Similarly, changes in the type or order of amino acids result in a different protein.

Enzymes An **enzyme** is a type of protein that speeds up a chemical reaction in a living thing. Without enzymes, many chemical reactions that are necessary for life would either take too long, or not occur at all. For example, enzymes in your saliva speed up the digestion of food by breaking down starches into sugars in your mouth.

☑ *Checkpoint* What is the role of enzymes?

What's That Taste?

Use this activity to discover one role that enzymes play in your body.

ACTIVITY

1. Put an unsalted soda cracker in your mouth. Chew it up, but do not swallow. Note what the cracker tastes like.

2. Continue to chew the cracker for a few minutes, mixing it well with your saliva. Note how the taste of the cracker changes.

Inferring Soda crackers are made up mainly of starch, with little sugar. How can you account for the change in taste after you chewed the cracker for a few minutes?

Proteins

Demonstration
Materials *pot of water, hot plate*

Time 10 minutes

Demonstrate to students how enzymes work to speed up chemical reactions by showing them a visual analogy. Use heat instead of an enzyme to speed up a chemical reaction, in this case making pudding. Mix a package of pudding (not instant) according to the directions on the package. Cook the mixture until it thickens, then ask: **What happened to the pudding?** (*It became thick.*) **How long would it have taken the pudding to thicken without heating it?** (*Much longer, perhaps not at all*) **How is the heat of the hot plate like an enzyme?** (*Both speed up chemical reactions.*) Explain that heat provides energy to speed up chemical reactions, whereas most enzymes work like chemical "matchmakers," bringing chemicals together so they can interact more quickly. **learning modality: visual**

TRY THIS

Skills Focus inferring
Materials *unsalted soda cracker*

Time 5 minutes
Expected Outcome After students have chewed the cracker for a minute or two, it should start to taste slightly sweet. Students should infer that enzymes in their saliva helped break down the cracker's starch into sugar.
Extend Ask: **How can you tell that a food is high in sugar?** (*It tastes sweet.*)
learning modality: kinesthetic

Answers to Self-Assessment

Caption Question
Figure 12 Sugars combine to form starches.

☑ *Checkpoint*
Enzymes speed up chemical reactions in living things.

Ongoing Assessment

Oral Presentation Call on students at random to give examples of foods high in carbohydrates or proteins. (*High-carbohydrate foods include fruits, potatoes, pasta, noodles, and bread; high-protein foods include meat, eggs, fish, nuts, and beans.*)

Lipids

Ask: **Based on the picture on the right, what are some specific foods you eat that are high in lipids?** *(Possible answers might include cheeseburgers, butter, and milkshakes.)* Point out that the main role of lipids in the body is to store energy. Ask: **Why might you gain weight if you ate large amounts of foods such as these?** *(You would not need all the energy they provided, and the excess lipids would be stored as fat.)* **learning modality: visual**

Integrating Health

To help students understand how cholesterol is both crucial for their cells and bad for their health, have them read the paragraph to find answers to the following series of questions. **What role does cholesterol play in your body?** *(It is an important component of cell membranes.)* Explain that, like most other important substances it needs, your body has a way of producing enough cholesterol. Then ask: **Where is cholesterol produced in your body?** *(the liver)* **How does your liver meet your body's cholesterol needs?** *(It produces enough cholesterol to meet the body's needs.)* **What might happen if you ate too much high-cholesterol food?** *(You would have too much cholesterol.)* **Why might this be bad for your health?** *(Excess cholesterol can block blood vessels.)* **learning modality: verbal**

Nucleic Acids

Building Inquiry Skills: Comparing and Contrasting

Challenge students to compare and contrast the two major types of nucleic acids in the body. Ask: **How are DNA and RNA similar?** *(Both are nucleic acids, which are very large compounds containing oxygen, hydrogen, nitrogen, and phosphorus. Both also contain genetic instructions for the cell.)* **How are DNA and RNA different?** *(DNA is found in the nucleus; RNA is found in both the cytoplasm and the nucleus.)* **learning modality: logical/mathematical**

Figure 14 Cholesterol is a lipid found in foods that come from animals. Excess cholesterol in your diet can cause blood vessels to become blocked, as shown at the left. *Making Judgments Why is it a good idea to limit the amount of cholesterol you eat?*

Lipids

Have you ever seen a cook trim the fat from a piece of meat before cooking it? The cook is trimming away a lipid. Fats, oils, and waxes are all **lipids.** Like carbohydrates, lipids are energy-rich organic compounds made of carbon, hydrogen, and oxygen.

Lipids contain even more energy than carbohydrates. Cells store energy in lipids for later use. For example, during winter a dormant bear lives on the energy stored as fat within its cells.

 INTEGRATING HEALTH One lipid that you may have heard about is cholesterol (kuh LES tuh rawl). Cholesterol is an important component of animal cell membranes. Your body requires a certain amount of this lipid. Your liver normally produces enough cholesterol to meet your body's needs. However, many of the foods you eat also contain cholesterol. Excess amounts of cholesterol can collect along the walls of blood vessels and block the flow of blood. For this reason, many nutritionists recommend that people limit their intake of foods that are high in cholesterol. Foods that come from animals, such as meat, cheese, and eggs, are high in cholesterol.

Nucleic Acids

Nucleic acids are very large organic molecules made of carbon, oxygen, hydrogen, nitrogen, and phosphorus. Nucleic acids contain the instructions that cells need to carry out all the functions of life.

There are two kinds of nucleic acids. Deoxyribonucleic acid (dee ahk see ry boh noo KLEE ik), or **DNA,** is the genetic material that carries information about an organism that is passed from

Background

Integrating Science Cholesterol is a waxy, fatlike substance found only in animal cells. A certain amount of cholesterol is needed by the human body to make cell membranes, nerve cells, certain hormones, vitamin D, and bile, an acid that aids in digestion. However, elevated levels of cholesterol are associated with heart disease.

Cholesterol is carried through the bloodstream in large molecules called lipoproteins.

There are two main types of lipoproteins—low-density lipoprotein (LDL) and high-density lipoprotein (HDL). LDL, sometimes called "bad cholesterol," increases the tendency for fatty build-up in blood vessels, while HDL, or "good cholesterol," reduces the tendency for fatty build-up. The higher the ratio of LDL to HDL, the greater the risk of heart attack.

parent to offspring. The information in DNA also directs all of the cell's functions. Most of the DNA in a cell is found in the chromatin in the nucleus. Ribonucleic acid (ry boh noo KLEE ik), or **RNA,** plays an important role in the production of proteins. RNA is found in the cytoplasm, as well as in the nucleus.

Water and Living Things

Did you know that water makes up about two thirds of your body? Water plays many vital roles in cells. For example, most chemical reactions that take place in cells can occur only when substances are dissolved in water. **Without water, most chemical reactions within cells could not take place.** Also, water molecules themselves take part in many chemical reactions in cells.

Water also helps cells keep their size and shape. In fact, a cell without water would be like a balloon without air. In addition, because water changes temperature slowly, it helps keep the temperature of cells from changing rapidly. In the next section, you'll learn about the role that water plays in carrying substances into and out of cells.

Figure 15 Water is essential for all living things to survive. The cells of these tulips need water to function.

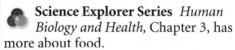 **Section 3 Review**

1. Name the four main groups of organic molecules in living things. Describe the function of each type of molecule.
2. What roles does water play in cells?
3. How are elements related to compounds?
4. **Thinking Critically Predicting** Suppose a cell did not have a supply of amino acids and could not produce them. What effect might this have on the cell?

Science at Home

With family members, look at the "Nutrition Facts" labels on a variety of food products. Identify foods that contain large amounts of the following organic compounds: carbohydrates, proteins, and fats. Discuss with your family what elements each of these compounds are made of and what roles they play in cells and in your body.

Program Resources

 Science Explorer Series *Human Biology and Health,* Chapter 3, has more about food.
◆ **Teaching Resources** 1-3 Review and Reinforce, p. 25; 1-3 Enrich, p. 26

Media and Technology

Interactive Student Tutorial CD-ROM C-1

Answers to Self-Assessment
Caption Question
Figure 14 Excess cholesterol can collect along the walls of blood vessels and block the flow of blood.

Building Inquiry Skills: Calculating

Remind students that about two thirds of their body mass is water. Then have them calculate how many kilograms of water their body contains. *(A 45-kg student contains about 30 kg of water.)* Tell students that a one-gallon jug of water has a mass of about 3.6 kg. Then ask: **About how many one-gallon jugs of water does your body contain?** *(A little over eight jugs for a 45-kg student)* **learning modality: logical/ mathematical**

3 Assess

Section 3 Review Answers

1. Carbohydrates provide energy and components of cell membranes and walls; proteins provide components of cell membranes and organelles and speed up chemical reactions; lipids provide components of cell membranes and store energy; nucleic acids contain the instructions for the cell to carry out all the functions of life.
2. Water helps chemical reactions take place, maintains cell size and shape, keeps cell temperature stable, and plays a role in carrying substances into and out of cells.
3. Compounds are made up of two or more elements.
4. The cell could not make proteins.

Science at Home

Tips Carbohydrates are made up of carbon, hydrogen, and oxygen and provide energy. Proteins are made up of carbon, hydrogen, oxygen, nitrogen, and sometimes sulfur, and form cell membranes and organelles. Fats are made up of carbon, hydrogen, and oxygen and provide energy.

Performance Assessment

Skills Check Have students compare and contrast lipids and nucleic acids.

What's in Your Lunch?

Preparing for Inquiry

Key Concept The presence of starches and lipids in foods can be determined using simple tests.

Skills Objectives Students will be able to
◆ predict whether foods contain starches or lipids;
◆ conclude from the tests they perform whether their predictions are correct.

Time 40 minutes

Advance Planning In addition to cornstarch and vegetable oil, provide students with a number of different foods to test. Other possibilities include: (1) pasta, beans, rice, onions, and potatoes for high-starch, low-lipid foods and (2) butter, lard, and cooked bacon for high-lipid, low-starch foods. Also include some foods that are not high in either starch or lipids, such as apples and strawberries, both of which contain sugar but not starch, as well as foods that contain both starches and lipids, such as peanut butter, bread, and potato chips. Cut up or mash solid foods for better test results. Also, cook starchy foods such as pasta, rice, and beans so the iodine will penetrate them more easily. Cut squares of brown paper ahead of time so each student will have enough squares to test several different food samples. You can obtain iodine solution from a pharmacy or biological supply company.

Alternative Materials Plastic culture dishes or petri dishes can be used instead of plastic cups. Squares of brown paper can be cut from grocery bags.

Guiding Inquiry

Invitation Show students a nutrition facts label on a package of food and challenge them to locate the information on carbohydrates and fats. Point out that fats are lipids and that the amount of starch in a food can be obtained by subtracting the amount of sugars and fiber from the total carbohydrate content. Ask: **How do you think food manufacturers determine how much**

What's in Your Lunch?

You might be surprised to learn that chemists help the food industry obey the law. Most foods must carry labels listing the types of compounds they contain. In this lab, you can find out how chemists obtain that kind of information.

Problem

Which foods contain starches and lipids?

Skills Focus

predicting, drawing conclusions

Materials

cornstarch, 1 gram   water
food samples   plastic cups
plastic stirrers   plastic dropper
plastic graduated cylinder
vegetable oil, 5 milliliters
iodine solution in dropper bottle
5-centimeter squares of brown paper

Procedure

Part 1 Identifying Tests for Starches and Lipids

1. Write a prediction describing one or more differences you expect to observe between starches and lipids. Then copy the data table into your notebook, adding at least five blank rows.

2. Obtain plastic cups containing samples of cornstarch (a starch) and vegetable oil (a lipid).

3. Take a pinch of cornstarch between your thumb and index finger. Feel the substance's texture, and record your observation. Wash your hands to remove the cornstarch.

4. Take a few drops of vegetable oil between your thumb and index finger. Feel the substance's texture, and record your observation. Wash your hands to remove the vegetable oil.

5. Pour 5 milliliters of water into a plastic cup, and add about half of the cornstarch. Use a plastic stirrer to blend the contents into a starch-water mixture.

6. Obtain a brown paper square and write "S" (for "starch") in the corner. Place 3 drops of the starch mixture on the square. Record your observations. Put the square aside to observe it again in about five minutes.

7. Obtain a fresh brown paper square and write "L" (for "lipid") in the corner. Place 3 drops of vegetable oil on the square. Record your observations. Put the square aside to observe again in about five minutes.

starch and lipids are in foods? *(By testing the foods in a lab)*

Introducing the Procedure

Have students read through the entire procedure, and ask: **In simple terms, what are the two procedures you will be using in this lab?** *(Adding iodine solution to foods, and rubbing foods on brown paper)*

Program Resources

◆ **Teaching Resources** Chapter 1 Real-World Lab, pp. 33–35

Safety

Review the safety guidelines in Appendix A.

DATA TABLE

	Substance Tested	Texture	Brown Paper Test	Iodine Test	Type of Compound
1.	Cornstarch				Starch
2.	Vegetable oil				Lipid
3.					
4.					
5.					

8. Add 4 drops of iodine to the remaining starch mixture. Use a clean plastic stirrer to mix the contents well. Record your observations. **CAUTION:** *Handle iodine carefully; it can stain skin and clothing.*

9. Add 4 drops of iodine to the remaining vegetable oil. Use a clean plastic stirrer to mix the contents well. Record your observations.

Part 2 Testing Food Samples

10. Use what you learned in Part 1 to plan starch and lipid tests for food samples such as bread, butter, onion, cooked pasta, peanut butter, potato, potato chips, and rice. If a food is in the form of a single chunk, such as a potato cube, mash it or cut it into smaller pieces. (*Hint:* You can test a sample for lipids by rubbing the sample directly on brown paper.) Be sure to submit your plan for your teacher's approval.

11. List each food you are testing in the first column of the data table. Before beginning your tests, predict what the results will be, and write a reason for each prediction. In making your predictions, consider that some foods may contain both starches and lipids.

12. Carry out the tests as in Part 1 of this lab. Record your observations in the data table. **CAUTION:** *Do not put iodine or any of the food samples in your mouth.* Wash your hands after handling the food samples.

Analyze and Conclude

1. Based on your investigation, what test results indicate the presence of starch? The presence of lipids?

2. What does it mean if one food sample reacts both to the iodine, as cornstarch did, and to the brown paper test, as the vegetable oil did?

3. What does it mean if a food does not react to either the iodine test or the brown paper test?

4. What did you discover from the tests you carried out on specific food samples? Did the results for any of the foods surprise you?

5. **Apply** Why might people want to know what kinds of organic compounds a food contains?

Design an Experiment

Some foods, such as milk and milk products, are available in both regular and low-fat forms. Plan a procedure in which you could test whether various milk products are low in fat.

Troubleshooting the Experiment

◆ To save time, you may want to do Part 1 of the lab as a class demonstration.
◆ If necessary, explain to students that the texture of a substance is how it feels to the touch.
◆ Make sure students do the tests on newspaper, wax paper, or a nonstaining surface.
◆ In Step 6, make sure students give the 3 drops of starch solution enough time to dry on the brown paper so they can see a clear difference between the starch residue and the greasy stain left by the 3 drops of oil in Step 7.

Expected Outcome

In Part 1, students should observe that iodine turns purple when added to starchy foods. Foods high in lipids leave grease stains on brown paper. In Part 2, they should conclude that foods such as potatoes and rice are high in starch and low in lipids. Foods such as butter and lard are high in lipids and low in starch.

Analyze and Conclude

1. When iodine is added to a food and it turns purple, it indicates the presence of starch. When a food leaves a grease stain on brown paper, it indicates the presence of lipids.

2. It means that the food is high in both starch and lipids.

3. It means that the food is low in both starch and lipids.

4. Answers will vary depending on the specific foods that students test. Students may be surprised to find that some foods are low in starch even though they are high in carbohydrates. They also may be surprised to find that some high-fat foods such as nuts also contain starch.

5. Possible answers might include: so people can avoid high-fat foods and choose foods high in other substances such as fiber.

Extending the Inquiry

Design an Experiment Students' plans to test whether various milk products, such as cheese, are low in fat should include performing the brown paper test on each food product and comparing the results for the different products.

Sample Data Table

	Substance Tested	Texture	Brown Paper Test	Iodine Test	Type of Compound
1.	Cornstarch	Not slippery	Leaves no stain	Iodine turns purple	Starch
2.	Vegetable oil	Slippery	Leaves grease stain	Iodine does not change color	Lipid
3.	Potato	Not slippery	Leaves no stain	Iodine turns purple	Starch
4.	Rice	Not slippery	Leaves no stain	Iodine turns purple	Starch
5.	Butter	Slippery	Leaves grease stain	Iodine does not change color	Lipid
6.	Lard	Slippery	Leaves grease stain	Iodine does not change color	Lipid
7.					

The Cell in Its Environment

Objectives

After completing the lesson, students will be able to
◆ describe the three methods by which materials move into and out of cells;
◆ compare passive transport to active transport.

Key Terms selectively permeable, diffusion, osmosis, passive transport, active transport

1 Engage/Explore

Activating Prior Knowledge

Introduce students to the idea of the cell membrane as a gatekeeper by helping them recall how a sieve or colander works. Ask: **Why might you use a sieve or colander?** *(Possible answers might include to strain lumps out of gravy or to drain vegetables or pasta.)* **What do all these things have in common?** *(They involve using a filter to separate large from small particles or solids from liquids.)* Tell students that the cell membrane acts like a filter, too, by allowing some substances, but not others, to pass in and out of the cell.

·········· DISCOVER ··········

Skills Focus developing hypotheses

Materials *air freshener spray*
Time 10 minutes
Tips When spraying the air freshener, spray up or down rather than in the direction of students.
Expected Outcome The spray should diffuse evenly throughout the classroom, reaching students at the same distance from the source at about the same time.
Think It Over The farther each student was from the teacher, the longer it took for the student to smell the air freshener. Students may hypothesize that particles in the spray moved from an area of higher concentration to an area of lower concentration.

The Cell in Its Environment

DISCOVER ·································· ACTIVITY

How Do Molecules Move?

1. With your classmates, stand so that you are evenly spaced throughout the classroom.
2. Your teacher will spray an air freshener into the room. When you first begin to smell the air freshener, raise your hand.
3. Note how long it takes for other students in the classroom to smell the scent.

Think It Over
Developing Hypotheses How was each student's distance from the teacher related to when he or she smelled the air freshener? Develop a hypothesis about why this pattern occurred.

GUIDE FOR READING

◆ By what three methods do materials move into and out of cells?
◆ What is the difference between passive transport and active transport?

Reading Tip Before you read, use the headings to make an outline about how materials move into and out of cells. As you read, make notes about each process.

▼ The *Mir* space station

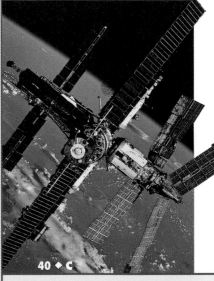

40 ◆ C

How is a cell like a space station? The walls of a space station protect the astronauts inside from the airless vacuum of space. Food, water, and other supplies must be brought to the space station by shuttles from Earth. In addition, the space station needs to be able to get rid of wastes. The doors of the space station allow the astronauts to bring materials in and move wastes out into the shuttle to be returned to Earth.

Like space stations, cells also have structures that protect them from the outside environment. As you learned, all cells are surrounded by a cell membrane that separates the cell from the outside environment. Just like the space station, the cell also has to take in needed materials and get rid of wastes. It is the cell membrane that controls what materials move into and out of the cell.

The Cell Membrane as Gatekeeper

The cell membrane is **selectively permeable,** which means that some substances can pass through it while others cannot. The term *permeable* comes from a Latin word that means "to pass through." You can think of the cell membrane as being like a gatekeeper at an ancient castle. It was the gatekeeper's job to decide when to open the gate to allow people to pass into and out of the castle. The gatekeeper made the castle wall "selectively permeable"—it was permeable to friendly folks but not to enemies.

A cell membrane is usually permeable to substances such as oxygen, water, and carbon dioxide. On the other hand, the cell membrane is usually not permeable to some large molecules and salts. **Substances that can move into and out of a cell do so by one of three methods: diffusion, osmosis, or active transport.**

READING STRATEGIES

Reading Tip After students have completed their outlines, have them exchange them with a partner. Then have partners work together to resolve any discrepancies. Suggest to students that they save their corrected outlines to use as study guides.

Study and Comprehension Encourage visual learners to preview the section by looking at the figures and reading the captions. This is also a good way for them to review the main points after reading the section.

Vocabulary To help students understand the technical terminology in this section, suggest that they rewrite the definitions of the boldfaced terms in their own words. Check their definitions when they are finished and point out any errors.

Diffusion—Molecules in Motion

The main method by which substances move into and out of cells is diffusion. **Diffusion** (dih FYOO zhun) is the process by which molecules tend to move from an area of higher concentration to an area of lower concentration. The concentration of a substance is the amount of the substance in a given volume.

If you did the Discover activity, you observed diffusion in action. The area where the air freshener was sprayed had many molecules of freshener. The molecules gradually moved from this area of higher concentration to the other parts of the classroom, where there were few molecules of freshener, and thus a lower concentration.

What Causes Diffusion? Molecules are always moving. As **INTEGRATING CHEMISTRY** they move, the molecules bump into one another. The more molecules there are in an area, the more collisions there will be. Collisions cause molecules to push away from one another. Over time, the molecules of a substance will continue to spread out. Eventually they will be spread evenly throughout the area.

Diffusion in Cells Have you ever used a microscope to observe one-celled organisms in pond water? These organisms obtain the oxygen they need to survive from the water around them. Luckily for them, there are many more molecules of oxygen in the water outside the cell than there are inside the cell. In other words, there is a higher concentration of oxygen molecules in the water than inside the cell. Remember that the cell membrane is permeable to oxygen molecules. The oxygen molecules diffuse from the area of higher concentration—the pond water—through the cell membrane to the area of lower concentration—the inside of the cell.

Figure 16 Molecules move by diffusion from an area of higher concentration to an area of lower concentration. **A.** The molecules diffuse into the cell. **B.** Eventually, there is an equal concentration of molecules inside and outside the cell. *Predicting What would happen if the concentration of the molecules outside the cell was lower than the concentration inside?*

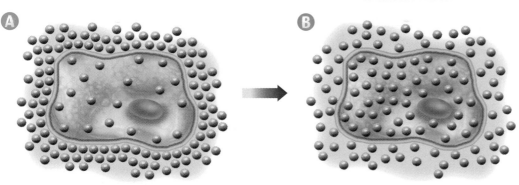

Program Resources

 Science Explorer Series *Chemical Building Blocks*, Chapter 2, has more about the behavior of molecules.
◆ **Teaching Resources** 1-4 Lesson Plan, p. 27; 1-4 Section Summary, p. 28

Media and Technology

Audiotapes English-Spanish Summary 1-4

Answers to Self-Assessment

Caption Question

Figure 16 If the concentration of molecules outside the cell was lower than the concentration inside, the molecules would diffuse out of the cell.

---

2 *Facilitate*

The Cell Membrane as Gatekeeper

Including All Students

Materials *cheesecloth, spoon, applesauce* **ACTIVITY**
Time 10 minutes

Have students place a small amount of applesauce in the middle of a piece of cheesecloth. Have them pull the edges together and, over a sink, try to squeeze the applesauce through the cloth. Have students examine what remains in the pouch, then ask: **How is the cheesecloth like a cell membrane?** (*It allows some but not all substances to pass through.*)
learning modality: kinesthetic

Diffusion—Molecules in Motion

 Integrating Chemistry

Materials *tablespoon, cornstarch, two cups, water, resealable plastic bag, plastic dropper, iodine* **ACTIVITY**

Time 15 minutes

To demonstrate diffusion through a selectively permeable membrane, stir a tablespoon of cornstarch into half a cup of water and pour the mixture into a plastic bag. Seal the bag, rinse it off to remove any cornstarch, and place it in a clean cup half full of plain water. Add 20 drops of iodine to the water in the cup. Later, show students the cup and ask. **Why did the water in the bag turn purple?** (*Iodine molecules passed through the plastic into the bag and interacted with the starch.*) **Why didn't the water in the cup turn purple?** (*The starch molecules were too big to pass through the bag.*) **learning modality: visual**

Ongoing Assessment

Drawing Have students draw a diagram to show what happens if the concentration outside a cell is lower than the concentration inside.

Osmosis—The Diffusion of Water Molecules

Demonstration

Materials *raw potato, knife, two shallow dishes, tap water, salt*

Time 5 minutes; 5 minutes

Use a potato to demonstrate the process of osmosis. At the beginning of class, cut a raw potato in half and hollow out a small depression in the curved side of each half. Place the halves flat-side down in shallow dishes containing a small amount of tap water. Place a pinch of salt in the depression of one of the potato halves, and then set the two halves aside. At the end of class, have students observe what has happened to the two potato halves. *(The depression without salt has become dried out, whereas the depression with salt has filled with water.)* Ask: **Where did the water in the depression come from?** *(The water moved by osmosis from an area of higher concentration in the potato cells to an area of lower concentration in the depression containing salt.)* **learning modality: visual**

TRY THIS

Skills Focus inferring
Materials *small clear plastic cup, cold water, plastic dropper, food coloring*
Time 10 minutes
Expected Outcome The large drop of food coloring will diffuse throughout the water in the cup, and the water will have an even shade of color.
Extend Encourage students to predict how changing the parameters of the experiment would affect the outcome. For example, ask: **How do you think the results of the activity would be different if you had used a larger amount of water?** *(Diffusion would have taken longer, and the water would have turned a lighter shade of color.)* **learning modality: logical/mathematical**

42 ◆ C

Diffusion in Action

Here's how you can observe the effects of diffusion.

1. Fill a small clear plastic cup with cold water. Place the cup on a table and allow it to sit until there is no movement in the water.
2. Use a plastic dropper to add one large drop of food coloring to the water.
3. Observe the water every minute. Note any changes that take place. Continue to observe until you can no longer see any changes.

Inferring What role did diffusion play in the changes you observed?

Osmosis—The Diffusion of Water Molecules

Like oxygen, water passes easily into and out of cells through the cell membrane. The diffusion of water molecules through a selectively permeable membrane is called **osmosis.** Osmosis is important to cells because cells cannot function properly without adequate water.

Remember that molecules tend to move from an area of higher concentration to an area of lower concentration. In osmosis, water molecules move by diffusion from an area where they are highly concentrated through the cell membrane to an area where they are less concentrated. This can have important consequences for the cell.

Look at Figure 17 to see the effect of osmosis on cells. In Figure 17 A, red blood cells are bathed in a solution in which the concentration of water is the same as it is inside the cells. This is the normal shape of a red blood cell.

Now look at Figure 17 B. The red blood cells are floating in water that contains a lot of salt. The concentration of water molecules outside the cells is lower than the concentration of water molecules inside the cells. This is because the salt takes up space in the salt water, so there are fewer water molecules. As a result, water moves out of the cells by osmosis, and the cells shrink.

Finally, consider Figure 17 C. The red blood cells are floating in water that contains a very small amount of salt. The water inside the cells contains more salt than the solution they are floating in. Thus, the concentration of water outside the cell is greater than it is inside the cell. The water moves into the cell, causing it to swell.

✓ *Checkpoint* *How is osmosis related to diffusion?*

Figure 17 Osmosis is the diffusion of water molecules through a selectively permeable membrane.

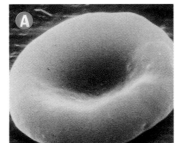

A. This is the normal shape of a red blood cell.

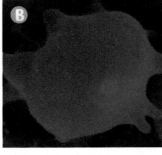

B. This cell has shrunk because water moved out of it by osmosis.

C. This cell is swollen with water that has moved into it by osmosis.

42 ◆ C

Background

Integrating Science Did you ever wonder why most fish cannot live in both freshwater and salt water? The answer lies in osmosis, which requires freshwater and saltwater fishes to have very different adaptations.

When fishes live in salt water, the water outside their body is saltier than the water inside their cells. Therefore, fishes lose a lot of water into the water around them by osmosis.

To compensate, they must drink a lot of water, use active transport to get rid of the excess salt, and produce very little urine.

In contrast, when fishes live in freshwater, the water inside their body cells is saltier than the water outside. Therefore, they gain a lot of water by osmosis. To compensate, they usually do not drink, and they produce large amounts of very dilute urine.

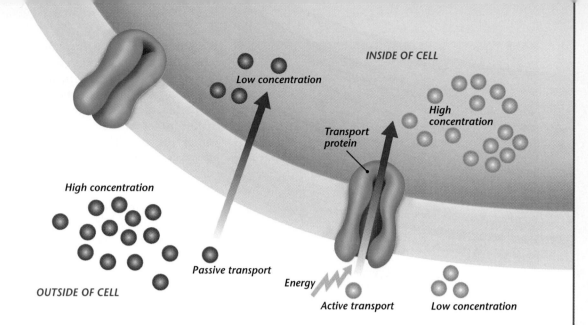

INSIDE OF CELL

Low concentration

High concentration

Transport protein

High concentration

Passive transport

OUTSIDE OF CELL

Energy

Active transport

Low concentration

Active Transport

If you have ever ridden a bicycle down a long hill, you know that it doesn't take any of your energy to go fast. But pedaling back up the hill does take energy. For a cell, moving materials through the cell membrane by diffusion and osmosis is like cycling downhill. These processes do not require the cell to use any energy. The movement of materials through a cell membrane without using energy is called **passive transport.**

What if a cell needs to take in a substance that is in higher concentration inside the cell than outside? The cell would have to move the molecules in the opposite direction than they naturally move by diffusion. Cells can do this, but they have to use energy—just as you would use energy to pedal back up the hill. **Active transport** is the movement of materials through a cell membrane using energy. **The main difference between passive transport and active transport is that active transport requires the cell to use energy while passive transport does not.**

Transport Proteins A cell has several ways of moving materials by active transport. In one method, transport proteins in the cell membrane "pick up" molecules outside the cell and carry them in, using energy in the process. Transport proteins also carry molecules out of cells in a similar way. Some substances that are carried into and out of cells in this way include calcium, potassium, and sodium.

Figure 18 Diffusion and osmosis are forms of passive transport. These processes do not require the cell to use any energy. Active transport, on the other hand, requires the use of energy. *Interpreting Diagrams How are passive and active transport related to the concentrations of the molecules inside and outside the cell?*

Inquiry Challenge

Materials *small board, stack of books, toy car*
Time 5 minutes

Challenge pairs of students to model active and passive transport using the materials listed above. *(The most likely way is to make an inclined plane with the board and books, and then to roll the toy car down the ramp to simulate passive transport and push it up the ramp to simulate active transport.)* Ask: **Why do you need to supply energy to move the toy car up the ramp?** *(To overcome the force of gravity)* **Why is energy needed to actively transport some substances into the cell?** *(To move the substances from an area of lower to an area of higher concentration)* **cooperative learning**

Building Inquiry Skills: Relating Cause and Effect

Help students better understand the role of transport proteins in active transport by developing the analogy in the text. Ask: **What plays a similar role in active transport as your muscles play when you pedal a bicycle up a hill?** *(Transport proteins, because they require energy to move something that could not move on its own)* **learning modality: logical/ mathematical**

Answers to Self-Assessment

☑ Checkpoint

Osmosis is water diffusion through a selectively permeable membrane.

Caption Question

Figure 18 Passive transport—molecules move from higher to lower concentration. Active transport—molecules move from lower to higher concentration.

Ongoing Assessment

Skills Check Have students draw a Venn diagram that relates active and passive transport. *(Students' diagrams should show that active transport requires energy and passive transport does not. The overlap area should indicate that in both processes, materials move in and out of cells.)*

Why Are Cells Small?

Demonstration

Materials *one-gallon aquarium, cold and room-temperature water, measuring cup, food coloring*

Time 5 minutes

Demonstrate how materials move through the cell in a stream of moving cytoplasm by creating a convection current in water. Pour half a cup of very cold water mixed with ten drops of food coloring into a one-gallon aquarium nearly full of room-temperature water. Students will see the cold, colored water move slowly to the bottom of the aquarium. Explain that the cold water sinks to the bottom because it is denser than the warmer room-temperature water. Ask: **How would increasing the size of the tank affect how long it takes the colored water to reach the bottom?** *(It would take longer in a larger tank.)* **learning modality: visual**

3 Assess

Section 4 Review Answers

1. In diffusion, molecules move from an area of higher to an area of lower concentration. In osmosis, water molecules move by diffusion. In active transport, molecules are helped across cell membranes by transport proteins.
2. Both passive and active transport refer to the movement of substances across cell membranes. Active transport requires energy; passive transport does not.
3. Substances can travel faster through the cytoplasm of small cells.
4. The cell will shrink as it loses water by osmosis.

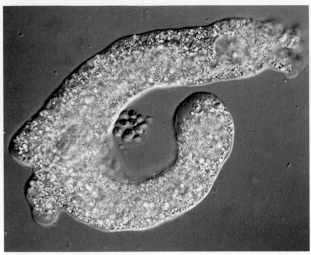

Figure 19 A cell can move some materials into the cell by engulfing them. This single-celled ameba is engulfing a smaller single-celled organism.

Transport by Engulfing You can see another method of active transport in Figure 19. First the cell membrane surrounds, or engulfs, a particle. Once the particle is engulfed, the cell membrane pinches off and forms a vacuole within the cell. The cell must use energy in this process.

Why Are Cells Small?

As you know, most cells are so small that you cannot see them without a microscope. Have you ever wondered why cells are so small? One reason is related to how materials move into and out of cells.

As a cell's size increases, more of its cytoplasm is located farther from the cell membrane. Once a molecule enters a cell, it is carried to its destination by a stream of moving cytoplasm, somewhat like the way currents of water in the ocean move a raft. But in a very large cell, the streams of cytoplasm must travel farther to bring materials to all parts of the cell. It would take much longer for a molecule to reach the center of a very large cell than it would in a small cell. Likewise, it would take a long time for wastes to be removed. If a cell grew too large, it could not function well enough to survive. When a cell reaches a certain size, it divides into two new cells. You will learn more about cell division in Chapter 2.

Section 4 Review

1. Describe three methods by which substances can move into and out of cells.
2. How are passive transport and active transport similar? How do they differ?
3. Why is small size an advantage to a cell?
4. **Thinking Critically Predicting** A single-celled organism is transferred from a tank of fresh water into a tank of salt water. How will the cell change? Explain.

Check Your Progress

CHAPTER PROJECT 1

Begin to think about why the egg changed as it did at each stage of the project. Consider how each of the different substances affected your egg. (*Hint:* Water plays a crucial role in the activities of a cell. How has water been involved in your investigation?) Organize your results into a report and make a graph of your egg's changing circumference. You may want to include diagrams to explain the processes that took place.

Program Resources

◆ **Teaching Resources** 1-4 Review and Reinforce, p. 29; 1-4 Enrich, p. 30

Media and Technology

Interactive Student Tutorial CD-ROM C-1

SECTION 1 — Discovering Cells

Key Ideas
- The invention of the microscope made the discovery of the cell possible.
- The cell theory states that: all living things are made of cells; cells are the basic units of structure and function in organisms; all cells come from other cells.
- The lens or lenses in a light microscope magnify an object by bending the light that passes through.

Key Terms
cell
microscope
compound microscope
cell theory

magnification
convex lens
resolution

SECTION 2 — Looking Inside Cells

Key Ideas
- The cell membrane protects the cell and controls what substances enter and leave it.
- The nucleus is the cell's control center. Chromatin in the nucleus contains genetic material that directs the cell's activities.
- Organelles in the cytoplasm include the mitochondria, endoplasmic reticulum, ribosomes, Golgi bodies, vacuoles, and lysosomes. Plant cells also contain chloroplasts.
- While a bacterial cell does have a cell membrane and a cell wall, it does not contain a nucleus.

Key Terms
organelle
cell wall
cell membrane
nucleus
chromatin

cytoplasm
mitochondrion
endoplasmic reticulum
ribosome

Golgi body
chloroplast
vacuole
lysosome

SECTION 3 — Chemical Compounds in Cells
INTEGRATING CHEMISTRY

Key Ideas
- When two or more elements combine chemically, they form a compound.
- The main groups of organic compounds found in living things are carbohydrates, lipids, proteins, and nucleic acids.
- Without water, most chemical reactions within cells could not take place.

Key Terms
element
atom
compound
molecule
organic compound
inorganic compound
carbohydrate

protein
amino acid
enzyme
lipid
nucleic acid
DNA
RNA

SECTION 4 — The Cell in Its Environment

Key Ideas
- Substances can move into and out of a cell by diffusion, osmosis, or active transport.
- Diffusion is the process by which molecules move from an area of higher concentration to an area of lower concentration. Osmosis is the diffusion of water molecules through a selectively permeable membrane.
- The main difference between passive transport and active transport is that active transport requires the cell to use energy while passive transport does not.
- If a cell grew too large, it could not function well enough to survive.

Key Terms
selectively permeable
diffusion
osmosis

passive transport
active transport

USING THE INTERNET *ACTIVITY*

www.science-explorer.phschool.com

Chapter 1 **C ◆ 45**

Check Your Progress

CHAPTER PROJECT 1

Have students graph their egg's diameter on one axis and the date it was measured on the other. They also should indicate on their graphs what liquid the egg was soaking in each day.

Program Resources

- **Teaching Resources** Chapter 1 Project Scoring Rubric, p. 14; Chapter 1 Performance Assessment, pp. 152–154; Chapter 1 Test, pp. 155–158

Media and Technology

 Interactive Student Tutorial CD-ROM C-1

 Computer Test Bank Test C-1

Performance Assessment

Concept Maps Have students make a concept map that includes the terms *diffusion, osmosis, passive transport,* and *active transport.*

Reviewing Content:
Multiple Choice
1. a   2. c   3. d   4. d   5. a

True or False
6. light   7. Mitochondria   8. true
9. nucleic acids   10. true

Checking Concepts
11. The microscope allowed scientists to observe the cells that make up living things. Over the years, they discovered that all living things are made up of cells.
12. The cell wall is rigid, and it helps to protect and support plant cells.
13. Organic compounds are compounds that contain the element carbon. They are found in living or once-living things. Inorganic compounds are compounds that do not contain carbon. (The only exception is carbon dioxide.) They are found in things that are not and never were alive.
14. Enzymes speed up chemical reactions in living things. Without enzymes, many of the chemical reactions that are necessary for life would either take too long or not occur at all.
15. Diffusion is the process by which molecules tend to move from an area of higher concentration to an area of lower concentration. Diffusion helps the cell take in the substances it needs and get rid of those it does not need.
16. Students' articles should describe the discoveries of either Robert Hooke or Anton van Leeuwenhoek and relate them to the microscope.

Thinking Visually
17. a. Carbohydrates **b.** Proteins **c.** Cholesterol **d.** Sugars **e.** DNA

Applying Skills
18. The plant cells got smaller after the plant was watered.
19. Osmosis, or loss of water by diffusion, would lead to the changes in the plant cells.
20. If the plant in B were to be watered with fresh water, it would return to its original size because it would gain water by osmosis.

Reviewing Content
 For more review of key concepts, see the Interactive Student Tutorial CD-ROM.

Multiple Choice
Choose the letter of the best answer.
1. The ability of microscopes to distinguish fine details is called
   a. resolution.
   b. bending.
   c. magnification.
   d. active transport.
2. In plant and animal cells, the control center of the cell is the
   a. chloroplast.
   b. ribosome.
   c. nucleus.
   d. Golgi body.
3. The storage compartment of a cell is the
   a. cell wall.
   b. lysosome.
   c. endoplasmic reticulum.
   d. vacuole.
4. Starch is an example of a
   a. nucleic acid.
   b. protein.
   c. lipid.
   d. carbohydrate.
5. The process by which water moves across a cell membrane is called
   a. osmosis.
   b. active transport.
   c. diffusion.
   d. resolution.

True or False
If the statement is true, write true. If it is false, change the underlined word or words to make the statement true.
6. Cells were discovered using <u>electron</u> microscopes.
7. <u>Vacuoles</u> are the "powerhouses" of the cell.
8. Bacterial cells differ from the cells of plants and animals in that they lack a <u>nucleus</u>.
9. Both DNA and RNA are <u>proteins</u>.
10. The <u>cell membrane</u> is selectively permeable.

Checking Concepts
11. What role did the microscope play in the development of the cell theory?
12. Describe the function of the cell wall in the cells that have these structures.
13. Explain the difference between organic and inorganic compounds.
14. How are enzymes important to living things?
15. What is diffusion? What role does diffusion play in the cell?
16. Writing to Learn Suppose you had been a reporter assigned to cover early scientists' discoveries about cells. Write a brief article for your daily newspaper that explains one scientist's discoveries. Be sure to explain both how the discoveries were made and why they are important.

Thinking Visually
17. Concept Map Copy the concept map about organic compounds onto a separate sheet of paper. Then complete the map and add a title. (For more about concept maps, see the Skills Handbook.)

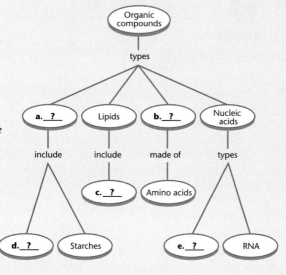

Thinking Critically
21. Answers may vary. Students might say a microscope that allowed scientists to see molecules inside a cell's organelles would help them understand how the organelles carry out the functions of the cell.
22. The cell theory states that all living things are composed of cells, that cells are the basic unit of structure and function in living things, and that all cells are produced from other cells. A dog is a living thing. Therefore, a dog is composed of cells, cells are the basic unit of structure and function in a dog, and all the dog's cells are produced from other cells.
23. A cell could not survive without a cell membrane because it would not have a barrier to control what substances moved into and out of the cell.
24. The study of chemistry is important to the understanding of living things because chemical elements and compounds make up the cells of living things and carry out their functions.

Applying Skills

A scientist watered the plant in Figure A with salt water. After 30 minutes, the plant looked as you see it in Figure B. Use the drawings to answer Questions 18–20.

18. **Observing** How did the plant cells change after the plant was watered?
19. **Inferring** Describe a process that would lead to the changes in the plant cells.

20. **Predicting** Suppose the scientist were to water the plant in B with fresh water. Predict what would happen to the plant. Explain your prediction.

Thinking Critically

21. **Relating Cause and Effect** Suppose a microscope is invented that scientists could use to see molecules inside a cell's organelles. How could the microscope contribute to their understanding of the cell?
22. **Applying Concepts** Explain how the cell theory applies to a dog.
23. **Predicting** Could a cell survive without a cell membrane? Give reasons to support your answer.
24. **Making Generalizations** Why is the study of chemistry important to the understanding of living things?
25. **Comparing and Contrasting** How is active transport different from osmosis?

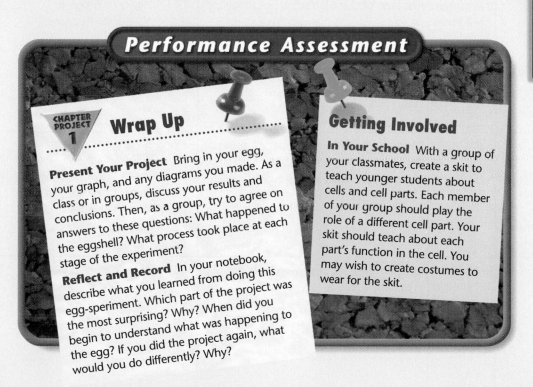

Performance Assessment

CHAPTER PROJECT 1
Wrap Up

Present Your Project Bring in your egg, your graph, and any diagrams you made. As a class or in groups, discuss your results and conclusions. Then, as a group, try to agree on answers to these questions: What happened to the eggshell? What process took place at each stage of the experiment?

Reflect and Record In your notebook, describe what you learned from doing this egg-speriment. Which part of the project was the most surprising? Why? When did you begin to understand what was happening to the egg? If you did the project again, what would you do differently? Why?

Getting Involved

In Your School With a group of your classmates, create a skit to teach younger students about cells and cell parts. Each member of your group should play the role of a different cell part. Your skit should teach about each part's function in the cell. You may wish to create costumes to wear for the skit.

---

25. Active transport and osmosis are both ways that molecules cross cell membranes, but osmosis is a passive form of transport that requires no energy, whereas active transport requires energy to take place. In addition, osmosis refers specifically to the transfer of water across the cell membrane, whereas active transport involves other kinds of molecules.

Program Resources

◆ **Inquiry Skills Activity Book** Provides teaching and review of all inquiry skills

---

Performance Assessment

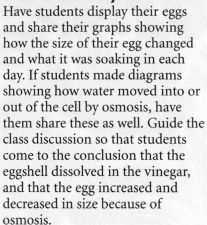

CHAPTER PROJECT 1
Wrap Up
Present Your Project
Have students display their eggs and share their graphs showing how the size of their egg changed and what it was soaking in each day. If students made diagrams showing how water moved into or out of the cell by osmosis, have them share these as well. Guide the class discussion so that students come to the conclusion that the eggshell dissolved in the vinegar, and that the egg increased and decreased in size because of osmosis.

Reflect and Record Students may say that this "egg-speriment" helped them understand the process of osmosis and how important the cell membrane is to the cell. The most surprising part may have been how the texture of the egg changed. Most students probably began to understand what was happening to the egg when they read about osmosis in Section 4. If they did the project over, students may say they would test a greater variety of liquids.

Getting Involved

In Your School Make sure groups are large enough for students to represent at least three different cell parts, such as the cell membrane, the nucleus, and an organelle. Suggest that group members brainstorm a creative way to present the information in a skit. Urge group members to divide the tasks fairly among themselves. Advise students to remember the grade level of their audience.

Cell Processes and Energy

Sections	Time	Student Edition Activities		Other Activities
CHAPTER PROJECT 2 **Shine On!** p. 49	Ongoing (3 weeks)	Check Your Progress, p. 54 Check Your Progress, p. 68 Check Your Progress, p. 73 Wrap Up, p. 77		
1 Photosynthesis pp. 50–54 ◆ Describe the process of photosynthesis. ◆ Explain how the sun supplies all living things with the energy they need.	2–3 periods/ 1–1½ blocks	**Discover** Where Does the Energy Come From?, p. 50 **Sharpen Your Skills** Inferring, p. 52	TE TE TE ISLM	Demonstration, p. 51 Building Inquiry Skills: Observing, p. 52 Building Inquiry Skills: Making Models, p. 53 C-2, "Stomata Functions"
2 Respiration pp. 55–60 ◆ Describe the events that occur during respiration. ◆ Describe the relationship between photosynthesis and respiration. ◆ Describe alcoholic and lactic-acid fermentation.	3–4 periods/ 1½–2 blocks	**Discover** What Is a Product of Respiration?, p. 55 **Try This** What's in Your Breath?, p. 57 **Science at Home,** p. 59 **Real-World Lab: You and Your Environment** Gases in Balance, p. 60	TE IES IES	Inquiry Challenge, p. 57 "Fate of the Rain Forest," pp. 20–21 "Where River Meets Sea," pp. 15–16
3 Cell Division pp. 61–69 ◆ List the events that take place during the three stages of the cell cycle. ◆ Describe the structure of DNA and how DNA replication occurs.	4–5 periods/ 2–2½ blocks	**Discover** What Are the Cells Doing?, p. 61 **Try This** Modeling Mitosis, p. 63 **Sharpen Your Skills** Interpreting Data, p. 66 **Skills Lab: Calculating** Multiplying by Dividing, p. 69	TE TE TE TE TE TE	Building Inquiry Skills: Calculating, p. 63 Inquiry Challenge, p. 64 Inquiry Challenge, p. 65 Inquiry Challenge, p. 67 Including All Students, p. 65 Demonstration, p. 66
4 **INTEGRATING HEALTH** **Cancer** pp. 70–74 ◆ State the relationship between cancer and the cell cycle. ◆ Describe how cancer begins and spreads. ◆ Describe several methods of cancer treatment and of cancer prevention.	2–3 periods/ 1–1½ blocks	**Discover** What Happens When There Are Too Many Cells?, p. 70	TE	Building Inquiry Skills: Calculating, p. 71
Study Guide/Chapter Review pp. 75–77	1 period/ ½ block		ISAB	Provides teaching and review of all inquiry skills

For Standard or Block Schedule The Resource Pro® CD-ROM gives you maximum flexibility for planning your instruction for any type of schedule. Resource Pro® contains Planning Express®, an advanced scheduling program, as well as the entire contents of the Teaching Resources and the Computer Test Bank.

CHAPTER PLANNING GUIDE

Program Resources	Assessment Strategies	Media and Technology
TR Chapter 2 Project Teacher Notes, pp. 36–37 **TR** Chapter 2 Project Overview and Worksheets, pp. 38–41 **TR** Chapter 2 Project Scoring Rubric, p. 42	**SE** Performance Assessment: Chapter 2 Project Wrap Up, p. 77 **TE** Check Your Progress, pp. 54, 68, 73 **TE** Performance Assessment: Chapter 2 Project Wrap Up, p. 77 **TR** Chapter 2 Project Scoring Rubric, p. 42	Science Explorer Internet Site
TR 2-1 Lesson Plan, p. 43 **TR** 2-1 Section Summary, p. 44 **TR** 2-1 Review and Reinforce, p. 45 **TR** 2-1 Enrich, p. 46 **SES** Book O, *Sound and Light,* Chapter 3 **SES** Book A, *From Bacteria to Plants,* Chapter 4	**SE** Section 1 Review, p. 54 **TE** Ongoing Assessment, pp. 51, 53 **TE** Performance Assessment, p. 54 **TR** 2-1 Review and Reinforce, p. 45	Audiotapes, English-Spanish Summary 2-1 Transparency 5, "Photosynthesis" Interactive Student Tutorial CD-ROM, C-2
TR 2-2 Lesson Plan, p. 47 **TR** 2-2 Section Summary, p. 48 **TR** 2-2 Review and Reinforce, p. 49 **TR** 2-2 Enrich, p. 50 **TR** Chapter 2 Real-World Lab, pp. 59–60 **SES** Book D, *Human Biology and Health,* Chapters 3 and 5 **SES** Book E, *Environmental Science,* Chapter 2	**SE** Section 2 Review, p. 59 **SE** Analyze and Conclude, p. 60 **TE** Ongoing Assessment, p. 57 **TE** Performance Assessment, p. 59 **TR** 2-2 Review and Reinforce, p. 49	Exploring Earth Science Videodisc, Unit 1 Side 1, "Sunny Days" Audiotapes, English-Spanish Summary 2-2 Transparency 6, "Respiration" Interactive Student Tutorial CD-ROM, C-2
TR 2-3 Lesson Plan, p. 51 **TR** 2-3 Section Summary, p. 52 **TR** 2-3 Review and Reinforce, p. 53 **TR** 2-3 Enrich, p. 54 **TR** Chapter 2 Skills Lab, pp. 61–63	**SE** Section 3 Review, p. 68 **SE** Analyze and Conclude, p. 69 **TE** Ongoing Assessment, pp. 63, 65, 67 **TE** Performance Assessment, p. 68 **TR** 2-3 Review and Reinforce, p. 53	Audiotapes, English-Spanish Summary 2-3 Transparencies 7, "Exploring the Cell Cycle"; 8, "DNA Structure"; 9, "DNA Replication" Interactive Student Tutorial CD-ROM, C-2
TR 2-4 Lesson Plan, p. 55 **TR** 2-4 Section Summary, p. 56 **TR** 2-4 Review and Reinforce, p. 57 **TR** 2-4 Enrich, p. 58	**SE** Section 4 Review, p. 73 **TE** Ongoing Assessment, p. 71 **TE** Performance Assessment, p. 73 **TR** 2-4 Review and Reinforce, p. 57	Audiotapes, English-Spanish Summary 2-4 Interactive Student Tutorial CD-ROM, C-2
TR Chapter 2 Performance Assessment, pp. 159–161 **TR** Chapter 2 Test, pp. 162–165	**SE** Chapter 2 Review, pp. 75–77 **TR** Chapter 2 Performance Assessment, pp. 159–161 **TR** Chapter 2 Test, pp. 162–165 **CTB** Test C-2	Interactive Student Tutorial CD-ROM, C-2 Computer Test Bank, Test C-2 Got It! Video Quizzes

Key: **SE** Student Edition   **TE** Teacher's Edition   **TR** Teaching Resources
     CTB Computer Test Bank   **SES** Science Explorer Series Text   **ISLM** Integrated Science Laboratory Manual
     ISAB Inquiry Skills Activity Book   **PTA** Product Testing Activities by *Consumer Reports*   **IES** Interdisciplinary Explorations Series

Meeting the National Science Education Standards and AAAS Benchmarks

National Science Education Standards	Benchmarks for Science Literacy	Unifying Themes

Science As Inquiry (Content Standard A)

◆ **Design and conduct a scientific investigation** Students investigate how different light conditions affect plants and how photosynthesis and respiration are related. *(Chapter Project; Real-World Lab)*

◆ **Use appropriate tools and techniques to gather, analyze, and interpret data** Students investigate how long the stages of the cell cycle take. *(Skills Lab)*

Life Science (Content Standard C)

◆ **Structure and function in living systems** Photosynthesis occurs inside chloroplasts in the cells of plants and some other organisms. During respiration, cells break down food molecules and release the energy they contain. The regular sequence of growth and division that cells undergo is called the cell cycle. Cancer is a disease in which cells grow and divide uncontrollably. *(Chapter Project; Sections 1, 2, 3, 4; Skills Lab)*

◆ **Populations and ecosystems** Nearly all living things obtain energy either directly or indirectly from the energy of sunlight captured during photosynthesis. Photosynthesis and respiration form a cycle that keeps the levels of oxygen and carbon dioxide fairly constant in the atmosphere. *(Sections 1, 2; Real-World Lab)*

Science in Personal and Social Perspectives (Content Standard F)

◆ **Science and technology in society** Students consider the issue of who has the right to a person's cells. *(Science and Society)*

1B Scientific Inquiry Students investigate how different light conditions affect plants, how photosynthesis and respiration are related, and how long the stages of the cell cycle take. *(Chapter Project; Real-World Lab; Skills Lab)*

3C Issues in Technology Students consider the issue of who has the right to a person's cells. *(Science and Society)*

5C Cells During respiration, cells break down food molecules and release the energy they contain. The regular sequence of growth and division that cells undergo is called the cell cycle. Cancer is a disease in which cells grow and divide uncontrollably. *(Sections 2, 3, 4; Skills Lab)*

5D Interdependence of Life Nearly all living things obtain energy either directly or indirectly from the energy of sunlight captured during photosynthesis. Photosynthesis and respiration form a cycle that keeps the levels of oxygen and carbon dioxide fairly constant in the atmosphere. *(Sections 1, 2; Real-World Lab)*

5E Flow of Matter and Energy During photosynthesis, plants and some other organisms use the sun's energy to make food. *(Chapter Project; Section 1)*

6E Physical Health Almost two thirds of all cancer deaths are caused by tobacco use or unhealthful diets. *(Section 4)*

◆ **Energy** During photosynthesis, plants and some other organisms use the sun's energy to make food. During respiration, cells break down food molecules and release the energy they contain. Fermentation provides energy for cells without using oxygen. *(Chapter Project; Sections 1, 2)*

◆ **Patterns of Change** During photosynthesis, carbon dioxide and water are converted into oxygen and sugars. The regular sequence of growth and division that cells undergo is called the cell cycle. Cancer begins when mutations disrupt the normal cell cycle, causing cells to divide uncontrollably. *(Sections 1, 3, 4; Skills Lab)*

◆ **Scale and Structure** Photosynthesis occurs inside chloroplasts in the cells of plants and some other organisms. Respiration takes place in the cytoplasm and mitochondria of an organism's cells. After a cell has grown to its mature size, it divides. A tumor is a mass of abnormal cells that develops when cancerous cells divide and grow uncontrollably. *(Sections 1, 2, 3, 4)*

◆ **Systems and Interactions** Through photosynthesis and respiration, the sun's energy is converted into energy that living organisms can use. *(Sections 1, 2; Real-World Lab)*

◆ **Stability** Photosynthesis and respiration form a cycle that keeps the levels of oxygen and carbon dioxide fairly constant in the atmosphere. DNA replication ensures that each daughter cell will have all the necessary genetic information. *(Sections 1, 2, 3)*

Media and Technology

Exploring Earth Science Videodisc

◆ **Section 2** "Sunny Days" describes the sun as the ultimate energy source responsible for time, the seasons, and food.

Interactive Student Tutorial CD-ROM

◆ **Chapter Review** Interactive questions help students self-assess their mastery of key chapter concepts.

Student Edition Connection Strategies

◆ **Section 1** Integrating Chemistry, p. 53
Integrating Environmental Science, p. 54

◆ **Section 2** Social Studies Connection, p. 58
Integrating Health, p. 59

◆ **Section 4** Integrating Health, pp. 70–74

Visit the Science Explorer Internet site to find an up-to-date activity for Chapter 2 of *Cells and Heredity*.

ACTIVITY	Time (minutes)	Materials — Quantities for one work group	Skills
Section 1			
Discover, p. 50	5	**Nonconsumable** solar-powered calculator that does not have batteries	**Inferring**
Sharpen Your Skills, p. 52	20	**Consumable** coffee filter, leaf, rubbing alcohol **Nonconsumable** scissors, metric ruler, dime, plastic cup	**Inferring**
Section 2			
Discover, p. 55	20	**Consumable** warm water, 5 mL sugar, 1.0 mL dried yeast, 2 straws **Nonconsumable** 2 test tubes with stoppers, test tube rack	**Observing**
Try This, p. 57	5	**Nonconsumable** mirror, window, or metal surface	**Inferring**
Science at Home, p. 59	home	**Consumable** ingredients for bread recipe **Nonconsumable** bread recipe	**Communicating**
Real-World Lab, p. 60	20/15	**Consumable** 2 *Elodea* plants, bromthymol blue solution, straws **Nonconsumable** marking pens, 100-mL plastic graduated cylinder, 3 250-ml flasks with stoppers, light source	**Controlling Variables, Interpreting Data**
Section 3			
Discover, p. 61	15	**Consumable** yeast culture, methylene blue stain **Nonconsumable** plastic dropper, microscope slide with coverslip, microscope	**Developing Hypotheses**
Try This, p. 63	10	**Consumable** construction paper, 3 different colored pipe cleaners	**Making Models**
Sharpen Your Skills, p. 66	5	No special materials are required.	**Interpreting Data**
Skills Lab, p. 69	40	**Nonconsumable** microscope, colored pencils, calculator, prepared slides of onion root tip cells undergoing cell division	**Observing, Calculating, Interpreting Data**
Section 4			
Discover, p. 70	15	**Consumable** masking tape **Nonconsumable** meter stick	**Predicting**

A list of all materials required for the Student Edition activities can be found on pages T14–T15. You can order Materials Kits by calling 1-800-828-7777 or by accessing the Science Explorer Internet site at **www.science-explorer.phschool.com.**

In Chapter 2, students will learn how plants use sunlight to make food in the process of photosynthesis. The Chapter 2 Project will help students understand how the amount or type of light a plant receives affects its ability to carry out photosynthesis.

Purpose Students will design a controlled experiment to determine the effects of different lighting conditions on plant growth and health.

Skills Focus After completing this project, students will be able to
◆ design a controlled experiment to grow plants under different lighting conditions while keeping other conditions constant;
◆ observe, measure, and record data on the health and growth of the plants;
◆ graph the data and draw conclusions from the data about the effect of light on plant health and growth.

Project Time Line The entire project will take about three weeks. On the first day, launch the project and have students read about the Chapter 2 Project on page 49 in the text. Also distribute and discuss the Chapter 2 Project Overview, pages 38–39 in Teaching Resources. In addition, you may wish to hand out the Chapter 2 Project Scoring Rubric on page 42 in Teaching Resources so students will know what is expected of them from the start of the project. If students will be working in groups, divide the class into groups at this time.

On the second day, give students time to brainstorm the answers to the questions listed in the text under Get Started on page 49. Then have students write an experimental plan and submit it to you for approval. Suggest any necessary revisions to their plans. Also have students complete the Chapter 2 Project Worksheets on pages 40–41 in Teaching Resources.

Urge students to set up their experiment and start measuring their plants as soon as possible, and to continue measuring their plants for at least two weeks. Check their progress at regular intervals, and set aside time at the end of two weeks for students to

prepare and deliver their presentations.

For more detailed information on planning and supervising the chapter project, see Chapter 2 Project Teacher Notes, pages 36–37 in Teaching Resources.

Suggested Shortcuts You can reduce the amount of time each student spends working on the project by having students work in groups. Group members should work together to brainstorm an experimental design and to draw conclusions from the data at the end of the project. Students can divide up the tasks

involved in caring for and measuring the plants, and graphing the data.

Students can grow the plants at home to reduce the amount of class time and classroom space needed to care for and measure the plants. Growing the plants at home also will allow students to continue to care for and measure their plants over weekends and school holidays.

Possible Materials The plants used for the project must be rapidly growing plants in order for different light conditions to produce a

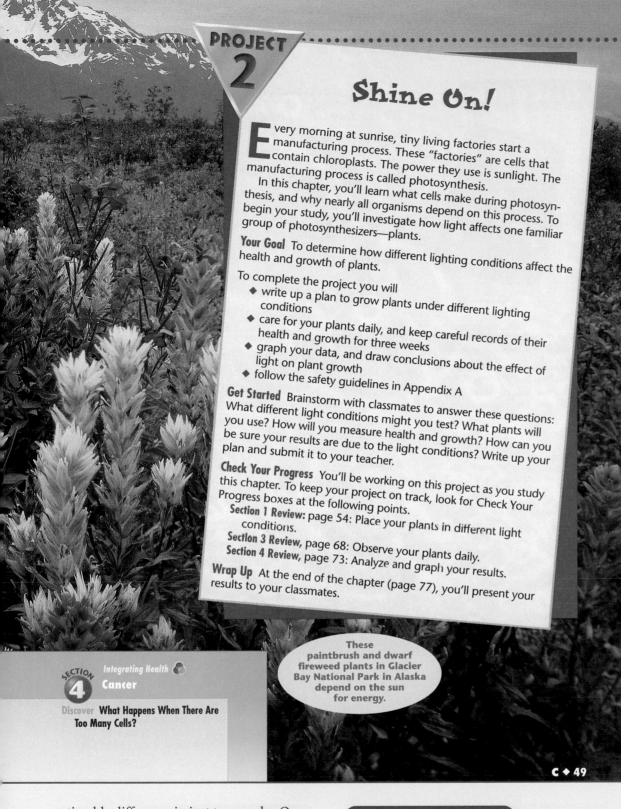

Shine On!

Every morning at sunrise, tiny living factories start a manufacturing process. These "factories" are cells that contain chloroplasts. The power they use is sunlight. The manufacturing process is called photosynthesis.

In this chapter, you'll learn what cells make during photosynthesis, and why nearly all organisms depend on this process. To begin your study, you'll investigate how light affects one familiar group of photosynthesizers—plants.

Your Goal To determine how different lighting conditions affect the health and growth of plants.

To complete the project you will

◆ write up a plan to grow plants under different lighting conditions
◆ care for your plants daily, and keep careful records of their health and growth for three weeks
◆ graph your data, and draw conclusions about the effect of light on plant growth
◆ follow the safety guidelines in Appendix A

Get Started Brainstorm with classmates to answer these questions: What different light conditions might you test? What plants will you use? How will you measure health and growth? How can you be sure your results are due to the light conditions? Write up your plan and submit it to your teacher.

Check Your Progress You'll be working on this project as you study this chapter. To keep your project on track, look for Check Your Progress boxes at the following points.

Section 1 Review: page 54: Place your plants in different light conditions.
Section 3 Review, page 68: Observe your plants daily.
Section 4 Review, page 73: Analyze and graph your results.

Wrap Up At the end of the chapter (page 77), you'll present your results to your classmates.

These paintbrush and dwarf fireweed plants in Glacier Bay National Park in Alaska depend on the sun for energy.

noticeable difference in just two weeks. One option is to use seedlings. You can germinate seeds, such as bean seeds, prior to the project or, depending on the time of year, obtain seedlings from a nursery or garden center. Another option is to use special fast-growing seeds available through several science supply companies.

Different lighting conditions can be achieved by varying the amount or the type of light. The simplest way to vary the amount of light is to put some plants on a sunny

Program Resources

◆ **Teaching Resources** Chapter 2 Project Teacher Notes, pp. 36–37; Chapter 2 Project Overview and Worksheets, pp. 38–41; Chapter 2 Project Scoring Rubric, p. 42

windowsill and to put other plants in a corner of the room as far from the windows as possible. A more elaborate setup is to place all the plants under plant lights with timers set so that some plants receive more light than others. Students could also vary the color of light by using colored cellophane paper or by using different artificial lighting sources.

Students also will need a watering can and water to care for their plants, a metric ruler for measuring them, and a data table for recording their measurements and observations. The table in Worksheet 2 can be used to record the data.

Address the needs of students in wheelchairs by placing plants and other needed materials on a low table so students have easy access to them.

Launching the Project Introduce the project by asking: **What do plants need to grow?** *(Possible answers include soil, nutrients, water, and light.)* Emphasize the importance of light to plant growth. Point out that plants need light in order to make food, which in turn provides them with the energy they need for growth and all other life processes. Ask: **What do you predict would happen to a plant that did not receive any light?** *(Students may say that the plant would not be able to make food, so it probably would die.)* Tell students that in the Chapter 2 Project they will grow plants under different lighting conditions to see how this affects the plants' health and growth.

Performance Assessment

To assess students' performance in this project, use the Chapter 2 Project Scoring Rubric on page 42 in Teaching Resources. Students will be assessed on
◆ their experimental design and how well they control variables;
◆ their record of observations and measurements of plant health and growth;
◆ their graphs of the data and their conclusions about the effect of light on plant health and growth;
◆ their group participation, if they worked in groups.

Objectives

After completing the lesson, students will be able to

◆ describe the process of photosynthesis;

◆ explain how the sun supplies all living things with the energy they need.

Key Terms photosynthesis, pigment, chlorophyll, stomata, autotroph, heterotroph

1 Engage/Explore

Activating Prior Knowledge

Ask students: **How many of you have houseplants in your home?** *(Most will probably say they do.)* **Where are houseplants usually placed?** *(Near a window or where they will receive light)* **What happens if a houseplant doesn't get enough light?** *(They get spindly, turn yellow, and may die.)* **Why do plants need light?** *(Some students may know that plants use light energy to make food. Accept all responses without comment at this time.)*

········ DISCOVER ········

Skills Focus inferring
Materials *solar-powered calculator that does not use batteries*
Time 5 minutes
Tips If necessary, show students where the solar cells are located on the calculator.
Expected Outcome When all the solar cells are covered, the number display should go blank. When all but one of the solar cells are covered, the number display should flicker and fade.
Think It Over Students should infer that energy to power the calculator comes from sunlight.

SECTION
1 Photosynthesis

DISCOVER .... ACTIVITY

Where Does the Energy Come From?

1. Obtain a solar-powered calculator that does not use batteries. Place the calculator in direct light.

2. Cover the solar cells with your finger. Note how your action affects the number display.

3. Uncover the solar cells. What happens to the number display?

4. Now cover all but one of the solar cells. How does that affect the number display?

Think It Over

Inferring From your observations, what can you infer about the energy that powers the calculator?

GUIDE FOR READING

◆ What happens during the process of photosynthesis?

◆ How does the sun supply living things with the energy they need?

Reading Tip As you read, create a flowchart that shows the steps involved in the process of photosynthesis.

It's a beautiful summer afternoon—a perfect day for a picnic in the park. The aroma of chicken cooking on the grill fills the air. Your dog is busy chasing sticks under a nearby tree. Up above, bluejays swoop down from the tree's branches, hunting for food. "Let's go for a bike ride before lunch," suggests your cousin. "Great idea," you say, and you ride off down the path.

Dogs running, birds flying, people biking—all of these activities require energy. Where do you think this energy comes from? Believe it or not, all the energy used to perform such activities comes from the sun. In fact, the sun provides almost all the energy used by living things on Earth.

READING STRATEGIES

Reading Tip Students' flowcharts should show photosynthesis as a two-stage process, with the first stage using chlorophyll to capture the sun's energy and the second stage using the captured energy to produce sugars and oxygen from carbon dioxide and water. To improve students' understanding of photosynthesis, challenge them to relate the steps of their flowcharts to the photosynthesis equation on page 53.

Program Resources

◆ **Teaching Resources** 2-1 Lesson Plan, p. 43; 2-1 Section Summary, p. 44

Science Explorer Series *Sound and Light,* Chapter 3, has more information on the electromagnetic spectrum.

What Is Photosynthesis?

Every living thing needs energy. All cells need energy to carry out their functions, such as making proteins and transporting substances into and out of the cell. Your picnic lunch supplies your cells with the energy they need. But plants and other organisms, such as algae and some bacteria, obtain their energy in a different way. These organisms use the energy in sunlight to make their own food.

The process by which a cell captures the energy in sunlight and uses it to make food is called **photosynthesis** (foh toh SIN thuh sis). The term *photosynthesis* comes from the root words *photo*, which means "light," and *synthesis*, which means "putting together." Photosynthesis means using light to make food.

A Two-Stage Process

Photosynthesis is a very complicated process. **During photosynthesis, plants and some other organisms use energy from the sun to convert carbon dioxide and water into oxygen and sugars, including glucose.** You can think of photosynthesis as taking place in two stages: capturing the sun's energy and producing sugars. You're probably familiar with many two-stage processes. To make a cake, for example, the first stage is to combine the ingredients to make the batter. The second stage is to bake the batter in an oven. To get the desired result—the cake—both stages must occur in the correct order.

Capturing the Sun's Energy The first stage of photosynthesis involves capturing the energy in sunlight. In plants, this energy-capturing process occurs in the leaves and other green parts of the plant. Recall from Chapter 1 that chloroplasts are green organelles inside plant cells. In most plants, leaf cells contain more chloroplasts than do cells in other parts of the plant.

Figure 1 Photosynthesis occurs inside chloroplasts in the cells of plants and some other organisms. The chloroplasts are the green structures in the cell in the inset. *Applying Concepts Where in a plant are cells with many chloroplasts found?*

---

2 Facilitate

What Is Photosynthesis?

Demonstration

Materials *green leaf, jar, rubbing alcohol, paper towel, shallow dish, iodine solution*
Time 10 minutes

Demonstrate to students that starch is produced in green leaves. Place a green leaf in a jar of rubbing alcohol and leave it overnight to remove the leaf's waxy covering and most of its chlorophyll. The next day in class, blot the leaf dry with a paper towel and place it in a shallow dish. Tell students that iodine turns purple when it comes into contact with starch, and then cover the leaf with iodine solution. Have students observe how the leaf changes color. Then ask: **Based on these observations, what compound does the leaf contain?** *(starch)* **Why does the leaf contain this compound?** *(It was produced from sugars that were produced by photosynthesis.)* **learning modality: visual**

A Two-Stage Process

Using the Visuals: Figure 1

Make sure students understand that the inset photo is a microscopic view of chloroplasts. Ask: **What makes the chloroplasts green?** *(Chlorophyll, a green pigment)* **What is the role of chlorophyll in photosynthesis?** *(It captures light energy that is used to power the second stage of photosynthesis.)* **learning modality: visual**

Answers to Self-Assessment

Caption Question

Figure 1 Cells with many chloroplasts are found in the leaves.

Ongoing Assessment

Oral Presentation Call on students at random to define photosynthesis and identify its two stages.

Sharpen your Skills

Inferring

Materials *coffee filter, scissors, leaf, metric ruler, dime, rubbing alcohol, plastic cup*

Time 20 minutes

Tips A geranium will work well for this activity. Tell students that chlorophyll and other plant pigments dissolve in alcohol.

Expected Outcome As the alcohol spreads through the green band, it dissolves the plant pigments and carries them up the paper strip. As the paper dries, the heavier pigments separate out first, so students may see separate lines of different pigments on the paper strip.

Extend Point out that, in temperate climates, the amount of chlorophyll in leaves greatly decreases in the fall. Ask: **Why does this cause the leaves to change color?** *(When the leaves contain less chlorophyll, the other pigments they contain can show through.)* **learning modality: kinesthetic**

Building Inquiry Skills: Observing

Materials *forceps, lettuce leaf, water, microscope slide, coverslip, microscope*

Time 15 minutes

Give students a chance to see stomata on the underside of a leaf. Have students use forceps to gently pull away a small piece of the thin membrane on the underside of a lettuce leaf. Then have students use the piece of leaf to make a slide. Students should scan the leaf under low power to find a few stomata, and then bring the stomata into focus under high power. Urge students to sketch the structures they see. Call their attention to the sausage-shaped guard cells on either side of each stoma, and ask: **What role do you think the guard cells play?** *(They regulate what enters the stomata.)* **What substance enters the leaf through the stomata?** *(Carbon dioxide)* **learning modality: visual**

Sharpen your Skills

Inferring
In this activity, you will observe the pigments in a leaf.

1. Cut a strip 5 cm by 20 cm out of a coffee filter.
2. Place a leaf on top of the paper strip, about 2 cm from the bottom.
3. Roll the edge of a dime over a section of the leaf, leaving a narrow band of color on the paper strip.
4. Pour rubbing alcohol into a plastic cup to a depth of 1 cm. Stand the paper strip in the cup so the color band is about 1 cm above the alcohol. Hook the other end of the strip over the top of the cup.
5. After 10 minutes, remove the paper strip and let it dry. Observe the strip.
6. Wash your hands.

What does the appearance of your paper strip reveal about the presence of pigments in the leaf?

The chloroplasts in plant cells give plants their green color. The green color comes from **pigments,** colored chemical compounds that absorb light. The main pigment found in the chloroplasts of plants is **chlorophyll.** Chloroplasts may also contain yellow and orange pigments, but they are usually masked by the green color of chlorophyll.

Chlorophyll and the other pigments function in a manner similar to that of the solar "cells" in a solar-powered calculator. Solar cells capture the energy in light and use it to power the calculator. Similarly, the pigments capture light energy and use it to power the second stage of photosynthesis.

Using Energy to Make Food In the second stage of photosynthesis, the cell uses the captured energy to produce sugars. The cell needs two raw materials for this stage: water (H_2O) and carbon dioxide (CO_2). In plants, the roots absorb water from the soil. The water then moves up through the plant's stem to the leaves. Carbon dioxide is one of the gases in the air. Carbon dioxide enters the plant through small openings on the undersides of the leaves called **stomata** (STOH muh tuh)(singular *stoma*). Once in the leaves, the water and carbon dioxide move into the chloroplasts.

Inside the chloroplasts, the water and carbon dioxide undergo a complex series of chemical reactions. The reactions are powered by the energy captured in the first stage. One of the products of the reactions is oxygen (O_2). The other products are sugars, including glucose ($C_6H_{12}O_6$). Recall from Chapter 1 that sugars are a type of carbohydrate. Cells can use the energy in the sugars to carry out important cell functions.

☑ *Checkpoint* Why are plants green?

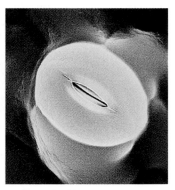

Figure 2 Stomata are small openings on the undersides of leaves. Stomata can open (left) or close (right) to control the movement of carbon dioxide and oxygen.

Background

Facts and Figures Most leaves contain large amounts of the pigment chlorophyll in the cell structures called chloroplasts. A single cell from a plant leaf may contain 50 or more chloroplasts. Visible light is made up of many wavelengths and these wavelengths interact differently with chlorophyll. The red and blue wavelengths of visible light are absorbed by chlorophyll, so you don't see these colors when you look at green leaves. The energy in these wavelengths is used to power photosynthesis. The green wavelengths of visible light are reflected by chlorophyll, so you see the color green when you look at leaves that contain a lot of chlorophyll. Little of the energy in the green wavelengths of light is used in photosynthesis.

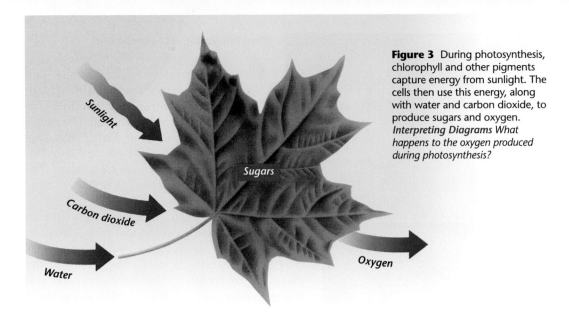

Figure 3 During photosynthesis, chlorophyll and other pigments capture energy from sunlight. The cells then use this energy, along with water and carbon dioxide, to produce sugars and oxygen. *Interpreting Diagrams What happens to the oxygen produced during photosynthesis?*

Sunlight

Sugars

Carbon dioxide

Oxygen

Water

The Photosynthesis Equation

The events of photosynthesis can be summed up by the following chemical equation:

$$6\,CO_2 + 6\,H_2O \xrightarrow{\text{light energy}} C_6H_{12}O_6 + 6\,O_2$$

carbon dioxide · water · glucose · oxygen

 INTEGRATING CHEMISTRY Notice that the raw materials—six molecules of carbon dioxide and six molecules of water—are on the left side of the equation. The products—one molecule of glucose and six molecules of oxygen—are on the right side of the equation. An arrow, which is read as "yields," connects the raw materials to the products. Light energy, which is necessary for the chemical reaction to occur, is written above the arrow.

What happens to the products of photosynthesis? Plant cells use some of the sugar for food. The cells break down the sugar molecules to release the energy they contain. This energy can then be used to carry out the plant's functions. Some sugar molecules are converted into other compounds, such as cellulose. Other sugar molecules may be stored in the plant's cells for later use. When you eat food from plants, such as potatoes or carrots, you are eating the plant's stored food.

The other product of photosynthesis is oxygen. Most of the oxygen passes out of the plant through the stomata and into the air. All organisms that carry out photosynthesis release oxygen.

Program Resources

◆ **Integrated Science Laboratory Manual**
C-2, "Stomata Functions"

Science Explorer Series *From Bacteria to Plants*, Chapter 4, has more information on photosynthesis.

Media and Technology

 Transparencies "Photosynthesis," Transparency 5

Answers to Self-Assessment

✓ Checkpoint
Plants are green because their chloroplasts contain the green pigment chlorophyll.

Caption Question
Figure 3 It passes out of the plant through the stomata and into the air.

The Photosynthesis Equation

Integrating Chemistry

Inform students that chemical equations must balance by having the same number of each type of atom on both sides of the equation. Point out that the subscript numerals show the number of atoms in each molecule in a compound and the numerals in front of the compound show how many molecules of that compound are involved in the reaction. Challenge students to determine if the chemical equation for photosynthesis is balanced by counting the number of each type of atom on the two sides of the equation. Check their counts by asking: **How many oxygen atoms are there on each side of the equation?** *(18)* **learning modality: logical/ mathematical**

Building Inquiry Skills: Making Models

Materials *bingo chips, buttons, cereal or pasta pieces, or other small objects in three different colors or shapes* **ACTIVITY**
Time 10 minutes

Divide the class into pairs, and provide each pair with enough small objects of each color or shape to represent the carbon, oxygen, and hydrogen atoms on one side of the photosynthesis equation. First have one member of each pair arrange the objects to represent the left side of the equation. Then have the other member of the pair rearrange the same objects to represent the right side of the photosynthesis equation. Urge partners to reverse their roles and repeat the activity. Then ask: **What part of the photosynthesis equation is not represented in the model?** *(The energy required to make the reaction occur)* **learning modality: kinesthetic**

Ongoing Assessment

Skills Check Have students make a flowchart to show what happens during photosynthesis.
 Students can save their flowcharts in their portfolios.

Photosynthesis and Life

 Integrating Environmental Science

Point out that not all the energy converted to food by autotrophs is available to the heterotrophs that depend on them. In fact, only about 10 percent of the energy at a given level in a food chain is available to organisms at the next level of the food chain. Ask: **Why are there fewer caterpillars than the plants they eat, and fewer birds than caterpillars?** (*Because there is less and less energy available to support life as you move up the food chain*) **learning modality: logical/mathematical**

3 Assess

Section 1 Review Answers

1. Raw materials: carbon dioxide, water; products: oxygen, sugars
2. Plants get energy from the sun. Animals get energy by eating plants or animals that eat plants.
3. Chlorophyll absorbs light, which provides the energy for photosynthesis. It is found in chloroplasts, which occur mainly in leaves.
4. Students may say that autotrophs provided them with oxygen, food for themselves, and food for the animals they depend on for food and other purposes.

 Check Your Progress

CHAPTER PROJECT 2

Make sure students have exposed their plants to different lighting conditions and are controlling all other variables. Remind students to give each plant the same amount of water (enough to keep the soil moist in each pot). By now, all students should have a data table ready to record their observations and measurements.

Performance Assessment

Writing Have students explain how life on Earth depends on the sun.

Figure 4 Both the caterpillar and the western bluebird obtain their energy indirectly from the sun.

Photosynthesis and Life

INTEGRATING ENVIRONMENTAL SCIENCE If you were a caterpillar, you might be sitting on a plant chewing on a leaf. The plant is an **autotroph** (AW toh trohf), an organism that makes its own food. The plant's leaves contain sugars made during photosynthesis. Leaves also contain starches, cellulose, and other compounds made from sugars. The energy in these compounds originally came from the sun.

The caterpillar is a **heterotroph** (HET uh roh trohf), an organism that cannot make its own food. To live, grow, and perform other caterpillar functions, it needs the energy in the plant's sugars. By eating plants, the caterpillar gets its energy from the sun, although in an indirect way.

Watch out—there's a bird! The bird, a heterotroph, gets its energy by eating caterpillars. Since the energy in caterpillars indirectly comes from the sun, the bird too is living off the sun's energy. **Nearly all living things obtain energy either directly or indirectly from the energy of sunlight captured during photosynthesis.**

Photosynthesis is also essential for the air you breathe. Most living things need oxygen to survive. About 21% of Earth's atmosphere is oxygen—thanks to plants and other organisms that carry out photosynthesis. Almost all the oxygen in Earth's atmosphere was produced by living things through the process of photosynthesis.

Section 1 Review

1. What are the raw materials needed for photosynthesis? What are the products?
2. How do plants get energy? How do animals get energy?
3. What role does chlorophyll play in photosynthesis? Where is chlorophyll found?
4. **Thinking Critically Applying Concepts** List three ways that autotrophs were important to you today.

Check Your Progress

CHAPTER PROJECT 2

Make any necessary revisions to your experimental plan. Then create a data table in which to record your observations each day. Now it's time to place your plants in the different lighting conditions. (*Hint:* Be sure to keep all other conditions the same throughout the project. For example, give all your plants the same amount of water.)

Background

History of Science The discovery of photosynthesis usually is attributed to the Dutch physician Jan Ingenhousz. In 1779, Ingenhousz demonstrated that plants need sunlight to replenish air. That is, plants produce oxygen in the presence of sunlight.

Program Resources

◆ **Teaching Resources** 2-1 Review and Reinforce, p. 45; 2-1 Enrich, p. 46

Media and Technology

 Interactive Student Tutorial CD-ROM C-2

DISCOVER · ACTIVITY · · · ·

What Is a Product of Respiration?

1. Put on your goggles. Fill two test tubes half full of warm water. Add 5 milliliters of sugar to one of the test tubes. Put the tubes in a test tube rack.

2. Add 0.5 milliliter of dried yeast (a single-celled organism) to each tube. Stir the contents of each tube with a straw. Place a stopper snugly in the top of each tube.

3. Observe any changes that occur in the two test tubes over the next 10 to 15 minutes.

Think It Over

Observing What changes occurred in each test tube? How can you account for any differences that you observed?

Your friend stops along the trail ahead of you and calls out, "Let's eat!" He looks around for a flat rock to sit on. You're ready for lunch. You didn't have much breakfast this morning, and you've been hiking for the past hour. As you look around you, you see that the steepest part of the trail is still ahead of you. You'll need a lot of energy to make it to the top.

Everyone knows that food provides energy. But not everyone knows *how* food provides energy. The food you eat does not provide your body with energy immediately after you eat it. First, the food must pass through your digestive system. There, the food is broken down into small molecules. These small molecules can then pass out of the digestive system and into your bloodstream. Next, the molecules travel through the bloodstream to the cells of your body. Inside the cells, the energy in the molecules is released. In this section, you'll learn how your body's cells obtain energy from the food you eat.

GUIDE FOR READING

◆ What events occur during respiration?

◆ How are photosynthesis and respiration related?

◆ What is fermentation?

Reading Tip Before you read, write a definition of *respiration*. As you read, revise your definition based on what you have learned.

Chapter 2   **C ◆ 55**

READING STRATEGIES

Reading Tip Most students will think initially that respiration just means breathing, which is its common meaning. By the time students have finished reading the section, they should realize that respiration also means the breakdown of food molecules in cells to produce energy. Make sure students are not confused by this dual use of the term.

Program Resources

◆ **Teaching Resources** 2-2 Lesson Plan, p. 47; 2-2 Section Summary, p. 48

Media and Technology

Audiotapes English-Spanish Summary 2-2

Transparencies "Respiration," Transparency 6

SECTION
2 Respiration

Objectives

After completing the lesson, students will be able to
◆ describe the events that occur during respiration;
◆ describe the relationship between photosynthesis and respiration;
◆ describe alcoholic and lactic-acid fermentation.

Key Terms respiration, fermentation

1 Engage/Explore

Activating Prior Knowledge

Introduce students to respiration by relating it to combustion. First help students recall what they know about combustion, by asking: **What does a fire need to burn?** *(fuel and oxygen)* **What is released when fuel is burned?** *(Energy in the form of heat and light)* Then tell students that a similar chemical process, called respiration, "burns" food molecules in cells. Like combustion, respiration uses fuel and oxygen to produce energy. The fuel comes from food, and the energy is used for cellular functions.

· · · · · · · · · · **DISCOVER** · · · · · · · · · ·

Skills Focus observing
Materials *2 test tubes with stoppers, warm water, 5 mL sugar, test tube rack, 1.0 mL dried yeast, 2 straws*
Time 20 minutes
Tips If possible, use fast-acting yeast, which you can purchase at a food store. The water should be warm, but not hot.
Expected Outcome Students should observe bubbles in the sugar water but none in the plain water.
Think It Over Students should infer that the bubbles in the test tube containing the sugar are due to some process involving the yeast and the sugar.

2 Facilitate

Storing and Releasing Energy

Building Inquiry Skills: Inferring

Ask students: **When do you think plants would need to "withdraw" the energy stored in their cells as complex carbohydrates?** *(During the winter when plants have lost their leaves and cannot photosynthesize)* **learning modality: logical/mathematical**

Respiration

Including All Students

Guide students who are still mastering English in comparing and contrasting breathing and cellular respiration. Ask: **How are breathing and cellular respiration similar?** *(Both involve using or taking in oxygen and releasing carbon dioxide and water.)* **How are breathing and cellular respiration different?** *(Breathing takes place in the lungs and provides the body with oxygen, whereas cellular respiration takes place inside cells and provides the cells with energy.)* **limited English proficiency**

Building Inquiry Skills: Communicating

Urge a small group of students who need extra challenges to work together to investigate the role of ATP in respiration and to communicate what they learn to the rest of the class. *(ATP, or adenosine triphosphate, is the molecule in which energy is stored during respiration. It is a very reactive molecule that readily breaks down and releases its energy for other cell functions.)* Make sure students fairly share the tasks of researching the problem and communicating the information. Challenge the group to communicate the information in a way that is creative, interesting, and easy to understand, such as a skit, cartoon strip, or illustrated flowchart. **cooperative learning**

Figure 5 All organisms need energy to live. **A.** This leopard frog uses the energy stored in carbohydrates to leap great distances. **B.** Although these mushrooms don't move, they still need a continuous supply of energy to grow and reproduce. *Applying Concepts What is the name of the process by which cells obtain the energy they need?*

Storing and Releasing Energy

To understand how cells use energy, think about how people save money in a bank. You might, for example, put some money in a savings account. Then, when you want to buy something, you withdraw some of the money. Cells store and use energy in a similar way. During photosynthesis, plants capture the energy from sunlight and "save" it in the form of carbohydrates, including sugars and starches. When the cells need energy, they "withdraw" it by breaking down the carbohydrates. This process releases energy. Similarly, when you eat a meal, you add to your body's energy savings account. When your cells need energy, they make a withdrawal and break down the food to release energy.

Respiration

After you eat a meal, your body converts the carbohydrates in the food into glucose, a type of sugar. The process by which cells "withdraw" energy from glucose is called **respiration. During respiration, cells break down simple food molecules such as glucose and release the energy they contain.** Because living things need a continuous supply of energy, the cells of all living things carry out respiration continuously.

The term *respiration* might be confusing. You have probably used it to mean breathing, that is, moving air in and out of your lungs. Because of this confusion, the respiration process that takes place inside cells is sometimes called cellular respiration.

The double use of the term *respiration* does point out a connection that you should keep in mind. Breathing brings oxygen into your lungs, and oxygen is necessary for cellular respiration to occur in most cells. Some cells can obtain energy from glucose without using oxygen. But the most efficient means of obtaining energy from glucose requires the presence of oxygen.

Background

Facts and Figures Respiration is often compared to combustion because both processes involve the breakdown of molecules in the presence of oxygen to produce energy and carbon dioxide. However, respiration is a much slower, more controlled process than combustion. If respiration is like carrying a bundle down five flights of stairs, combustion is like dropping it from a fifth-story window.

History of Science The discovery of the nature of cellular respiration is attributed jointly to the French chemist Antoine Laurent Lavoisier and the French physicist, mathematician, and astronomer Pierre Laplace. In 1780 they published the results of their experiments showing that animal respiration is a form of combustion.

The Respiration Equation Although respiration occurs in a series of complex steps, the overall process can be summarized in the following equation:

$$C_6H_{12}O_6 + 6\,O_2 \longrightarrow 6\,CO_2 + 6\,H_2O + energy$$

glucose   oxygen   carbon dioxide   water

Notice that the raw materials for respiration are glucose and oxygen. Plants and other organisms that undergo photosynthesis make their own glucose. The glucose in the cells of animals and other organisms comes from the food they consume. The oxygen comes from the air or water surrounding the organism.

The Two Stages of Respiration Like photosynthesis, respiration is a two-stage process. The first stage takes place in the cytoplasm of the organism's cells. There, glucose molecules are broken down into smaller molecules. Oxygen is not involved in this stage of respiration. Only a small amount of the energy in glucose is released during this stage.

The second stage of respiration takes place in the mitochondria. There, the small molecules are broken down into even smaller molecules. These chemical reactions require oxygen, and a great deal of energy is released. This is why the mitochondria are sometimes called the "powerhouses" of the cell.

Figure 6 summarizes the process of respiration. If you trace the steps in the breakdown of glucose, you'll see that energy is released in both stages. Two other products of respiration are carbon dioxide and water. These products diffuse out of the cell. In animals, the carbon dioxide and some water leave the body when they breathe out. Thus, when you breathe in, you take in oxygen, a raw material for respiration. When you breathe out, you release carbon dioxide and water, products of respiration.

☑ *Checkpoint* *What are the raw materials for respiration?*

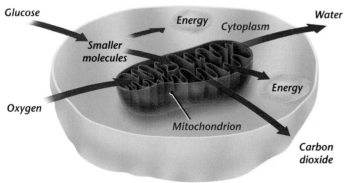

Figure 6 The first stage of respiration, which takes place in the cytoplasm, releases a small amount of energy. The second stage takes place in the mitochondria. A large amount of energy is released at this stage.

Chapter 2 **C ◆ 57**

Comparing Photosynthesis and Respiration

Building Inquiry Skills: Comparing and Contrasting

Urge students to compare the respiration equation on the previous page with the photosynthesis equation on page 53. Ask: **How are the two equations similar?** *(Both involve the same chemical compounds.)* **How are the two equations different?** *(The left and right sides of the equations are reversed; also the photosynthesis reaction uses energy, and the respiration reaction produces energy.)* **Based on your comparison, what can you conclude about the relationship between respiration and photosynthesis?** *(Complex molecules formed during photosynthesis are broken down during respiration to produce energy and simple molecules that are the raw materials for photosynthesis.)* **learning modality: logical/mathematical**

Fermentation

Social Studies CONNECTION

Emphasize that lactic acid is a product of one type of fermentation. Explain that lactic acid, like most other acids, has a sour taste. Bring to class samples of some of the fermented foods mentioned in the connection feature, such as sauerkraut, soy sauce, or miso. Give students an opportunity to taste the foods and describe how they taste. (CAUTION: Check for food allergies.)

In Your Journal In their ads, students should write about one of the fermented foods mentioned in the feature or another fermented food, such as yogurt. Suggest that they try to find a recipe for the food they have chosen. Their ads should include a description of the process of lactic-acid fermentation that is written in easily understood terms. **learning modality: verbal**

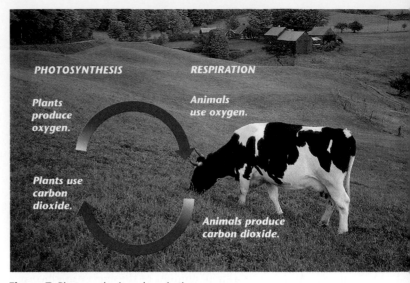

Figure 7 Photosynthesis and respiration can be thought of as opposite processes. *Interpreting Photographs How do these two processes keep the levels of oxygen and carbon dioxide in the atmosphere fairly constant?*

Social Studies CONNECTION

Many popular Asian foods are produced by fermentation. Kimchee, for example, is a Korean side dish that is similar to sauerkraut. It is made from Asian cabbage, salt, and spices. Naturally occuring bacteria ferment sugars in the cabbage by lactic-acid fermentation. The lactic acid produced during the fermentation process gives the kimchee a tangy flavor. Other Asian foods produced by fermentation include soy sauce and miso.

In Your Journal

Write an ad for kimchee or another fermented food product. Include information about how the food is made and used.

Comparing Photosynthesis and Respiration

Do you notice anything familiar about the equation for respiration? You are quite right if you said it is the opposite of the equation for photosynthesis. This is an important point to remember. During photosynthesis, carbon dioxide and water are used to produce sugars and oxygen. During respiration, glucose (a sugar) and oxygen are used to produce carbon dioxide and water. **Photosynthesis and respiration can be thought of as opposite processes.** Together, these two processes form a cycle that keeps the levels of oxygen and carbon dioxide fairly constant in the atmosphere. As you can see in Figure 7, living things use both gases over and over again.

Fermentation

Some cells are able to obtain energy from food without using oxygen. For example, some single-celled organisms live where there is no oxygen, such as deep in the ocean or in the mud of lakes or swamps. These organisms obtain their energy through **fermentation,** an energy-releasing process that does not require oxygen. **Fermentation provides energy for cells without using oxygen.** The amount of energy released from each sugar molecule during fermentation, however, is much lower than the amount released during respiration.

Background

Integrating Science The thyroid gland produces the hormone thyroxine, which regulates metabolic rate. A person's thyroid gland can produce too much or too little thyroxine. In hyperthyroidism, the thyroid produces too much thyroxine, leading to an increased rate of cellular respiration and a speeding up of all body processes. Symptoms of hyperthyroidism include rapid heart rate, weight loss, and difficulty sleeping. In hypothyroidism, the thyroid produces too little hormone. This leads to a decreased rate of cellular respiration and a slowing down of all body processes. The symptoms of hypothyroidism include slow heart rate, weight gain, and fatigue.

Alcoholic Fermentation One type of fermentation occurs in yeast and some other single-celled organisms. This process is sometimes called alcoholic fermentation because alcohol is one of the products made when these organisms break down sugars. The other products are carbon dioxide and a small amount of energy.

The products of alcoholic fermentation are important to bakers and brewers. The carbon dioxide produced by yeast causes dough to rise, and it creates the air pockets you see in bread. Carbon dioxide is also the source of bubbles in alcoholic drinks such as beer and sparkling wine.

Lactic-Acid Fermentation Another type of **INTEGRATING HEALTH** fermentation takes place at times in your body, and you've probably felt its effects. Think of a time when you've run as fast as you could for as long as you could. Your leg muscles were pushing hard against the pavement, and you were breathing quickly. Eventually, however, your legs became tired and you couldn't run any more.

No matter how hard you breathed, your muscle cells used up the oxygen faster than it could be replaced. Because your cells lacked oxygen, fermentation occurred. One product of this type of fermentation is an acid known as lactic acid. When lactic acid builds up, you feel a painful sensation in your muscles. Your muscles feel weak and sore.

Figure 8 When an athlete's muscles run out of oxygen, lactic-acid fermentation occurs. The athlete's muscles feel tired and sore.

Section 2 Review

1. Why is respiration important for a cell?
2. Explain the relationship between photosynthesis and respiration.
3. Which raw material is *not* needed for fermentation to occur?
4. How do plants and animals maintain the level of oxygen in the atmosphere?
5. **Thinking Critically Applying Concepts** Do plant cells need to carry out respiration? Explain.

Science at Home

With an adult family member, follow a recipe in a cookbook to make a loaf of bread using yeast. Explain to your family what causes the dough to rise. After you bake the bread, observe a slice and look for evidence that fermentation occurred.

Program Resources

- **Teaching Resources** 2-2 Review and Reinforce, p. 49; 2-2 Enrich, p. 50
- **Interdisciplinary Exploration Series** "Fate of the Rain Forest," pp. 20–21; "Where River Meets Sea," pp. 15–16
- **Science Explorer Series** *Environmental Science,* Chapter 2, has more information on cycles in nature.

Answers to Self-Assessment

Caption Question

Figure 7 Photosynthesis uses carbon dioxide and produces oxygen; respiration uses oxygen and produces carbon dioxide.

Media and Technology

 Interactive Student Tutorial CD-ROM C-2

Tell students that researchers have hypothesized that eating a high-carbohydrate diet before a long race slows the buildup of lactic acid in the muscles and helps prevent muscle soreness and fatigue. Challenge students to design an experiment to test this hypothesis. Call on volunteers to describe their experimental designs. *(The most likely design compares muscle soreness and fatigue in two groups of runners, one group that has been eating a high-carbohydrate diet and one that has been eating a low-carbohydrate diet.)* **learning modality: logical/mathematical**

3 Assess

Section 2 Review Answers

1. It supplies the energy the cell needs.
2. They can be thought of as opposite processes: During photosynthesis, carbon dioxide and water are used to produce sugar and oxygen. During respiration, sugar and oxygen are used to produce carbon dioxide and water.
3. oxygen
4. The level of oxygen in the atmosphere is maintained mainly by plants producing oxygen during photosynthesis and animals using oxygen during respiration.
5. Yes; plant cells carry out respiration to produce energy for cell functions from molecules such as glucose.

Science at Home

Students should explain **ACTIVITY** that yeast use the sugar in the dough for alcoholic fermentation, which releases carbon dioxide. The carbon dioxide, in turn, causes the dough to rise and small holes to form in the baked bread.

Performance Assessment

Writing Have students describe the similarities and differences between alcoholic and lactic-acid fermentation.

Gases in Balance

Preparing for Inquiry

Key Concept Photosynthesis and respiration are opposite processes.

Skills Objectives Students will be able to
- control other variables while investigating whether photosynthesis requires light;
- interpret data on color to detect carbon dioxide in solutions.

Time 20 minutes on Day 1; 15 minutes on Day 2

Advance Planning Purchase *Elodea* plants at an aquarium supply store.

Guiding Inquiry

Troubleshooting the Experiment
- Make sure students realize that the solution will turn blue again if the carbon dioxide is used up.

Expected Outcome
The solution in flask L should change from yellow to blue; the solution in flasks D and C should remain yellow.

Analyze and Conclude
1. The solution in flask L changed because photosynthesis used up the carbon dioxide. The solution in flask D remained the same because the plant had no light for photosynthesis. The solution in flask C remained the same because there was no plant to undergo photosynthesis.
2. Flask C was needed to rule out the possibility that the solution in flask L changed color just because it was placed in the light.
3. The solution would turn yellow again because it would contain carbon dioxide.
4. The lab showed that carbon dioxide is given off in respiration and used in photosynthesis. These two processes form a cycle that keeps levels of oxygen and carbon dioxide constant.

Extending the Inquiry

More to Explore The levels would reach a stable balance as the plant and fish recycled the two gases.

Real-World Lab

You and Your Environment

Gases in Balance

Problem
How are photosynthesis and respiration related?

Skills Focus
controlling variables, interpreting data

Materials
marking pens	straws
2 *Elodea* plants	light source
plastic graduated cylinder, 100-mL	
bromthymol blue solution	
3 flasks with stoppers, 250-mL	

Procedure

1. Bromthymol blue can be used to test for carbon dioxide. To see how this dye works, pour 100 mL of bromthymol blue solution into a flask. Record its color. **CAUTION:** *Bromthymol blue can stain skin and clothing. Avoid spilling or splashing it on yourself.*
2. Provide a supply of carbon dioxide by gently blowing into the solution through a straw until the dye changes color. Record the new color. **CAUTION:** *Do not inhale any of the solution through the straw.*
3. Copy the data table into your notebook. Add 100 mL of bromthymol blue to the other flasks. Then blow through clean straws into each solution until the color changes.
4. Now you will test to see what gas is used by a plant in the presence of light. Obtain two *Elodea* plants of about the same size.
5. Place one plant into the first flask. Label the flask "L" for light. Place the other plant in the second flask. Label the flask "D" for darkness. Label the third flask "C" for control. Put stoppers in all three flasks.

6. Record the colors of the three solutions under Day 1 in your data table.
7. Place the flasks labeled L and C in a lighted location as directed by your teacher. Place the flask labeled D in a dark location as directed by your teacher. Wash your hands thoroughly when you have finished.
8. On Day 2, examine the flasks and record the colors of the solutions in your data table.

Analyze and Conclude

1. Explain why the color of each solution did or did not change from Day 1 to Day 2.
2. Why was it important to include the flask labeled C as part of this experiment?
3. Predict what would happen if you blew into the flask labeled L after you completed Step 8. Explain your prediction.
4. **Apply** How does this lab show that photosynthesis and respiration are opposite processes? Why are both processes necessary to maintain an environment suitable for living things?

More to Explore

Suppose you were to put an *Elodea* plant and a small fish in a stoppered flask. Predict what would happen to the levels of oxygen and carbon dioxide in the flask. Explain your prediction.

DATA TABLE

Flask	Color of Solution	
	Day 1	Day 2
L (light)		
D (dark)		
C (control)		

Sample Data Table

Flask	Color of Solution	
	Day 1	Day 2
L (light)	yellow	blue
D (dark)	yellow	yellow
C (control)	yellow	yellow

Program Resources

- **Teaching Resources** Chapter 2 Real-World Lab, pp. 59–60

Safety

Stress to students that they should not inhale the bromthymol blue solution through the straw. Review the safety guidelines in Appendix A.

SECTION 3 Cell Division

DISCOVER ACTIVITY

What Are the Cells Doing?

1. Use a plastic dropper to transfer some yeast cells from a yeast culture to a microscope slide. Your teacher has prepared the slide by drying methylene blue stain onto it. Add a coverslip and place the slide under a microscope.

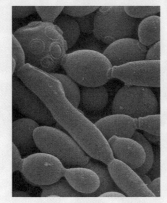

2. Examine the cells on the slide. Use low power first, then high power. Look for what appears to be two cells attached to each other. One cell may be larger than the other. Draw what you see.

Think It Over

Developing Hypotheses What process do you think the "double cells" are undergoing? Develop a hypothesis that might explain what you see.

I n the early autumn, many local fairs run pumpkin contests. Proud growers enter their largest pumpkins, hoping to win a prize. If you've never seen these prize-winning pumpkins, you would be amazed. Some have masses close to 400 kilograms and can be as big as a doghouse. What's even more amazing is that these giant pumpkins began as small flowers on pumpkin plants. How did the pumpkins grow so big?

A pumpkin grows in size by increasing both the size and the number of its cells. A single cell divides, forming two cells. Then two cells divide, forming four, and so on. This process of cell division does not occur only in pumpkins, though. In fact, many cells in your body are undergoing cell division as you read this page.

GUIDE FOR READING

◆ What events take place during the three stages of the cell cycle?

◆ What is the role of DNA replication?

Reading Tip Before you read, use the headings to outline the process of cell division. As you read, fill in information under each heading.

READING STRATEGIES

Study and Comprehension Before students read the section, suggest that they reread the material on DNA in Chapter 1. After students read this section, encourage them to create a concept map using the boldfaced terms. Call on students to name the stages of the cell cycle and the phases of mitosis to make sure they are not confusing the two.

Program Resources

◆ **Teaching Resources** 2-3 Lesson Plan, p. 51; 2-3 Section Summary, p. 52

Media and Technology

Audiotapes English-Spanish Summary 2-3

SECTION 3 Cell Division

Objectives

After completing the lesson, students will be able to
◆ list the events that take place during the three stages of the cell cycle;
◆ describe the structure of DNA and how DNA replication occurs.

Key Terms cell cycle, interphase, replication, mitosis, chromosome, chromatid, cytokinesis

1 Engage/Explore

Activating Prior Knowledge

Introduce students to the cell cycle by relating it to the human life cycle. Ask: **What are the stages that people go through during their life, starting with infancy and ending with old age?** *(Students are likely to name or describe the additional stages of childhood, adolescence, and adulthood.)* Point out that cells, like people, undergo a life cycle, called the cell cycle. During the stages of the cell cycle, cells grow and mature. But unlike the human life cycle, the cell cycle starts over again when the cell divides.

DISCOVER

Skills Focus developing hypotheses

Materials *plastic dropper, yeast culture, stained microscope slide, coverslip, microscope*

Time 15 minutes

Tips You can prepare a yeast culture by stirring dry yeast and sugar into warm (not hot) water. Stain slides ahead of time by adding a drop of methylene blue to each slide and letting it dry. Alternatively, you can use prepared slides of yeast cells.

Expected Outcome Students should observe and sketch yeast cells, some of which are in the process of budding to form daughter cells.

Think It Over Students may say that the "double cells" are dividing. The most likely hypothesis is that yeast cells split in two when they reproduce.

2 Facilitate

The Cell Cycle

Including All Students

Guide students who need more help in organizing the information in this section. Point out that the focus of the section is cell division, but cell division is just part of the cell cycle. Ask: **What are the three stages of the cell cycle?** *(interphase, mitosis, and cytokinesis)* As students identify the names of the three stages, list them on the chalkboard under the heading "Cell Cycle." Point out that the stages of mitosis and cytokinesis, which comprise cell division, are relatively short, whereas interphase is by far the longest stage. **limited English proficiency**

Stage 1: Interphase

Building Inquiry Skills: Inferring

Help students appreciate the role of DNA replication by having them infer what would happen if cell division occurred without DNA replication occurring first during interphase. Ask: **How would this affect the daughter cells?** *(Each daughter cell would have just half the DNA of the parent cell. With only half the DNA, the daughter cells would be unable to direct all cell activities and the cells probably would not survive.)* **learning modality: logical/mathematical**

Language Arts Connection

Remind students that analogies help us understand difficult ideas by relating them to things that are more familiar. Tell students that interphase in the cell cycle is like childhood and adolescence in the human life cycle. Ask: **Do you think this is a good analogy? Why or why not?** *(Students may say it is a good analogy because during interphase, like childhood and adolescence, the cell grows and matures.)* **learning modality: verbal**

Figure 9 The cells that make up this young monkey are the same size as those that make up its mother. However, the adult has many more cells in its body.

The Cell Cycle

Think about the cells you learned about in Chapter 1. Each cell contains many different structures, including a cell membrane, a nucleus, mitochondria, and ribosomes. To divide into two equal parts, the cell would need to either duplicate the structures or divide them equally between the two new cells. Both cells would then contain everything they need in order to survive and carry out their life functions.

The regular sequence of growth and division that cells undergo is known as the **cell cycle.** You can see details of the cell cycle in *Exploring the Cell Cycle* on pages 64 and 65. Notice that the cell cycle is divided into three main stages. As you read about each stage, follow the events that occur as one "parent" cell divides to form two identical "daughter" cells.

Stage 1: Interphase

The first stage of the cell cycle is called **interphase.** Interphase is the period before cell division occurs. Even though it is not dividing, the cell is quite active during this stage. **During interphase, the cell grows to its mature size, makes a copy of its DNA, and prepares to divide into two cells.**

Growth During the first part of interphase, the cell doubles in size and produces all the structures needed to carry out its functions. For example, the cell enlarges its endoplasmic reticulum, makes new ribosomes, and produces enzymes. Both mitochondria and chloroplasts make copies of themselves during the growth stage. The cell matures to its full size and structure.

DNA Replication After a cell has grown to its mature size, the next part of interphase begins. The cell makes a copy of the DNA in its nucleus in a process called **replication.** Recall that DNA is a nucleic acid found in the chromatin in a cell's nucleus. DNA holds all the information that the cell needs to carry out its functions. The replication of a cell's DNA is very important, since each daughter cell must have a complete set of DNA to survive. At the end of DNA replication, the cell contains two identical sets of DNA. One set will be distributed to each daughter cell. You will learn the details of DNA replication later in this section.

Integrating Science The cells in our body divide at varying rates as we grow older, causing the body not only to grow in size, but also to change in shape. During early life, cells in the head divide rapidly so that by birth, the head is very large relative to the body. During early childhood, the cells in the arms and legs divide rapidly, causing the young child's limbs to grow long relative to the trunk. At puberty, the child's body undergoes another spurt in growth and development. Sex hormones influence cells of the bones and muscles to divide rapidly, and within a few years the child reaches adult body size and proportions. The hormones also stimulate rapid growth and development of the sex organs and the secondary sex characteristics, such as breasts and body hair.

Preparation for Division Once the cell's DNA has replicated, preparation for cell division begins. The cell produces structures that it will use to divide during the rest of the cell cycle. At the end of interphase, the cell is ready to divide.

Stage 2: Mitosis

Once interphase is complete, the second stage of the cell cycle begins. **Mitosis** (my TOH sis) is the stage during which the cell's nucleus divides into two new nuclei. **During mitosis, one copy of the DNA is distributed into each of the two daughter cells.**

Scientists divide mitosis into four parts, or phases: prophase, metaphase, anaphase, and telophase. During prophase, the threadlike chromatin in the cell's nucleus begins to condense and coil, like fishing line wrapping around a ball. Under a light microscope, the condensed chromatin looks like tiny rods, as you can see in Figure 10. Since the cell's DNA has replicated, each rod has doubled. Each is an exact copy of the other. Scientists call each doubled rod of condensed chromatin a **chromosome.** Each identical rod, or strand, of the chromosome is called a **chromatid.** The two strands are held together by a structure called a centromere.

As the cell progresses through metaphase, anaphase, and telophase, the chromatids separate from each other and move to opposite ends of the cell. Then two nuclei form around the chromatids at the two ends of the cell. You can follow this process in *Exploring the Cell Cycle.*

✓ *Checkpoint* *During which stage of mitosis does the chromatin condense and form rodlike structures?*

Modeling Mitosis

ACTIVITY

Refer to *Exploring the Cell Cycle* as you carry out this activity.

1. Construct a model of a cell that has three chromosomes. Use a piece of construction paper to represent the cell. Use different colored pipe cleaners to represent the chromosomes. Make sure that the chromosomes look like double rods.

2. Position the chromosomes in the cell where they would be during prophase.

3. Repeat Step 2 for metaphase, anaphase, and telophase.

Making Models How did the model help you understand the events of mitosis?

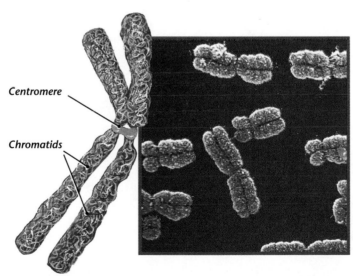

Centromere

Chromatids

Figure 10 During mitosis, the chromatin condenses to form rodlike chromosomes. Each chromosome consists of two identical strands, or chromatids. *Interpreting Diagrams What is the name of the structure that holds the chromatids together?*

Answers to Self-Assessment

✓ *Checkpoint*

The chromatin condenses into rodlike structures during prophase of mitosis.

Caption Question

Figure 10 The centromere holds the chromatids together.

TRY THIS

Skills Focus making models **ACTIVITY**

Materials *construction paper, different colored pipe cleaners*

Time 10 minutes

Expected Outcome Students should place three pairs of pipe cleaners, which represent three chromosomes, on the construction paper, which represents the cell. In prophase, both pipe cleaners in each pair should be joined at the center, and all the paired pipe cleaners should be clustered together. In metaphase, the paired pipe cleaners should be lined up across the center. In anaphase, the pipe cleaners in each pair should be separated and moved part way toward opposite ends. In telophase, the separated pipe cleaners should be located at opposite ends. Students may say that their model helped them see mitosis as a continuous process.

Extend Ask: **How could you use your model to show the next stage of the cell cycle?** (*Cytokinesis could be modeled by cutting the paper into two equal pieces and placing half the pipe cleaners on each piece.*) **learning modality: kinesthetic**

Building Inquiry Skills: Calculating

Materials *calculator* **ACTIVITY**
Time 5 minutes

Help students appreciate how quickly cell division can lead to a large number of cells. Challenge students to calculate how many cells there would be after a cell divides once, twice, three times, and so on, up to ten times. Then ask: **With each division that occurs, how does the number of cells change?** (*The number doubles.*) **learning modality: logical/mathematical**

Ongoing Assessment

Oral Presentation Call on students at random to state what happens during interphase and mitosis.

EXPLORING
the Cell Cycle

After students have examined the feature, ask: **How are the photographs related to the drawings?** *(They show actual cells at each stage of the cell cycle as they appear under a microscope, whereas the drawings are simplified sketches of the stages.)* Challenge students to find the genetic material in each illustration. Point out that, in prophase, each pair of chromatids consists of the original DNA of the parent cell plus a copy of the DNA, which was made during interphase. To help students appreciate the continuous nature of the cell cycle, tell them that cytokinesis and the last phase of mitosis, telophase, actually overlap in time. Ask: **Why is a circular diagram like this a better way to represent the cell cycle than a straight-line flowchart?** *(Because after the last stage of the cell cycle, the cycle starts over again)* **learning modality: visual**

Inquiry Challenge

Materials *poster board, colored markers, index cards, dice, small objects such as different colored erasers for game tokens*

ACTIVITY

Time 20 minutes

Divide the class into groups, and provide each group with the materials listed above. Challenge each group to create a board game that models the cell cycle. To get from "start" to "finish" on the game board, players must advance through each stage of the cell cycle by correctly answering questions about that stage. For example, to advance from prophase to metaphase, they might be required to answer: **How does the position of the chromosomes in metaphase differ from their position in prophase?** *(In prophase, the chromosomes are clustered in a group in the nucleus; in metaphase, the chromosomes are lined up across the center of the cell.)* When groups have finished creating their games, have them exchange and play the games. **cooperative learning**

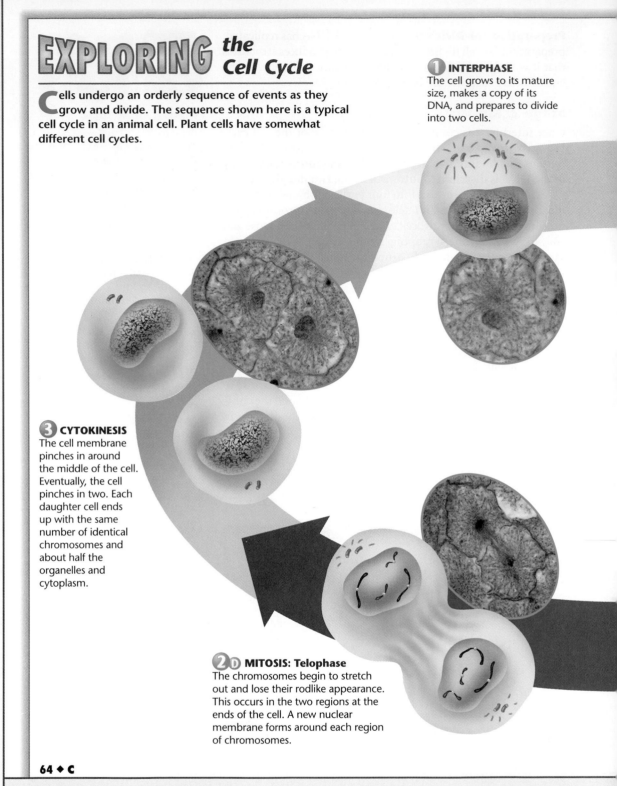

EXPLORING the Cell Cycle

Cells undergo an orderly sequence of events as they grow and divide. The sequence shown here is a typical cell cycle in an animal cell. Plant cells have somewhat different cell cycles.

① INTERPHASE
The cell grows to its mature size, makes a copy of its DNA, and prepares to divide into two cells.

③ CYTOKINESIS
The cell membrane pinches in around the middle of the cell. Eventually, the cell pinches in two. Each daughter cell ends up with the same number of identical chromosomes and about half the organelles and cytoplasm.

②D MITOSIS: Telophase
The chromosomes begin to stretch out and lose their rodlike appearance. This occurs in the two regions at the ends of the cell. A new nuclear membrane forms around each region of chromosomes.

Background

History of Science With the development of dyes for staining microscope specimens in the 1800s, scientists could see organelles in the nucleus and learn the details of mitosis. Some of the dyes stained the granular material in the nucleus, so it was given the name *chromatin*, from the Greek word *chroma*, meaning "color." With the dye, chromatin could be seen condensing into rodlike structures during cell division. These rodlike structures were called chromosomes, or "colored bodies" (the Greek word *soma* means "body.") By the late 1800s, German zoologist Theodor Boveri was able to show that, following mitosis, both daughter cells contain an exact copy of the chromosomes of the parent cell.

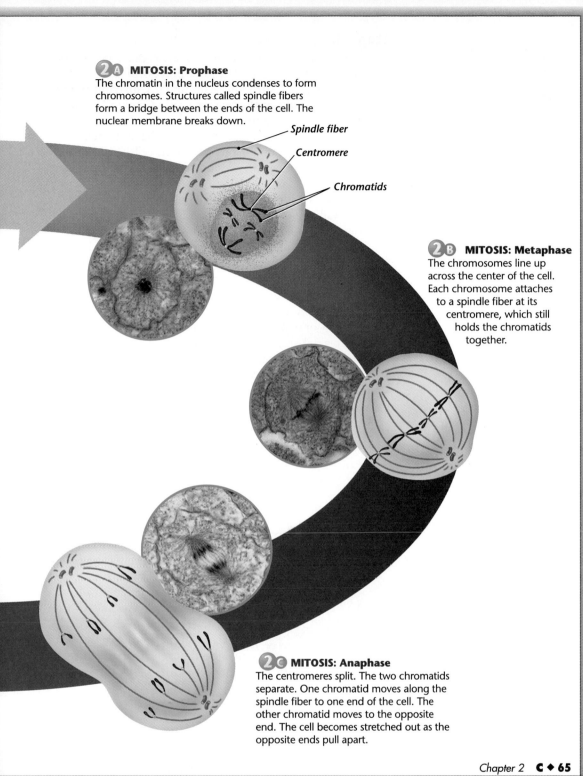

2A MITOSIS: Prophase

The chromatin in the nucleus condenses to form chromosomes. Structures called spindle fibers form a bridge between the ends of the cell. The nuclear membrane breaks down.

— *Spindle fiber*

— *Centromere*

— *Chromatids*

2B MITOSIS: Metaphase

The chromosomes line up across the center of the cell. Each chromosome attaches to a spindle fiber at its centromere, which still holds the chromatids together.

2C MITOSIS: Anaphase

The centromeres split. The two chromatids separate. One chromatid moves along the spindle fiber to one end of the cell. The other chromatid moves to the opposite end. The cell becomes stretched out as the opposite ends pull apart.

Including All Students

Materials index cards
Time 20 minutes

Urge students who are still mastering English to create flash cards for the stages of the cell cycle and the phases of mitosis. Suggest that they write the name of each stage or phase on one side of an index card, and describe it in their own words on the other side. After students have finished making their flash cards, check to see that they have included all the stages of the cell cycle and all the phases of mitosis. Also make sure that students have correctly described each stage or phase. For example, ask: **What occurs during metaphase?** (*The chromosomes form a line across the middle of the cell, and each chromosome is joined to a spindle fiber.*) Encourage pairs of students to quiz each other using their flash cards. **limited English proficiency**

Inquiry Challenge

Materials *construction paper, colored markers, tape or safety pins*
Time 15 minutes

Challenge the class to make a human model of the nucleus to show how mitosis occurs. (*One possible model is for a few pairs of students, representing paired chromatids, to stand face to face and join hands, while the other students, representing the nuclear membrane, join hands in a circle around them.*) Provide students with the materials listed above so they can make and wear signs that show which part of the nucleus they represent. After the class has formed the model, challenge students to move in ways that demonstrate the major events of mitosis. Ask: **How could you model the chromatin inside the nucleus during the other stages of the cell cycle?** (*To model cytokinesis and interphase, the formerly paired students might stand at random inside the "nuclear membrane" and no longer hold hands.*) **learning modality: kinesthetic**

Ongoing Assessment

Writing Have students write a list, in chronological order, of the major events that occur during mitosis.

Stage 3: Cytokinesis

Demonstration

Materials *balloon, water* **ACTIVITY**
Time 5 minutes

Make a three-dimensional model of an animal cell to show students how the cell membrane and cytoplasm change during cytokinesis. Fill a balloon about three fourths full with water, and then tightly tie the end of the balloon. Tell students that the balloon represents the cell membrane and the water represents the cytoplasm. Ask: **How could you use this model to show what happens to the cell membrane and cytoplasm during cytokinesis?** (*The most likely response is to squeeze the balloon together in the middle so that it forms two separate "daughter cells."*) Demonstrate with the balloon. **learning modality: visual**

Length of the Cell Cycle

Sharpen your *Skills*

Interpreting Data

Time 5 minutes **ACTIVITY**
Tips Make sure students realize that cell division includes *both* mitosis and cytokinesis and lasts a total of one hour.

Expected Outcome The cell cycle in the graph is 22 hours long. More cells would be in interphase at any given time because interphase is the longest stage, lasting for 21 hours.

Extend Ask: **Which part of interphase would you expect more cells to be in at any given time?** (*DNA replication*)
learning modality: logical/mathematical

Using the Visuals: Figure 11

Use the graph to help students better understand the relative lengths of the stages of the cell cycle. Call students' attention to the figure, and ask: **If each stage of the cell cycle took place in half the time, would the lines on the graph change? Why or why not?** (*The lines on the graph would not change, because each stage of the cycle would still make up the same percentage of the total cycle.*)
learning modality: logical/mathematical

66 ◆ C

Sharpen your *Skills*

Interpreting Data

Use the circle graph shown **ACTIVITY** in Figure 11 to answer the following questions.
1. How long is the cell cycle shown in the graph?
2. Which stage of the cell cycle would you expect more of the cells to be in at any given time— interphase, mitosis, or cytokinesis? Explain.

Stage 3: Cytokinesis

After mitosis, the final stage of the cell cycle, called **cytokinesis** (sy toh kih NEE sis), completes the process of cell division. **During cytokinesis, the cytoplasm divides, distributing the organelles into each of the two new cells.** Cytokinesis usually starts at about the same time as telophase.

During cytokinesis in animal cells, the cell membrane squeezes together around the middle of the cell. The cytoplasm pinches into two cells with about half of the organelles in each daughter cell.

Cytokinesis is somewhat different in plant cells. A plant cell's rigid cell wall cannot squeeze together in the same way that a cell membrane can. Instead, a structure called a cell plate forms across the middle of the cell. The cell plate gradually develops into new cell membranes between the two daughter cells. New cell walls then form around the cell membranes.

There are many variations of the basic pattern of cytokinesis. For example, yeast cells divide, though not equally. A small daughter cell, or bud, pinches off of the parent cell. The bud then grows into a full-sized yeast cell.

Cytokinesis marks the end of the cell cycle. Two new cells have formed. Each daughter cell has the same number of chromosomes as the original parent cell. At the end of cytokinesis, each cell enters interphase, and the cycle begins again.

✓ Checkpoint When in the cell cycle does cytokinesis begin?

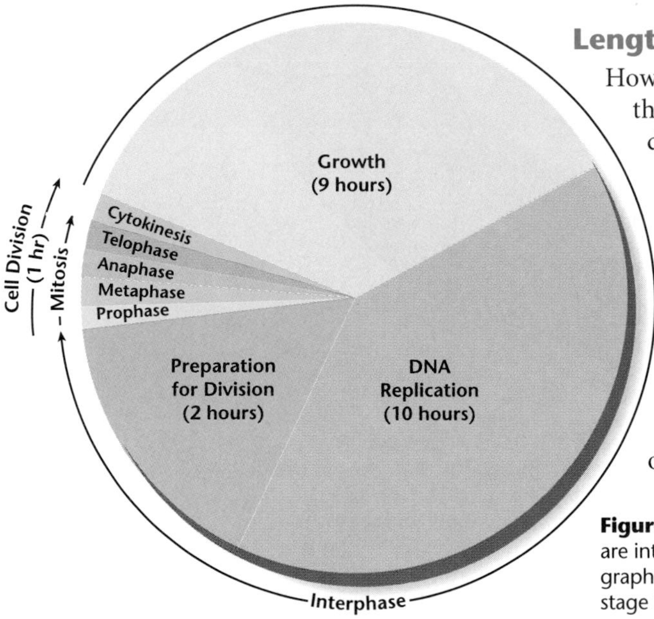

Length of the Cell Cycle

How long does it take for a cell to go through one cell cycle? The answer depends on the type of cell. In a young sea urchin, for example, one cell cycle takes about 2 hours. In contrast, a human liver cell completes one cell cycle in about 22 hours, as shown in Figure 11. The length of each stage in the cell cycle also varies greatly from cell to cell. Some cells, such as human brain cells, never divide—they remain in the first part of interphase for as long as they live.

Figure 11 The main stages of the cell cycle are interphase, mitosis, and cytokinesis. This graph shows the average length of each stage in a human liver cell.

Growth (9 hours)
Cell Division (1 hr) — Mitosis
Cytokinesis
Telophase
Anaphase
Metaphase
Prophase
Preparation for Division (2 hours)
DNA Replication (10 hours)
— Interphase —

66 ◆ C

Background

History of Science In 1955, Watson and Crick described the structure of the DNA molecule. To determine DNA's structure, they used English chemist Rosalind Franklin's X-ray photographs showing the helical appearance of DNA along with much other data. Franklin died in 1956, before Watson and Crick were awarded the Nobel Prize for their work on DNA's structure.

Facts and Figures When DNA replicates, the process requires more than 20 different enzymes to separate the strands of parent DNA and join the nucleotides in the correct sequence in the DNA copies. Although mistakes sometimes happen during this process, they are rare, occurring, on average, once in every one billion replications of any given base pair in a DNA molecule.

DNA Replication

A cell makes a copy of its DNA before mitosis occurs. **DNA replication ensures that each daughter cell will have all of the genetic information it needs to carry out its activities.**

Only in the last 50 years have scientists understood the importance of DNA. By the early 1950s, the work of several scientists showed that DNA carries all of the cell's instructions. They also learned that DNA is passed from a parent cell to its daughter cells. In 1953, two scientists, James Watson and Francis Crick, figured out the structure of DNA. This discovery revealed important information about how DNA copies itself.

The Structure of DNA Notice in Figure 12 that a DNA molecule looks like a twisted ladder, or spiral staircase. Because of its shape, a DNA molecule is often called a "double helix." A helix is a shape that twists like the threads of a screw.

The two sides of the DNA ladder are made up of molecules of a sugar called deoxyribose, alternating with molecules known as phosphates. Each rung of the DNA ladder is made up of a pair of molecules called nitrogen bases. Nitrogen bases are molecules that combine the element nitrogen with other elements. There are four kinds of nitrogen bases: adenine (AD uh neen), thymine (THY meen), guanine (GWAH neen), and cytosine (SY tuh seen). The capital letters A, T, G, and C are used to represent the four bases.

Look closely at Figure 12. Notice that the bases on one side of the ladder match up in a specific way with the bases on the other side. Adenine (A) only pairs with thymine (T), while guanine (G) only pairs with cytosine (C). This pairing pattern is the key to understanding how DNA replication occurs.

Figure 12 A DNA molecule is shaped like a twisted ladder. The sides are made up of sugar and phosphate molecules. The rungs are formed by pairs of nitrogen bases. *Classifying* Which base always pairs with adenine?

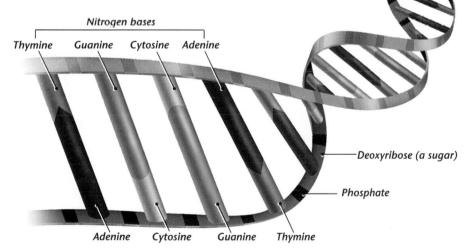

Nitrogen bases

Thymine   Guanine   Cytosine   Adenine

Deoxyribose (a sugar)

Phosphate

Adenine   Cytosine   Guanine   Thymine

Inquiry Challenge

Materials *toothpicks, white and colored miniature marshmallows*

Time 15 minutes

Challenge hands-on learners to make a three-dimensional model of a DNA molecule using the materials listed above. *(The most likely way is to use toothpicks to join together white marshmallows, representing sugar and phosphate molecules, and colored marshmallows, representing nitrogen bases.)* Suggest to students that they make a key for their model that shows which part of the DNA molecule the different components represent. Then ask: **How does your model show that adenine only pairs with thymine and guanine only pairs with cytosine?** *(In their models, students should have joined colored marshmallows representing different bases in the correct pairings.)* **learning modality: kinesthetic**

Building Inquiry Skills: Inferring

Encourage students to infer what would happen if an error in DNA replication occurred. Ask: **What do you think would be the outcome if one or more of the nitrogen bases were assembled in the wrong order in a new DNA molecule?** *(Answers may vary. Students may say that the new DNA molecule might not be able to properly direct cell functions. They also might say that any future copies of the new DNA molecule would contain bases in the wrong order, so the error would spread if the cells survived and divided.)* **learning modality: logical/mathematical**

Media and Technology

Transparencies "DNA Structure," Transparency 8; "DNA Replication," Transparency 9

Answers to Self-Assessment

☑ *Checkpoint*

Cytokinesis is the final stage of the cell cycle, and it usually begins at about the same time as telophase.

Caption Question

Figure 12 Thymine always pairs with adenine.

Ongoing Assessment

Skills Check Have students create a concept map that includes the following terms: *DNA structure, phosphate molecules, sugar molecules, nitrogen bases, adenine, thymine, guanine,* and *cytosine.*

 Students can save their concept maps in their portfolios.

C ◆ 67

Section 3 Review Answers

1. The stages are interphase, mitosis, and cytokinesis. In interphase, the cell grows and DNA replicates; in mitosis, the nucleus divides and a copy of DNA goes to each daughter cell; in cytokinesis, the cytoplasm divides into two new cells.

2. The DNA must replicate so that each daughter cell will have all the genetic information it needs.

3. In plant cells, new cell membranes develop across the middle of the cell and separate the cytoplasm of the daughter cells. In animal cells, the cell membrane squeezes together around the middle of the cell and pinches the cytoplasm into the daughter cells.

4. One of the daughter cells would receive two of each chromosome, while the other daughter cell would receive no chromosomes. Probably neither daughter cell would survive.

Check Your Progress CHAPTER PROJECT 2

Make sure students are making daily observations and measurements of their plants and recording the data. Check that the data are reasonable and that students are doing their best to control variables. Urge students to continue to water and measure their plants until they have obtained at least two weeks of data.

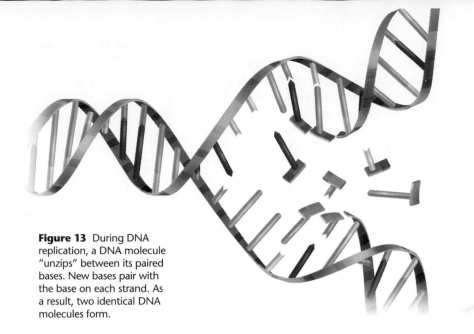

Figure 13 During DNA replication, a DNA molecule "unzips" between its paired bases. New bases pair with the base on each strand. As a result, two identical DNA molecules form.

The Replication Process DNA replication begins when the two sides of the DNA molecule unwind and separate, like a zipper unzipping. As you can see in Figure 13, the molecule separates between the paired nitrogen bases on each rung. Next, nitrogen bases that are floating in the nucleus pair up with the bases on each half of the DNA molecule. Remember that the pairing of bases follows definite rules: A always pairs with T, while G always pairs with C. Once the new bases are attached, two new DNA molecules are formed. The order of the bases in each new DNA molecule will exactly match the order in the original DNA molecule.

Section 3 Review

1. What are the three main stages of the cell cycle? Briefly describe the events that occur at each stage.
2. Why must the DNA in a cell replicate before the cell divides?
3. How does cytokinesis differ in plant and animal cells?
4. **Thinking Critically Predicting** Suppose that during anaphase, the centromeres did not split and the chromatids did not separate. Predict the results.

Check Your Progress CHAPTER PROJECT 2

At this point, you should be observing the health of your plants, and measuring their growth. Make drawings to show the appearance of the plants at different stages of the project. (*Hint:* In addition to overall height, you may wish to note the number and length of stems, and the number, size, color, and firmness of the leaves.)

Performance Assessment

Writing Have students explain why the pairing of nitrogen bases is the key to understanding DNA replication.

Program Resources

◆ **Teaching Resources** 2-3 Review and Reinforce, p. 53; 2-3 Enrich, p. 54

Media and Technology

Interactive Student Tutorial CD-ROM C-2

Program Resources

◆ **Teaching Resources** Chapter 2 Skills Lab, pp. 61–63

Safety

Remind students to handle slides and coverslips carefully. Review the safety guidelines in Appendix A.

Multiplying by Dividing

Skills Lab

Problem

How long do the stages of the cell cycle take?

Materials

microscope
colored pencils
calculator (optional)
prepared slides of onion root tip cells
   undergoing cell division

Procedure

1. Place the slide on the stage of a microscope. Use low power to locate a cell in interphase. Then switch to high power, and make a labeled drawing of the cell. **CAUTION:** *Slides and coverslips break easily. Do not allow the objective to touch the slide. If the slide breaks, notify your teacher. Do not touch broken glass.*
2. Repeat Step 1 to find cells in prophase, metaphase, anaphase, and telophase. Then copy the data table into your notebook.
3. Return to low power. Find an area of the slide with many cells undergoing cell division. Switch to the magnification that lets you see about 50 cells at once (for example, 100 ×).

DATA TABLE

Stage of Cell Cycle	First Sample	Second Sample	Total Number
Interphase			
Mitosis: Prophase			
Metaphase			
Anaphase			
Telophase			
Total number of cells counted			

4. Examine the cells row by row, and count the cells that are in interphase. Record that number in the data table under *First Sample.*
5. Examine the cells row-by-row four more times to count the cells in prophase, metaphase, anaphase, and telophase. Record the results.
6. Move to a new area on the slide. Repeat Steps 3–5 and record your counts in the column labeled *Second Sample.*
7. Fill in the column labeled *Total Number* by adding the numbers across each row in your data table.
8. Add the totals for the five stages to find the total number of cells counted.

Analyze and Conclude

1. Which stage of the cell cycle did you observe most often?
2. The cell cycle for onion root tips takes about 720 minutes (12 hours). Use your data and the formula below to find the number of minutes each stage takes.

$$\text{Time for each stage} = \frac{\text{Number of cells at each stage}}{\text{Total number of cells counted}} \times 720 \text{ min}$$

3. **Think About It** Use the data to compare the amount of time spent in mitosis with the total time for the whole cell cycle.

More to Explore

Examine prepared slides of animal cells undergoing cell division. Use drawings and descriptions to compare plant and animal mitosis.

Sample Data Table

Stage of Cell Cycle	First Sample	Second Sample	Total Number
Interphase	43	46	89
Mitosis: Prophase	3	4	7
Metaphase	1	1	2
Anaphase	1	0	1
Telophase	0	1	1

Extending the Inquiry

More to Explore Interphase and mitosis are very similar in plant and animal cells, except that the centrioles appear during prophase in animal cells. Challenge students to predict whether animal or plant cells spend longer in mitosis. Then have them design an experiment to test their prediction.

Calculating

Multiplying by Dividing

Preparing for Inquiry

Key Concept Mitosis occurs quickly, and cells spend most of their time in interphase.

Skills Objectives Students will be able to
◆ observe cells in different stages of the cell cycle;
◆ calculate the amount of time cells spend in each stage of the cell cycle;
◆ interpret data to compare how long cells spend in mitosis with the total time of the cell cycle.

Time 40 minutes

Advance Planning Prepared slides can be purchased from a biological supply company.

Alternative Materials Slides of other rapidly dividing cells undergoing division may be used if nuclear structures show up clearly.

Guiding Inquiry

Troubleshooting the Experiment

◆ Urge students to review the photographs in *Exploring the Cell Cycle* on pages 64–65.

Expected Outcome

Students should observe and sketch cells undergoing interphase and the four phases of mitosis. Most of the cells they count should be in the interphase stage of the cell cycle, but errors in counting and differences in samples may give varying results.

Analyze and Conclude

1. The most likely answer is interphase.
2. Answers will vary depending on students' data. Answers for the sample data are: interphase, 641 minutes; prophase, 50 minutes; metaphase, 14 minutes; anaphase, 7 minutes; telophase, 7 minutes.
3. Based on the sample data, the amount of time spent in mitosis is 11 percent. Students' answers will vary depending on their data.

SECTION 4 Cancer

Objectives

After completing the lesson, students will be able to
◆ state the relationship between cancer and the cell cycle;
◆ describe how cancer begins and spreads;
◆ describe several methods of cancer treatment and of cancer prevention.

Key Terms cancer, mutation, tumor, chemotherapy

1 Engage/Explore

Activating Prior Knowledge

Help students recall their prior knowledge of cancer by asking: **What is cancer?** *(Students are likely to say cancer is a disease that often kills people.)* **What causes cancer?** *(Students may say that cancer is caused by genes, diet, smoking, environment, or similar factors. Accept any reasonable answers.)* **How can cancer be treated?** *(Possible answers might include surgery, drugs, or other treatments.)* **How can the risk of cancer be reduced?** *(Students may say by not smoking or by eating a healthy diet.)* Tell students they will learn about the causes, treatment, and prevention of cancer in this section.

•••••• DISCOVER ••••••

Skills Focus predicting
Materials *masking tape,*
meter stick
Time 15 minutes
Tips Make sure students understand that each time one student leaves the square, two more students should enter. Ask a volunteer to keep track of the time.
Expected Outcome The square fills up quickly with students as the "cells" divide.
Think It Over Students may predict that part of the body would grow too fast and crowd other parts, perhaps causing damage or disease.

SECTION 4 Cancer

DISCOVER •••••• ACTIVITY

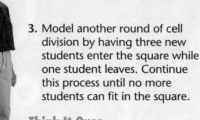

What Happens When There Are Too Many Cells?

1.  Use tape to mark off a one meter-by-one meter square on the floor. The square represents an area inside the human body. Have two students stand in the square to represent cells.

2. Suppose each cell divides every 30 seconds, and then one cell dies. With a group of students, model this situation. After 30 seconds, two new students should enter the square and one student should leave the square.

3. Model another round of cell division by having three new students enter the square while one student leaves. Continue this process until no more students can fit in the square.

Think It Over

Predicting Use this activity to predict what would happen if some cells in a person's body divided faster than they should.

GUIDE FOR READING

◆ How is cancer related to the cell cycle?
◆ What are some ways that cancer can be treated?

Reading Tip As you read, make a list of the main causes of cancer and how to prevent them.

Imagine that you are planting a flower garden near your home. After careful planning, you plant snapdragons, geraniums, and petunias exactly where you think they will look best. You also plant a ground ivy that you think will look nice between the flowers. You water your garden and wait for it to grow.

Much to your dismay, after a few months you notice that the ground ivy has taken over the garden. Where there should be flowers, there is nothing but a tangle of vines. Only a few flowers have survived. The ivy has used up more than its share of garden space and soil nutrients. A neighbor remarks, "That vine is so out of control, it's like a cancer."

READING STRATEGIES

Vocabulary Make sure students understand the difference between *cancer* and *tumor,* because these terms often are used interchangeably. Point out that cancer is a disease, whereas a tumor is a growth that results from the disease.

Study and Comprehension Have students make an outline using the main headings. Then, as they read the section, have them add details to their outlines.

Program Resources

◆ **Teaching Resources** 2-4 Lesson Plan, p. 55; 2-4 Section Summary, p. 56

Media and Technology

 Audiotapes English-Spanish Summary 2-4

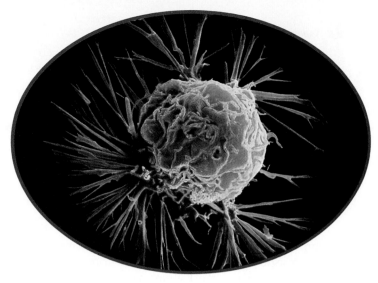

Figure 14 A cancer tumor begins as a single abnormal cell, like this breast cancer cell. A mutation occurs in the cell's DNA and disrupts the normal cell cycle.
Relating Cause and Effect How does the cell behave as a result of the mutation?

What Is Cancer?

Your neighbor compared the ground ivy to a cancer because it grew uncontrollably and destroyed the other plants. **Cancer** is a disease in which cells grow and divide uncontrollably, damaging the parts of the body around them.

Cancer is actually not just one disease. In fact, there are more than 100 types of cancer. Cancer can occur in almost any part of the body. Cancers are often named by the place in the body where they begin. In the United States today, lung cancer is the leading cause of cancer deaths among both men and women.

How Cancer Begins Scientists think that cancer begins when something damages a portion of the DNA in a chromosome. The damage causes a change in the DNA called a **mutation.** Remember that DNA contains all the instructions necessary for life. Damage to the DNA can cause cells to function abnormally.

Normally, the cells in one part of the body live in harmony with the cells around them. Cells that go through the cell cycle divide in a controlled way. Other cells don't divide at all. **Cancer begins when mutations disrupt the normal cell cycle, causing cells to divide in an uncontrolled way.** The cells stop behaving as they normally do. Without the normal controls on the cell cycle, the cells grow too large and divide too often.

How Cancer Spreads At first, one cell develops in an abnormal way. As the cell divides, more and more abnormal cells like it grow near it. In time, these cells form a tumor. A **tumor** is a mass of abnormal cells that develops when cancerous cells divide and grow uncontrollably.

Answers to Self-Assessment

Caption Question

Figure 14 As a result of the mutation, the cell divides in an uncontrolled way.

2 Facilitate

What Is Cancer?

Addressing Naive Conceptions

Help students avoid developing the naive conception that all mutations cause cancer. Ask: **How does cancer begin?** *(Students should say that cancer begins when a mutation damages a portion of the DNA in a chromosome, disrupting the cell cycle.)* Explain that, although some mutations do indeed cause cancer in this way, many mutations are not harmful. In fact, some mutations may even increase the fitness of the individuals who have them. For example, as students will read in the Science and Society feature on page 74, some people have mutations that help protect them from certain types of cancer. **learning modality: verbal**

Building Inquiry Skills: Calculating

Materials calculator
Time 5 minutes

Help students appreciate how uncontrolled cell division can lead to the formation of a tumor. First challenge students to calculate how many cell divisions would occur and how many cells there would be if cells divided every 30 minutes for 10 hours. *(There would be 20 divisions and 1,048,576 cells.)* Then challenge students to calculate how many cell divisions would occur and how many cells there would be if cells divided every 2 hours for 10 hours. *(There would be 5 divisions and 32 cells.)* **How do your calculations relate to the formation of a tumor?** *(Cancer cells divide very rapidly, forming a mass of cells called a tumor.)* **learning modality: logical/ mathematical**

What Is Cancer?, continued

Using the Visuals: Figure 15

Help students relate the figure to the text by having them select sentences from the text to make longer captions for each part of the figure. Ask: **Which sentence(s) would be a good expanded caption for part 1?** *(Students might select from page 71: "Cancer begins when mutations disrupt the normal cell cycle, causing cells to divide in an uncontrolled way.")* **Which sentence(s) would be a good expanded caption for part 2?** *(Students might select from page 71: "As the cell divides, more and more abnormal cells like it grow near it. In time, these cells form a tumor.")* **Which sentence(s) would be a good expanded caption for part 3?** *(One possible selection from page 72: "Some of the cancerous cells may break off the tumor and enter the bloodstream. In this way, the cancer can spread to other areas of the body.")* **learning modality: visual**

Treating Cancer

 ### Integrating Chemistry

Explain to students that many plants produce chemicals that protect the plants from diseases, parasites, and predators. Scientists investigate these chemicals from plants to determine if they can be used to fight human diseases. One such chemical, called taxol, is now being used to treat certain types of cancer. Taxol comes from the bark of the Pacific yew tree. This tree's bark is very resistant to diseases and insects. In cancer patients, taxol forms cagelike structures around individual cancer cells, preventing them from dividing. Encourage interested students to find out more about taxol or other medicines from plants. **learning modality: verbal**

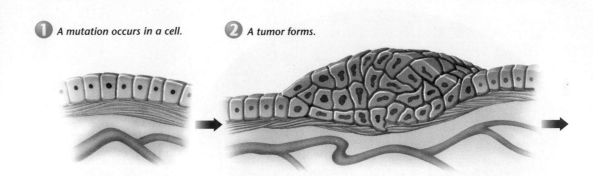

① *A mutation occurs in a cell.*   **②** *A tumor forms.*

Figure 15 A tumor is a mass of cells that divide uncontrollably. It may take years for a tumor to grow large enough to be noticed. *Interpreting Diagrams How can cancer spread from one part of the body to another?*

Figure 15 shows the process by which a tumor forms. Tumors often take years to grow to a noticeable size. During that time, the cells become more and more abnormal as they continue to divide. Some of the cancerous cells may break off the tumor and enter the bloodstream. In this way, the cancer can spread to other areas of the body.

☑ *Checkpoint* What is the first step that leads to the development of a tumor?

Treating Cancer

If a person is stricken with cancer, there are a variety of treatments that may be effective in fighting the disease. **Doctors usually treat cancer in one or more of three ways: surgery, radiation, or drugs that destroy the cancer cells.**

When a cancer is detected before it has spread to other parts of the body, surgery is usually the best treatment. If doctors can completely remove the cancerous tumor, a person may be cured of the disease. If, however, the cancer has spread or if the tumor cannot be removed, doctors may use radiation, beams of high-energy waves. Fast-growing cancer cells are more likely than normal cells to be destroyed by radiation.

Chemotherapy, or the use of drugs to kill cancer cells, is another form of treatment. Chemotherapy is effective because the drugs spread throughout the body, killing cancer cells or slowing their growth.

Unfortunately, none of these cancer treatments is perfect. Most have unpleasant, or even dangerous, side effects. Scientists continue to look for new ways to treat cancer. If, for example, scientists can discover how the cell cycle is controlled, they may find ways to stop cancer cells from going through the cell cycle.

Background

Facts and Figures After almost 20 years of rising cancer rates, the rate of new cancer cases among Americans finally started to decline in the early 1990s. The rates declined for most ages, both sexes, and most racial and ethnic groups. The only exceptions were African-American males and Asian and Pacific Islander females. The main forms of cancer that declined were lung and prostate cancers in males and colorectal cancers in both males and females. The decline in these and some other cancers may be due to decreased tobacco use, better screening to detect and treat precancerous conditions, and, possibly, improved diet. Despite the good news, not all types of cancer are decreasing. In fact, some types of cancer, including melanoma and non-Hodgkin's lymphoma, occur more often now than they did in the past.

Cancer cells enter the bloodstream.

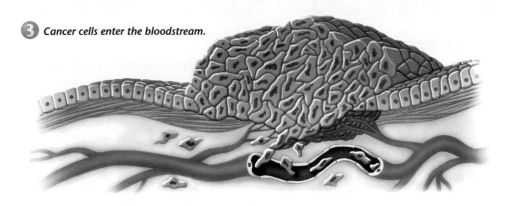

They might be able to "turn off" cancer before it causes too much damage to the body. Another possible treatment for cancer is to use drugs that block the flow of blood to tumors. Without a blood supply, tumors might not be able to continue growing.

Cancer Prevention

Scientists estimate that almost two thirds of all cancer deaths are caused either by tobacco use or unhealthful diets. Smoking is the main cause of lung cancer. When people repeatedly expose their bodies to the chemicals in tobacco, their cells will likely become damaged. Cancer may result.

It might surprise you to learn that unhealthful diets may lead to almost as many cancer deaths as does tobacco. A diet high in fat is especially harmful. Regularly eating high-fat foods, such as fatty meats and fried foods, can put a person at risk for cancer. A diet that includes a lot of fruits, vegetables, and grain products can help lower a person's risk of some types of cancer.

Section 4 Review

1. Explain the relationship between cancer and the cell cycle.
2. Describe three ways that cancer can be treated.
3. What two health habits can help prevent cancer?
4. **Thinking Critically Relating Cause and Effect** How could smoking tobacco cause cancer to develop inside the lungs?

> **Check Your Progress**
> CHAPTER PROJECT 2
> It is now time to make your final observations of your plants. Then examine all of the data that you have collected. Which data can you present in graphs? Which of your diagrams show the major differences between your two plants? Write a brief summary that describes your experimental plan and your results.

Program Resources

◆ **Teaching Resources** 2-4 Review and Reinforce, p. 57; 2-4 Enrich, p. 58

Media and Technology

Interactive Student Tutorial CD-ROM C-2

Answers to Self-Assessment

Caption Question

Figure 15 Cancer can spread from one part of the body to another when cancer cells break off a tumor and enter the bloodstream.

☑ *Checkpoint*

The first step that leads to the development of a tumor is a mutation.

Cancer Prevention

Real-Life Learning

Have small groups of students each make a poster to educate the public about cancer prevention. Suggest that students contact the American Cancer Society to get more information. Students can display their posters throughout their school or community. **cooperative learning**

3 Assess

Section 4 Review Answers

1. Cancer begins when mutations disrupt the normal cell cycle, causing cells to divide in an uncontrolled way.
2. Surgery to remove the cancerous tumor, radiation to destroy cancer cells, or drugs to kill cancer cells
3. Avoiding tobacco use and eating a low-fat diet containing a lot of fruits, vegetables, and grains
4. By causing mutations in the cells of the lungs

> **Check Your Progress**
> CHAPTER PROJECT 2
> Students should present their quantitative measurements of growth, such as growth in height or number of leaves, in graphs. Other observations, such as leaf color or shape, might be presented in drawings. Tell students to save their plants for their presentation.

Performance Assessment

Writing Have students write a 50- to 75-word public service message informing people how they can help protect themselves from cancer.

Who Owns Your Cells?

Purpose

To provide students with an example of the legal and ethical issues that medical advances can create.

Role-Play

Time a day to prepare; 20 minutes for role-play

Divide the class into small groups, and have each group discuss the position of one of the people in this situation: John Moore, his doctors, his lawyer, and a mediator. Then have volunteers role-play a meeting in which the two sides, with the help of the mediator, try to reach a mutually agreeable compromise solution. In their role-play, the two sides should state their positions clearly and explain why they have taken their positions. After the role-play has been presented, ask the other students if they think the solution that was achieved is fair to both parties and also in the best interests of society.

Extend Encourage interested students to find out how people in their state can volunteer to donate organs when they die. Have students report their findings to the class.

You Decide

Urge students to use analogies to make their writing more convincing. For example, students might write that using people's cells without their consent is like using authors' or artists' words or images without their permission. Challenge students to try to counter arguments presented in the feature as they weigh their decision. *(For example, although you lose control over the blood you donate, the decision to donate it in the first place is yours; and although the doctors turned John Moore's cells into something valuable, the cells would have had no value if they weren't special in the first place.)* Ask several students with different viewpoints to share their solutions and the reasons behind them with the class.

Who Owns Your Cells?

John Moore was seriously ill. He had leukemia—cancer of the blood cells—and his spleen was in danger of bursting. Doctors removed his spleen, but Moore's condition was still serious. Surprisingly, however, Moore made a remarkable recovery. The doctors wondered whether Moore's body produced disease-fighting cells that fought off the cancer.

Without telling Moore why, his doctors gathered more of his cells. They discovered that Moore's cells were a natural "factory" of lifesaving chemicals. After years of investigation, the doctors sold the cells for several million dollars to a company that wanted to use the cells to manufacture medicines. When Moore found out, he sued the doctors, claiming that he owned his cells. Who do you think was right?

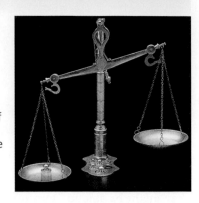

The Issues

Do Patients Have a Right to Their Cells?
Once a person's cells are outside his or her body, the person usually can no longer control what is done with them. For example, people who donate blood cannot tell blood banks what to do with their blood. On the other hand, people are able to decide whether or not to donate their organs when they die. Similarly, many people think they should be able to decide whether their cells can be used in medical research.

Do Doctors Have the Right to Use People's Cells? If people could control what was done with their cells, some doctors think it would be harder to find new cures for diseases. Scientists need to be free to experiment and to learn from their research. But who should make money from life-saving research? The doctors argued that the profits from Moore's cells

belonged to them. Moore had signed a consent form that gave the doctors permission to operate and remove his cells. It was the doctors' hard work and knowledge that turned the cells into something valuable.

Other people argue that there is not enough protection for patients. When Moore agreed to have the operation, he wasn't thinking about what would happen to his cells. His only concern was his need for the life-saving operation.

What Decision Was Reached? In Moore's case, the California Supreme Court ruled that the doctors owned the cells once they were out of Moore's body. However, the Court also said that Moore's doctors should have specifically asked for permission to use his cells. Moore was awarded a small amount of money, barely enough to pay his legal fees.

You Decide

1. Identify the Problem
In your own words, describe the controversy raised in John Moore's lawsuit against his doctors.

2. Analyze the Options
List some of the options the California Supreme Court might have considered in their decision. Be sure to include solutions in which neither Moore nor his doctors would get everything they want.

3. Find a Solution
Suppose you were one of the judges in Moore's court case. Choose a solution that you think is fair to both Moore and his doctors, and is best for society. Give reasons to support your decision.

Background

Facts and Figures Advances in fertility research have created ethical and legal issues similar to those raised by the John Moore case. In in-vitro fertilization procedures, dozens of a woman's eggs are fertilized in a test tube by a man's sperm. An embryo is then implanted in the woman. Couples may choose to have the remaining unused

embryos frozen. Over the years, many thousands of unclaimed frozen embryos have accumulated in storage facilities. In 1996 in England, 3,000 such embryos were destroyed. A policy about what to do with unclaimed frozen human embryos has not yet been developed in the United States.

SECTION 1 — Photosynthesis

Key Ideas
◆ During photosynthesis, plants and some other organisms use energy from the sun to convert carbon dioxide and water into oxygen and sugars, including glucose.
◆ In the first stage of photosynthesis, chlorophyll and other plant pigments capture energy from sunlight. In the second stage, the cell uses the energy to produce sugars from carbon dioxide and water.
◆ Nearly all living things obtain the energy they need either directly or indirectly from the sun.

Key Terms
photosynthesis	chlorophyll	autotroph
pigment	stomata	heterotroph

SECTION 2 — Respiration

Key Ideas
◆ Respiration is a process in which cells break down simple food substances, such as glucose, and release the energy they contain.
◆ During respiration, glucose and oxygen are converted into carbon dioxide and water.
◆ Photosynthesis and respiration can be thought of as opposite processes. These two processes form a cycle that keeps the levels of oxygen and carbon dioxide fairly constant in the atmosphere.
◆ Fermentation provides energy for cells without using oxygen.

Key Terms
respiration	fermentation

SECTION 3 — Cell Division

Key Ideas
◆ Cells go through a regular cycle of growth and division called the cell cycle.
◆ During interphase, the cell grows to its mature size, makes a copy of its DNA, and prepares to divide into two cells. During mitosis, one copy of the DNA is distributed into each of the two daughter cells. During cytokinesis, the cell's cytoplasm divides, distributing the organelles into each of the two new cells.
◆ DNA replication ensures that each daughter cell will have all of the genetic information it needs to carry out its activities.

Key Terms
cell cycle	chromosome
interphase	chromatid
replication	cytokinesis
mitosis	

SECTION 4 — Cancer

INTEGRATING HEALTH

Key Ideas
◆ Cancer begins when the normal cell cycle is disrupted by mutations, causing cells to divide in an uncontrolled way.
◆ A tumor grows as the cells continue to divide. Cancerous cells may break off the tumor, enter the bloodstream, and spread to other areas of the body.
◆ Cancer is usually treated with surgery, radiation, or chemotherapy.

Key Terms
cancer	tumor
mutation	chemotherapy

USING THE INTERNET

www.science-explorer.phschool.com

Program Resources
◆ **Teaching Resources** Chapter 2 Project Scoring Rubric, p. 42; Chapter 2 Performance Assessment, pp. 159–161; Chapter 2 Test, pp. 162–165

Media and Technology
 Interactive Student Tutorial CD-ROM C-2

 Computer Test Bank Test C-2

Reviewing Content:
Multiple Choice
1. b 2. a 3. c 4. c 5. a

True or False
6. true 7. true 8. fermentation
9. interphase 10. true

Checking Concepts
11. During photosynthesis, energy from sunlight is changed into chemical energy, which is used to convert carbon dioxide and water into oxygen and sugars, including glucose.
12. Heterotrophs get energy by eating plants or other organisms that eat plants. Plants get energy from the sun.
13. Organisms need to carry out respiration in order to provide energy for cell processes.
14. During interphase, the cell grows, DNA is replicated, and the cell prepares to divide.
15. During interphase exact copies of the DNA are made, and during mitosis the DNA and cell organelles are divided equally between the daughter cells.
16. Cancer usually begins when a portion of a chromosome in a cell is damaged and the cell cycle is disturbed.
17. Students' paragraphs should include the following points: The oxygen molecule is formed in a chloroplast in a cell of a plant during photosynthesis. It leaves the plant cell through a stoma and passes into the air, where another organism can use it for respiration.

Thinking Visually
18. **a.** Chromatin condenses to form chromosomes, spindle fibers form, and the nuclear membrane breaks down. **b.** The chromatids separate and move to opposite ends of the cell. **c.** The cell membrane pinches in around the middle of the cell, and the cell divides.

Applying Skills
19. The bars in the graph should correspond to the percentages in the table. There should be four bars for each organism.
20. The percents of adenine and thymine are equal. The percents of guanine and cytosine also are equal.

Reviewing Content

 For more review of key concepts, see the Interactive Student Tutorial CD-ROM.

Multiple Choice
Choose the letter of the best answer.

1. The organelle in which photosynthesis takes place is the
   a. mitochondrion.
   b. chloroplast.
   c. chlorophyll.
   d. nucleus.
2. What process is responsible for producing most of Earth's oxygen?
   a. photosynthesis **b.** replication
   c. mutation   **d.** respiration
3. The process in which a cell makes an exact copy of its DNA is called
   a. fermentation.   **b.** respiration.
   c. replication.   **d.** reproduction.
4. Chromatids are held together by a
   a. spindle.
   b. chloroplast.
   c. centromere.
   d. cell membrane.
5. A mass of cancer cells is called a
   a. tumor.
   b. chromosome.
   c. mutation.
   d. mitochondrion.

True or False
If the statement is true, write true. If it is false, change the underlined word or words to make the statement true.

6. An organism that makes its own food is an <u>autotroph</u>.
7. The process of respiration takes place mainly in the <u>mitochondria</u>.
8. An energy-releasing process that does not require oxygen is <u>replication</u>.
9. The stage of the cell cycle when DNA replication occurs is <u>telophase</u>.
10. Uncontrolled cell division is a characteristic of <u>cancer</u>.

Checking Concepts
11. Briefly explain what happens to energy from the sun during photosynthesis.
12. Explain how heterotrophs depend on the sun for energy.
13. Why do organisms need to carry out the process of respiration?
14. Describe what happens during interphase.
15. How do the events of the cell cycle ensure that the daughter cells will be identical to the parent cell?
16. Describe how cancer usually begins to develop in the body.
17. **Writing to Learn** Write a paragraph describing the journey of an oxygen molecule as it moves between a plant and another organism.

Thinking Visually

18. **Cycle Diagram** Copy the cycle diagram about the cell cycle onto a separate sheet of paper. Then complete it and add a title. (For more on cycle diagrams, see the Skills Handbook.)

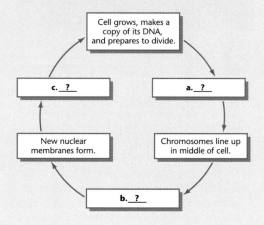

Cell grows, makes a copy of its DNA, and prepares to divide.
c. _?_
a. _?_
New nuclear membranes form.
Chromosomes line up in middle of cell.
b. _?_

---

21. In all of the organisms, adenine is paired with thymine and guanine is paired with cytosine.

Thinking Critically
22. Answers may vary. *Sample answer:* The ash from the volcano would block the sun and prevent plants from using its energy to make food. Plants would die out, and the animals and other organisms that get their energy from plants would die out as well.
23. Breathing brings oxygen into the body for respiration. Respiration uses the oxygen to break down food and provide energy for the body's needs.
24. Photosynthesis uses water and carbon dioxide, produces oxygen and sugars, and occurs in chloroplasts. Respiration uses oxygen and sugars, produces water and carbon dioxide, and occurs in mitochondria.
25. T G C A G A C
26. Answers may vary but should include not smoking, eating a low-fat diet, and eating a lot of fruits, vegetables, and grain products.

Applying Skills

Use the table below to answer Questions 19–21.

Percentages of Nitrogen Bases In the DNA of Various Organisms

Nitrogen Base	Human	Wheat	*E. coli* bacterium
Adenine	30%	27%	24%
Guanine	20%	23%	26%
Thymine	30%	27%	24%
Cytosine	20%	23%	26%

19. **Graphing** For each organism, draw a bar graph to show the percentages of each nitrogen base in its DNA.
20. **Interpreting Data** What is the relationship between the amounts of adenine and thymine in the DNA of each organism? Between the amounts of guanine and cytosine?
21. **Inferring** Based on your answer to Question 20, what can you infer about the structure of DNA in these three organisms?

Thinking Critically

22. **Predicting** Suppose a volcano spewed so much ash into the air that it blocked most of the sunlight that usually strikes Earth. How might this affect the ability of animals to obtain the energy they need to live?
23. **Applying Concepts** Explain the relationship between the processes of breathing and respiration.
24. **Comparing and Contrasting** Compare and contrast photosynthesis and respiration in terms of raw materials, products, and where each occurs.
25. **Inferring** Suppose one strand of a DNA molecule contained the following bases: A C G T C T G. What would the bases on the other strand be?
26. **Making Generalizations** Suppose you want to reduce your risks for getting cancer. Outline three steps you could take to lower your risk.

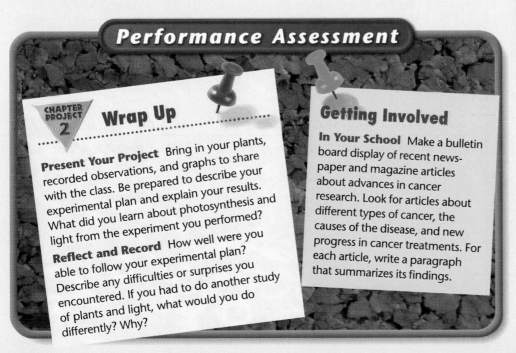

Performance Assessment

CHAPTER PROJECT 2

Wrap Up

Present Your Project Bring in your plants, recorded observations, and graphs to share with the class. Be prepared to describe your experimental plan and explain your results. What did you learn about photosynthesis and light from the experiment you performed?

Reflect and Record How well were you able to follow your experimental plan? Describe any difficulties or surprises you encountered. If you had to do another study of plants and light, what would you do differently? Why?

Getting Involved

In Your School Make a bulletin board display of recent newspaper and magazine articles about advances in cancer research. Look for articles about different types of cancer, the causes of the disease, and new progress in cancer treatments. For each article, write a paragraph that summarizes its findings.

Performance Assessment

CHAPTER PROJECT 2

Wrap Up

Present Your Project Students should describe how they varied lighting conditions and controlled other variables, as well as how they assessed plant health and growth. Students should have learned that plants cannot undertake normal photosynthesis without adequate light.

Reflect and Record Students may not have varied the lighting conditions enough to affect plant growth. In another study, students might vary the color of light plants receive.

Program Resources

◆ **Inquiry Skills Activity Book** Provides teaching and review of all inquiry skills

Getting Involved

In Your School You may want students to search the Internet for information for this activity. Good sources for reliable information include the American Cancer Society, National Cancer Institute, and Centers for Disease Control and Prevention. To make sure several different types of cancer are covered, you might want to assign each student or group of students a specific type of cancer to research. Lung, prostate, and colorectal cancer are especially important cancers to include because they are among the most common.

Genetics: The Science of Heredity

Sections	Time	Student Edition Activities	Other Activities	
CHAPTER PROJECT 3 **All In The Family** p. 79	Ongoing (2–3 weeks)	Check Your Progress, p. 85 Check Your Progress, p. 100 Check Your Progress, p. 106 Wrap Up, p. 109		
1 **Mendel's Work** pp. 80–87 ◆ Describe Mendel's genetics experiments. ◆ Identify the factors that control the inheritance of traits in organisms. ◆ Explain how geneticists use symbols to represent alleles.	3–4 periods/ $1\frac{1}{2}$–2 blocks	**Discover** What Does the Father Look Like?, p. 80 **Skills Lab: Developing Hypotheses** Take a Class Survey, pp. 86–87	TE TE TE TE	Building Inquiry Skills: Observing, p. 81 Inquiry Challenge, p. 81 Demonstration, p. 83 Inquiry Challenge, p. 84
2 **INTEGRATING MATHEMATICS** **Probability and Genetics** pp. 88–95 ◆ Describe the principles of probability and how Mendel applied them to inheritance. ◆ State how geneticists use Punnett squares. ◆ Explain the meanings of the terms *phenotype, genotype, homozygous, heterozygous,* and *codominance.*	3–4 periods/ $1\frac{1}{2}$–2 blocks	**Discover** What's the Chance?, p. 88 **Try This** Coin Crosses, p. 91 **Science at Home,** p. 93 **Skills Lab: Making Models** Make the Right Call!, pp. 94–95	TE TE TE TE IES	Including All Students, p. 89 Inquiry Challenge, p. 89 Inquiry Challenge, p. 90 Demonstration, p. 91 "The Power of Patterns," p. 42
3 **The Cell and Inheritance** pp. 96–100 ◆ Describe the role of chromosomes in inheritance. ◆ Identify and describe the events that occur during meiosis.	2–3 periods/ 1–$1\frac{1}{2}$ blocks	**Discover** Which Chromosome Is Which?, p. 96	TE TE TE TE ISLM	Inquiry Challenge, p. 97 Building Inquiry Skills: Making Models, p. 98 Building Inquiry Skills, Observing, p. 99 Including All Students, p. 100 C-3, "Chromosomes and Inheritance"
4 **The DNA Connection** pp. 101–106 ◆ Explain the term "genetic code." ◆ Describe the process by which a cell produces proteins. ◆ Describe the different types of mutations and how they affect an organism.	2–3 periods/ 1–$1\frac{1}{2}$ blocks	**Discover** Can You Crack the Code?, p. 101 **Sharpen Your Skills** Predicting, p. 103	TE TE	Inquiry Challenge, p. 103 Building Inquiry Skills: Making Models, p. 105
Study Guide/Chapter Review pp. 107–109	1 period/ $\frac{1}{2}$ block		ISAB	Provides teaching and review of all inquiry skills.

 For Standard or Block Schedule The Resource Pro® CD-ROM gives you maximum flexibility for planning your instruction for any type of schedule. Resource Pro® contains Planning Express®, an advanced scheduling program, as well as the entire contents of the Teaching Resources and the Computer Test Bank.

CHAPTER PLANNING GUIDE

Program Resources	Assessment Strategies	Media and Technology
TR Chapter 3 Project Teacher Notes, pp. 64–65 TR Chapter 3 Project Overview and Worksheets, Materials, pp. 66–69 TR Chapter 3 Project Scoring Rubric, p. 70	SE Performance Assessment: Chapter 3 Project Wrap Up, p. 109 TE Check Your Progress, pp. 85, 100, 106 TE Performance Assessment: Chapter 3 Project Wrap Up, p. 109 TR Chapter 3 Project Scoring Rubric, p. 70	Science Explorer Internet Site
TR 3-1 Lesson Plan, p. 71 TR 3-1 Section Summary, p. 72 TR 3-1 Review and Reinforce, p. 73 TR 3-1 Enrich, p. 74 TR Chapter 3 Skills Lab, pp. 87–88 TR Book A, *From Bacteria to Plants,* Chapter 5	SE Section 1 Review, p. 85 SE Analyze and Conclude, p. 87 TE Ongoing Assessment, pp. 81, 83 TE Performance Assessment, p. 85 TR 3-1 Review and Reinforce, p. 73	Exploring Life Science Videodisc, Unit 5 Side 1, "We Are All Heirs" Audiotapes, English-Spanish Summary 3-1 Transparency 10, "Genetics of Pea Plants" Interactive Student Tutorial CD-ROM, C-3
TR 3-2 Lesson Plan, p. 75 TR 3-2 Section Summary, p. 76 TR 3-2 Review and Reinforce, p. 77 TR 3-2 Enrich, p. 78 TR Chapter 3 Skills Lab, pp. 89–91	SE Section 2 Review, p. 93 SE Analyze and Conclude, p. 95 TE Ongoing Assessment, pp. 89, 91 TE Performance Assessment, p. 93 TR 3-2 Review and Reinforce, p. 77	Audiotapes, English-Spanish Summary 3-2 Transparency 11, "Punnett Square—Pea Plants" Interactive Student Tutorial CD-ROM, C-3
TR 3-3 Lesson Plan, p. 79 TR 3-3 Section Summary, p. 80 TR 3-3 Review and Reinforce, p. 81 TR 3-3 Enrich, p. 82 SES Book D, *Human Biology and Health,* Chapter 8	SE Section 3 Review, p. 100 TE Ongoing Assessment, pp. 97, 99 TE Performance Assessment, p. 100 TR 3-3 Review and Reinforce, p. 81	Exploring Life Science Videodisc, Unit 5 Side 1, "The Chromosome Theory" Audiotapes, English-Spanish Summary 3-3 Transparency 12, "Exploring Meiosis" Interactive Student Tutorial CD-ROM, C-3
TR 3-4 Lesson Plan, p. 83 TR 3-4 Section Summary, p. 84 TR 3-4 Review and Reinforce, p. 85 TR 3-4 Enrich, p. 86 SES Book C, *Cells and Heredity,* Chapter 2	SE Section 4 Review, p. 106 TE Ongoing Assessment, pp. 103, 105 TE Performance Assessment, p. 107 TR 3-4 Review and Reinforce, p. 85	Exploring Life Science Videodisc, Unit 5 Side 1, "DNA: The Double Helix" and "Protein Synthesis" Audiotapes, English-Spanish Summary 3-4 Transparency 13, "Exploring Protein Synthesis" Interactive Student Tutorial CD-ROM, C-3
TR Chapter 3 Performance Assessment, pp. 166–168 TR Chapter 3 Test, pp. 169–172	SE Chapter 3 Review, pp. 107–109 TR Chapter 3 Performance Assessment, pp. 166–168 TR Chapter 3 Test, pp. 169–172 CTB Test C-3	Interactive Student Tutorial CD-ROM, C-3 Computer Test Bank, Test C-3 Got It! Video Quizzes

Key: **SE** Student Edition **TE** Teacher's Edition **TR** Teaching Resources
CTB Computer Test Bank **SES** Science Explorer Series Text **ISLM** Integrated Science Laboratory Manual
ISAB Inquiry Skills Activity Book **PTA** Product Testing Activities by *Consumer Reports* **IES** Interdisciplinary Explorations Series

Meeting the National Science Education Standards and AAAS Benchmarks

National Science Education Standards	Benchmarks for Science Literacy	Unifying Themes

Science As Inquiry (Content Standard A)

◆ **Use appropriate tools and technology to gather, analyze, and interpret data** Students investigate genetic traits among classmates. (*Skills Lab*)

◆ **Develop descriptions, explanations, predictions, and models using evidence** Students model genetic crosses. Students predict the possible results of genetic crosses. (*Chapter Project; Skills Lab*)

◆ **Use mathematics in all aspects of scientific inquiry** Geneticists use Punnett squares to determine the probability of a particular outcome. (*Chapter Project; Section 2; Skills Lab*)

Life Science (Content Standard C)

◆ **Structure and function in living systems** Meiosis is the process by which the number of chromosomes is reduced by half to form sex cells. During protein synthesis, the cell uses information from genes to produce proteins. (*Sections 3, 4*)

◆ **Reproduction and heredity** The passing of traits from parents to offspring is called heredity. Genes are carried from parents to offspring on chromosomes. Mutations can be a source of genetic variety. (*Chapter Project; Sections 1, 3, 4; Skills Lab*)

History and Nature of Science (Content Standard G)

◆ **History of science** Many of the genetic principles that Mendel discovered still stand to this day. (*Sections 1, 2*)

1B Scientific Inquiry Students model genetic crosses, investigate genetic traits among classmates, and predict the possible results of genetic crosses. (*Chapter Project; Skills Lab; Skills Lab*)

1C The Scientific Enterprise Many of the genetic principles that Gregor Mendel discovered still stand to this day. Mendel was the first scientist to recognize that the principles of probability can be used to predict the results of genetic crosses. Walter Sutton concluded that chromosomes carry genes from one generation to the next. (*Sections 1, 2, 3*)

5B Heredity The passing of traits from parents to offspring is called heredity. Genes are carried from parents to offspring on chromosomes. Mutations can be a source of genetic variety. (*Chapter Project; Sections 1, 3, 4; Skills Lab*)

5C Cells Meiosis is the process by which the number of chromosomes is reduced by half to form sex cells. During protein synthesis, the cell uses information from a gene to produce a specific protein. (*Sections 3, 4*)

9D Uncertainty Geneticists use Punnett squares to show all the possible outcomes of a genetic cross and to determine the probability of a particular outcome. (*Chapter Project; Section 2; Skills Lab*)

◆ **Evolution** Genes are the basic units of heredity. Genes are carried from parents to offspring on chromosomes. Mutations can be a source of genetic variety. (*Sections 1, 3, 4*)

◆ **Modeling** Students model genetic crosses. (*Chapter Project; Skills Lab*)

◆ **Patterns of Change** Individual alleles control the inheritance of traits. During meiosis, a cell undergoes two divisions to produce sex cells with half the number of chromosomes. Mutations can cause a cell to produce an incorrect protein. (*Sections 1, 3, 4*)

◆ **Scale and Structure** Genes are located on chromosomes. Sex cells have half the normal number of chromosomes. DNA and RNA are made up of nitrogen bases. (*Sections 3, 4*)

◆ **Stability** Heredity is the passing of traits from parents to offspring. A dominant allele is one whose trait always shows up in the organism when the allele is present. Before meiosis begins, every chromosome in the cell is copied. In the genetic code, a group of three bases codes for the attachment of a specific amino acid. (*Sections 1, 3, 4*)

◆ **Systems and Interactions** During meiosis, chromosome pairs separate and are distributed to two different cells. During protein synthesis, the cells use information from a gene to produce specific proteins. (*Sections 2, 3, 4*)

◆ **Unity and Diversity** The different forms of a gene are called alleles. (*Section 1*)

Media and Technology

Exploring Life Science Videodiscs

◆ **Section 1** "We Are All Heirs" explains Mendel's discoveries about the inheritance of dominant and recessive traits.

◆ **Section 3** "The Chromosome Theory" describes the discovery of chromosomes, sex cells, and the steps in meiosis.

◆ **Section 4** "DNA: The Double Helix" describes the work of Watson and Crick. "Protein Synthesis" illustrates the interactions of DNA, RNA, and ribosomes.

Interactive Student Tutorial CD-ROM

◆ **Chapter Review** Interactive questions help students to self-assess their mastery of key chapter concepts.

Student Edition Connection Strategies

◆ **Section 1** Language Arts Connection, p. 82

◆ **Section 2** Integrating Mathematics, pp. 88–95
Math Toolbox, p. 89

◆ **Section 4** Integrating Health, p. 106

USING THE INTERNET

www.science-explorer.phschool.com

Visit the Science Explorer Internet site to find an up-to-date activity for Chapter 3 of *Cells and Heredity.*

ACTIVITY	**Time** (minutes)	**Materials** Quantities for one work group	**Skills**
Section 1			
Discover, p. 80	10	No special materials are required.	Inferring
Skills Lab, pp. 86–87	40	**Consumable** PTC paper **Nonconsumable** mirror (optional)	Developing Hypotheses, Interpreting Data, Drawing Conclusions
Section 2			
Discover, p. 88	15	**Nonconsumable** coin	Predicting
Try This, p. 91	15	**Consumable** masking tape **Nonconsumable** 2 coins, scissors	Interpreting Data
Science at Home, p. 93	home	No special materials are required.	Predicting
Skills Lab, pp. 94–95	40	**Consumable** 2 small paper bags **Nonconsumable** marking pen, 3 blue marbles, 3 white marbles	Making Models, Predicting, Analyzing Data, Comparing and Contrasting
Section 3			
Discover, p. 96	10	**Consumable** 4 craft sticks **Nonconsumable** 3 pieces of paper, marking pen	Inferring
Section 4			
Discover, p. 101	15	No special materials are required.	Forming Operational Definitions
Sharpen Your Skills, p. 103	10	No special materials are required.	Predicting

A list of all materials required for the Student Edition activities can be found on pages T14–T15. You can order Materials Kits by calling 1-800-828-7777 or by accessing the Science Explorer Internet site at **www.science-explorer.phschool.com.**

All In The Family

Most students are curious about why family members share some physical similarities. Some might even have their own ideas about how physical traits run in families.

Purpose In the Chapter 3 Project, students will create a family of "paper pets" based on phenotypes they have selected. In doing so, students will learn about phenotypes, genotypes, traits, and alleles. They will also learn how traits are passed from parent to offspring and how it is possible to predict the outcomes of genetic crosses.

Skills Focus After completing the Chapter 3 Project, students will be able to
◆ model the inheritance of traits using a paper pet;
◆ infer their pets' genotypes;
◆ predict the genotypes and phenotypes of their pets' offspring;
◆ communicate the results of genetic crosses in a class presentation.

Project Time Line The entire project will require about two or three weeks. See Chapter 3 Project Teacher Notes on pages 64–65 in Teaching Resources for more detailed instructions. Begin the project by distributing Chapter 3 Project Overview, pages 66–67 in Teaching Resources. Discuss the project with students and begin talking about the materials they will need to decorate their pets. Students will use Chapter 3 Project Worksheet 1, page 68 in Teaching Resources, to help them create their pets.

Once they have created their pets, allow class time for students to set up crosses with another pet. After students have found partners, distribute Chapter 3 Project Worksheet 2, page 69 in Teaching Resources, to help students determine the results of the crosses between their pets and create the offspring. Student pairs might need class time to prepare displays of their pet families.

Suggested Shortcuts You can simplify this project by having students record the phenotype and genotype of their pets on paper. Student pairs can set up Punnett

squares for the crosses without making paper models of the pet parents and offspring. Each pair can simply assume that one of their pets is female and the other is male.

Possible Materials Students need blue or yellow construction paper for the pet's body. They will also need scissors, colored pencils, glue, and markers to create their pets. Encourage students to decorate their pets with additional materials. You can provide these materials or have students use materials from home. Materials students might use include

glitter, beads, feathers, sequins, yarn, and buttons. Students will need a coin to toss to determine the offspring's genotypes and poster board or other large paper to display their pet families.

Launching the Project To introduce the Chapter 3 Project, invite students to look at the photo of the boxer puppies on these pages. Ask: **How are these puppies similar to each other and to their mother? How are they different?** *(Accept all answers. Most students will describe similarities in the shape of the nose and ears and*

WHAT'S AHEAD

Integrating Mathematics

SECTION 1 Mendel's Work
Discover **What Does the Father Look Like?**
Skills Lab **Take a Class Survey**

SECTION 2 Probability and Genetics
Discover **What's the Chance?**
Try This **Coin Crosses**
Skills Lab **Make the Right Call!**

SECTION 3 The Cell and Inheritance
Discover **Which Chromosome Is Which?**

All In The Family

Did you ever wonder why some offspring resemble their parents while others do not? In this chapter, you'll learn how offspring come to have traits similar to those of their parents. In this project, you'll create a family of "paper pets" to explore how traits pass from parents to offspring.

Your Goal To create a "paper pet" that will be crossed with a pet belonging to a classmate, and to determine what traits the offspring will have.

To complete this project successfully, you must
◆ create your own unique paper pet with five different traits
◆ cross your pet with another pet to produce six offspring
◆ determine what traits the offspring will have, and explain how they came to have those traits

Get Started Cut out your pet from either blue or yellow construction paper. Choose other traits for your pet from this list: female or male; square eyes or round eyes; oval nose or triangular nose; pointed teeth or square teeth. Then create your pet using materials of your choice.

Check Your Progress You'll be working on this project as you study this chapter. To keep your project on track, look for Check Your Progress boxes at the following points.
Section 1 Review, page 85: Identify your pet's genotype.
Section 3 Review, page 100: Determine what traits your pet's offspring have.
Section 4 Review, page 106: Make a display of your pet's family.

Wrap Up At the end of the chapter (page 108), you and your partner will display your pet's family and analyze the inheritance patterns.

These boxer puppies and their mother resemble each other in many ways. However, there are also noticeable differences between one dog and the next.

SECTION 4 The DNA Connection

Discover **Can You Crack the Code?**
Sharpen Your Skills **Predicting**

C ◆ 79

differences in color.) Encourage students to offer explanations for these similarities and differences.

Finally, have students read the description of the project in their text and in the Chapter 3 Project Overview. Encourage students to begin thinking about what traits their pets will have without considering which alleles are dominant or recessive.

Program Resources

◆ **Teaching Resources** Chapter 3 Project Teacher Notes, pp. 64–65; Chapter 3 Project Overview and Worksheets, pp. 66–69; Chapter 3 Project Scoring Rubric, p. 70

Performance Assessment

The Chapter 3 Project Scoring Rubric on page 70 of Teaching Resources will help you evaluate how well students complete the Chapter 3 Project. Students will be assessed on
◆ how neatly and creatively they design their paper pets and how correctly they identify the phenotypes and genotypes;
◆ how accurately they identify the genotypes and phenotypes of their pets' offspring;
◆ how accurately and completely they design a display of their pets' families.
By sharing the Chapter 3 Project Scoring Rubric with students at the beginning of the project, you will make it clear to them what they are expected to do.

Objectives

After completing the lesson, students will be able to
- Describe Mendel's genetics experiments;
- identify the factors that control the inheritance of traits in organisms;
- explain how geneticists use symbols to represent alleles.

Key Terms trait, heredity, genetics, purebred, gene, allele, dominant allele, recessive allele, hybrid

1 Engage/Explore

Activating Prior Knowledge

Invite students to share observations they have made about the physical similarities and differences among family members. Ask: **Have you ever wondered why some family members look very similar while others look very different?** *(Many students will have considered this in one way or another.)* Encourage students to share their ideas about the inheritance of traits in families. Be alert for misconceptions students might have, and address these throughout the section.

DISCOVER

Skills Focus inferring
Time 10 minutes
Expected Outcome Two kittens are orange and white. The mother and the third kitten are black, orange, and white.
Think It Over Students will probably infer that the father may be orange and white. They may also infer that the orange and white kittens may have inherited their color pattern from the father.

DISCOVER •••••••••••••••••••••••••••• ACTIVITY

What Does the Father Look Like?

1. Observe the colors of each kitten in the photo. Record each kitten's coat colors and patterns. Include as many details as you can.
2. Observe the mother cat in the photo. Record her coat color and pattern.

Think It Over

Inferring Based on your observations, describe what you think the kittens' father might look like. Identify the evidence on which you based your inference.

GUIDE FOR READING

◆ What factors control the inheritance of traits in organisms?

Reading Tip Before you read, preview the section and make a list of the boldfaced terms. As you read, write a definition for each term in your own words.

Gregor Mendel in the monastery garden ▼

The year was 1851. Gregor Mendel, a young priest from a monastery in Central Europe, entered the University of Vienna to study mathematics and science. Two years later, Mendel returned to the monastery and began teaching at a nearby high school.

Mendel also cared for the monastery's garden, where he grew hundreds of pea plants. He became curious about why some of the plants had different physical characteristics, or **traits.** Some pea plants grew tall while others were short. Some plants produced green seeds, while others had yellow seeds.

Mendel observed that the pea plants' traits were often similar to those of their parents. Sometimes, however, the pea plants had different traits than their parents. The passing of traits from parents to offspring is called **heredity.** For more than ten years, Mendel experimented with thousands of pea plants to understand the process of heredity. Mendel's work formed the foundation of **genetics,** the scientific study of heredity.

Mendel's Peas

Mendel made a wise decision when he chose to study peas rather than other plants in the monastery garden. Pea plants are easy to study because they have many traits that exist in only two forms. For example, pea plant stems are either tall or short, but not medium height. Also, garden peas produce a large number of offspring in one generation. Thus, it is easy to collect large amounts of data to analyze.

READING STRATEGIES

Reading Tip Make sure students use their own words to define each boldfaced term. After students have previewed the section, pronounce each boldfaced term for the class to make sure that students are pronouncing them correctly. Students could write each term on one side of an index card and the definition on the other side. They can then use these cards as study aids.

Concept Mapping Have students make a concept map in which they show the relationships among the terms in the section. Students may include their definitions on the concept maps, if they wish.

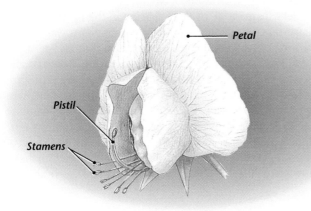

Petal

Pistil

Stamens

Figure 1 Garden peas usually reproduce by self-pollination. Pollen from a flower's stamens lands on the pistil of the same flower. Plants that result from self-pollination inherit all of their characteristics from the single parent plant. *Applying Concepts How did Mendel prevent his pea plants from self-pollinating?*

Figure 1 shows a flowering pea plant. Notice that the flower's petals surround the pistil and the stamens. The pistil produces female sex cells, or eggs, while the stamens produce the male sex cells, or pollen.

In nature, pea plants are usually self-pollinating. This means that pollen from one flower lands on the pistil of the same flower. Mendel developed a method by which he could cross-pollinate, or "cross," pea plants. To cross two plants, he removed pollen from a flower on one plant and brushed it onto a flower on a second plant. To prevent the pea plants from self-pollinating, he carefully removed the stamens from the flowers on the second plant.

Mendel's Experiments

Suppose you had a garden full of pea plants, and you wanted to study the inheritance of traits. What would you do? Mendel decided to cross plants with opposite forms of a trait, for example, tall plants and short plants. He started his experiments with purebred plants. A **purebred** plant is one that always produces offspring with the same form of a trait as the parent. For example, purebred short pea plants always produce short offspring. Purebred tall pea plants always produce tall offspring. To produce purebred plants, Mendel allowed peas with one particular trait to self-pollinate for many generations. By using purebred plants, Mendel knew that the offspring's trait would always be identical to that of the parents.

In his first experiment, Mendel crossed purebred tall plants with purebred short plants. He called these parent plants the parental generation, or P generation. He called the offspring from this cross the first filial (FIL ee ul) generation, or the F_1 generation. The word *filial* means "son" in Latin.

Program Resources

◆ **Teaching Resources** 3-1 Lesson Plan, p. 71; 3-1 Section Summary, p. 72
Science Explorer Series *From Bacteria to Plants,* Chapter 5, has more information about flower structure and pollination.

Answers to Self-Assessment

Caption Question

Figure 1 Mendel removed the stamens from the flowers that he cross-pollinated.

Media and Technology

Audiotapes English-Spanish Summary 3-1

2 Facilitate

Mendel's Peas

Building Inquiry Skills: Observing

Materials *tulip or lily flower, hand lens, small blunt-tipped scissors*
Time 15 minutes

Encourage students to closely observe the intact flower with a hand lens. Then instruct students to snip apart the pistil and stamens with scissors and examine these parts individually. Have students draw a labeled diagram of the flower and its parts. Then have them compare their diagrams with the pea flower in Figure 1. Ask: **What makes the pea flower well suited for self-pollination?** *(The petals almost completely enclose the pistil and stamen.)* Tell students that self-pollinating plants are a better choice for studying inheritance because it is easier to obtain purebreeding plants.
learning modality: kinesthetic

Mendel's Experiments

Inquiry Challenge

Materials *posterboard*
Time 20 minutes

Challenge small groups to evaluate Mendel's experimental procedure. Groups should create a poster on which they identify Mendel's question and hypothesis and outline his experimental design. Groups should also include a summary of their opinions about Mendel's procedures. Have them consider why Mendel allowed the F_1 plants to self-pollinate. *(To see if they were purebred)* Groups can present their posters to the class. **cooperative learning**

Ongoing Assessment

Writing Have students identify three characteristics of pea plants that make them useful for studying inheritance. *(Only two forms of many traits, large number of offspring, self-pollinating)*

Other Traits

Have students compare Mendel's description with the round and wrinkled peas in Figure 3. Invite them to suggest changes to Mendel's description. Then ask: **Why do you think detailed descriptions are important in scientific papers?** *(So readers will clearly understand the author's ideas)*

In Your Journal Before students list the features of their objects, discuss adjectives and adverbs, the kinds of words used to describe objects. Tell students not to use the name of their objects in their paragraphs. Then have students trade paragraphs and guess their partners' objects. **learning modality: verbal**

Dominant and Recessive Alleles

Using the Visuals: Figure 3

Review with students the forms of each trait in the peas that Mendel studied. Ask: **Why are these traits well suited for studying inheritance?** *(The traits are easy to observe and have two distinct forms.)* Then have students solve simple genetic crosses between peas that differ in one trait. For example: **What color seeds will the offspring have when a purebred pea plant with yellow seeds is crossed with a purebred plant with green seeds?** *(yellow seeds)* **learning modality: visual**

Including All Students

Students can add the following terms to their lists of boldfaced terms from the Reading Tip activity to create their own genetics dictionary: *factor, characteristic, self-pollination, cross-pollination, cross, filial, F₁ generation, P generation, inheritance,* and *purebred*. Students should write their own definitions of these words and include drawings if needed. Allow students whose native language is not English to write definitions in their own language. **limited English proficiency**

Gregor Mendel presented a detailed description of his observations in a scientific paper in 1866. In the excerpt that follows, notice how clearly he describes his observations of the two different seed shapes in peas.

"These are either round or roundish, the depressions, if any, occur on the surface, being always only shallow; or they are irregularly angular and deeply wrinkled."

In Your Journal

Choose an everyday object, such as a piece of fruit or a pen. Make a list of the object's features. Then write a short paragraph describing the object. Use clear, precise language in your description.

You can see the results of Mendel's first cross in Figure 2. To Mendel's surprise, all of the offspring in the F_1 generation were tall. Despite the fact that one of the parent plants was short, none of the offspring were short. The shortness trait had disappeared!

Mendel let the plants in the F_1 generation grow and allowed them to self-pollinate. The results of this experiment also surprised Mendel. The plants in the F_2 (second filial) generation were a mix of tall and short plants. This occurred even though none of the F_1 parent plants were short. The shortness trait had reappeared. Mendel counted the number of tall and short plants in the F_2 generation. He found that about three fourths of the plants were tall, while one fourth of the plants were short.

☑ *Checkpoint* What is a purebred plant?

Other Traits

In addition to stem height, Mendel studied six other traits in garden peas: seed shape, seed color, seed coat color, pod shape, pod color, and flower position. Compare the two forms of each trait in Figure 3. Mendel crossed plants with these traits in the same manner as he did for stem height. The results in each experiment were similar to those that he observed with stem height. Only one form of the trait appeared in the F_1 generation. However, in the F_2 generation the "lost" form of the trait always reappeared in about one fourth of the plants.

Figure 2 When Mendel crossed purebred tall and short pea plants, all the offspring in the F_1 generation were tall. In the F_2 generation, three fourths of the plants were tall, while one fourth were short.

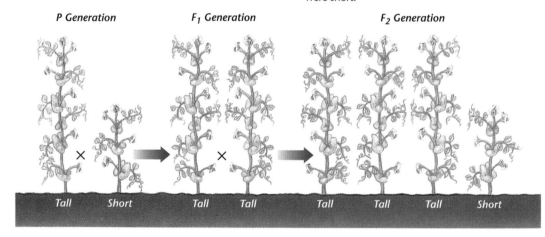

P Generation   F₁ Generation   F₂ Generation

Tall   Short   Tall   Tall   Tall   Tall   Tall   Short

History of Science Mendel's work is relevant today because of his careful experimental design. Unlike other scientists and plant and animal breeders of his time, Mendel carefully chose to study distinct traits. He allowed plants to self-pollinate until he was certain that the plants he used were purebreeding. Most importantly, he applied the principles of statistics when setting up his crosses and interpreting his results. This prevented him from interpreting his results using his personal opinions and beliefs. Other scientists and breeders at that time set up their crosses randomly with parents of unknown breeding and often tried to follow more than one trait at a time. They also thought that inheritance was much too complicated to analyze using the principles of statistics.

Genetics of Pea Plants

Traits	Seed Shape	Seed Color	Seed Coat Color	Pod Shape	Pod Color	Flower Position	Stem Height
Controlled by Dominant Allele	Round	Yellow	Gray	Smooth	Green	Side	Tall
Controlled by Recessive Allele	Wrinkled	Green	White	Pinched	Yellow	End	Short

Figure 3 Mendel studied seven different traits in pea plants. Each trait has two different forms. *Interpreting Diagrams Is yellow seed color controlled by a dominant allele or a recessive allele? What type of allele controls pinched pod shape?*

Dominant and Recessive Alleles

From his results, Mendel reasoned that individual factors must control the inheritance of traits in peas. The factors that control each trait exist in pairs. The female parent contributes one factor, while the male parent contributes the other factor.

Mendel went on to reason that one factor in a pair can mask, or hide, the other factor. The tallness factor, for example, masked the shortness factor in the F_1 generation.

Today, scientists call the factors that control traits **genes.** They call the different forms of a gene **alleles** (uh LEELZ). The gene that controls stem height in peas, for example, has one allele for tall stems and one allele for short stems. Each pea plant inherits a combination of two alleles from its parents—either two alleles for tall stems, two alleles for short stems, or one of each.

Individual alleles control the inheritance of traits. Some alleles are dominant, while other alleles are recessive. A **dominant allele** is one whose trait always shows up in the organism when the allele is present. A **recessive allele,** on the other hand, is masked, or covered up, whenever the dominant allele is present. A trait controlled by a recessive allele will only show up if the organism does not have the dominant allele.

In pea plants, the allele for tall stems is dominant over the allele for short stems. Pea plants with one allele for tall stems and one allele for short stems will be tall. The allele for tall stems masks the allele for short stems. Only pea plants that inherit two recessive alleles for short stems will be short.

Chapter 3 **C ◆ 83**

Answers to Self-Assessment

✓ Checkpoint
A plant that always produces offspring with the same form of a trait as the parent

Caption Question
Figure 3 a dominant allele; recessive

Demonstration

Materials 2 Drosophila melanogaster *cultures—wild-type and ebony, culture vials and plugs,* Drosophila *media, nonether anesthesia kit, hand lens, paint brush, white index card, marking pen* (NOTE: Drosophila *cultures are available from science supply companies.*)

Time 20 minutes

Advance Preparation Set up the parental cross about two weeks in advance by placing 2 to 3 ebony males with 2 to 3 wild-type virgin females in each of three vials. To collect virgin females, remove all adult flies from the culture vial. Then, within 4 to 6 hours, collect the newly emerged females. Females have pointed abdomens with stripes almost to the end. Males have rounded abdomens that are black at the end. Anesthetize flies to sort them and to set up the crosses. Place vials on their sides until the flies wake up. Remove parent flies from the vials when pupae begin to develop. When F_1 adults begin to emerge, remove the flies daily to prevent F_2 offspring from mixing with F_1 offspring. Dispose of flies in a jar of mineral oil. Empty this "morgue" into a garbage disposal.

Tips Anesthetize the parent flies and place them on index cards for students to examine. Ask: **How do these flies differ?** *(Ebony flies have darker bodies than wild-type flies.)* Challenge students to predict which trait is controlled by a dominant allele and which is controlled by a recessive allele. Then anesthetize the F_1 flies and place them on index cards for students to count. Ask: **Which trait is controlled by a dominant allele?** *(lighter body color)* **How do you know?** *(None of the F_1 flies have ebony bodies.)* **What body color will F_2 flies have?** *(Some will have ebony bodies, but most will have lighter bodies.)* **learning modality: logical/mathematical**

Ongoing Assessment

Drawing Have students diagram Mendel's crosses between tall and short pea plants. Tell them to label the traits controlled by dominant and recessive alleles.

 Students can save their drawings in their portfolios.

Understanding Mendel's Crosses

Building Inquiry Skills: Applying Concepts

Have students choose a pea trait from Figure 3, and challenge them to diagram the crosses that Mendel made. In their diagrams, students should show how dominant and recessive alleles are inherited from the P generation through the F_1 generation to the F_2 generation. Encourage students to share their diagrams with the class. **learning modality: logical/mathematical**

Using Symbols in Genetics

Including All Students

Students who need more help can practice using genetic symbols by assigning letters to the dominant and recessive alleles for each trait that Mendel studied. Students can use any letter to represent each trait, although the convention is to use the letter that begins the word of the dominant allele. For example, *R* stands for round seeds and *r* stands for wrinkled. Dominant alleles must have a capital letter; recessive alleles, lower-case. **learning modality: verbal**

Inquiry Challenge

Materials *F_2 ear of corn with purple and yellow kernels (available from science supply companies)*
Time 15 minutes

Give each small group an ear of corn. Explain that the ears were produced by F_2 generation plants and that kernel color is controlled by dominant and recessive alleles—purple is controlled by the dominant allele, and yellow is controlled by the recessive allele. Then challenge students to trace the inheritance of the dominant and recessive alleles for kernel color by working backward from the F_2 ear to the F_1 cross and finally to the parental cross. Students should use symbols to represent the alleles for kernel color. (*F_1 parents: both purple* (Pp); *P parents: one purple* (PP), *one yellow* (pp)) **learning modality: logical/mathematical**

Figure 4 These rabbits have some traits controlled by dominant alleles and other traits controlled by recessive alleles. For example, the allele for black fur is dominant over the allele for white fur. *Inferring What combination of alleles must the white rabbit have?*

Understanding Mendel's Crosses

You can understand Mendel's results by tracing the inheritance of alleles in his experiments. The purebred plants in the P generation had two identical alleles for stem height. The purebred tall plants had two alleles for tall stems. The purebred short plants had two alleles for short stems. In the F_1 generation, all of the plants received one allele for tall stems from the tall parent. They received one allele for short stems from the short parent. The F_1 plants are called **hybrids** (HY bridz) because they have two different alleles for the trait. All the F_1 plants are tall because the dominant allele for tall stems masks the recessive allele for short stems.

When Mendel crossed the hybrid plants in the F_1 generation, some of the plants inherited two dominant alleles for tall stems. These plants were tall. Other plants inherited one dominant allele for tall stems and one recessive allele for short stems. These plants were also tall. Other plants inherited two recessive alleles for short stems. These plants were short.

☑ *Checkpoint* *If a pea plant has a tall stem, what possible combinations of alleles could it have?*

Using Symbols in Genetics

Geneticists today use a standard shorthand method to write about alleles in genetic crosses. Instead of using words such as "tall stems" to represent alleles, they simply use letters. A

Background

History of Science At the time of Mendel's studies of inheritance, most of the scientific community believed in the blending theory of inheritance. This theory assumed that both parents contributed equally to the characteristics of the offspring. According to the theory, parents of contrasting appearance always produced offspring with an intermediate appearance. When parental traits reappeared in the offspring, it was thought to be due to some genetic disturbance. Mendel also subscribed to the blending theory. When he started working on his experiments with peas, he was not trying to discover the laws of inheritance. Rather, he was trying to find a hybrid that would breed true. This is one reason why his results went unnoticed for some time. The scientific community could not interpret them for what they really showed.

dominant allele is represented by a capital letter. For example, the allele for tall stems is represented by *T*. A recessive allele is represented by the lowercase version of the letter. So, the allele for short stems would be represented by *t*. When a plant inherits two dominant alleles for tall stems, its alleles are written as *TT*. When a plant inherits two recessive alleles for short stems, its alleles are written as *tt*. When a plant inherits one allele for tall stems and one allele for short stems, its alleles are written as *Tt*.

Mendel's Contribution

In 1866, Mendel presented his results to a scientific society that met regularly near the monastery. In his paper, Mendel described the principles of heredity he had discovered. Unfortunately, other scientists did not understand the importance of Mendel's work. Some scientists thought that Mendel had oversimplified the process of inheritance. Others never read his paper, or even heard about his work. At that time, scientists in different parts of the world were isolated from each other. Mendel was especially isolated because he wasn't at a university. Remember, there were no telephones, and no computers to send electronic mail.

Mendel's work was forgotten for 34 years. In 1900, three different scientists rediscovered Mendel's work. They had made many of the same observations as Mendel had. The scientists quickly recognized the importance of Mendel's work. Many of the genetic principles that Mendel discovered still stand to this day. Because of his work, Mendel is often called the Father of Genetics.

Figure 5 The dominant allele for yellow skin color in summer squash is represented by the letter *Y*. The recessive allele for green skin color is represented by the letter *y*.

 Section 1 Review

1. Explain how the inheritance of traits is controlled in organisms. Use the terms *genes* and *alleles* in your explanation.
2. What is a dominant allele? What is a recessive allele? Give an example of each.
3. The allele for round seeds is represented by *R*. Suppose that a pea plant inherited two recessive alleles for wrinkled seeds. How would you write the symbols for its alleles?
4. **Thinking Critically Applying Concepts** Can a short pea plant ever be a hybrid? Why or why not?

> **Check Your Progress** CHAPTER PROJECT 3
>
> By now you should have constructed your paper pet. On the back, write what alleles your pet has for each trait. Use XX for a female, and XY for a male. The dominant alleles for the other four traits are: *B* (blue skin), *R* (round eyes), *T* (triangular nose), and *P* (pointed teeth). (*Hint:* If your pet has a trait controlled by a dominant allele, you can choose which of the possible combinations of alleles your pet has.)

Answers to Self-Assessment

Caption Question

Figure 4 two alleles for white fur

☑ *Checkpoint*

Two alleles for tall stems or one allele for tall stems and one allele for short stems

Mendel's Contribution

Real-Life Learning

Explain to students that it is not unusual for scientists who have discovered new ideas to be misunderstood or even ridiculed. It is very difficult to change popular opinion. Some ideas that were once controversial include that Earth orbits the sun and that Earth is round. Challenge student groups to work together to write a broadcast news story about a scientific idea that is controversial. Students might choose Mendel's results or another idea, either current or historical. You might wish to videotape the groups' broadcasts in a pretend news show. **cooperative learning**

3 Assess

Section 1 Review Answers

1. Each allele of a gene controls the inheritance of a specific trait.
2. *Dominant:* trait always shows up when the allele is present; tall stems in peas. *Recessive:* trait is covered up whenever dominant allele is present; short pea stems.
3. The symbols would be *rr*.
4. No, it has two recessive alleles *(tt)*; hybrids have two different alleles for a trait.

> *Check Your Progress* CHAPTER PROJECT 3
>
> Check each paper pet to make sure students have correctly assigned pairs of alleles based on the traits they chose. Monitor the number of male and female pets so that there is an equal number of each. If the class has an odd number of students, create an extra pet. Encourage students to be creative when they decorate their pets.

Performance Assessment

Writing Have students summarize Mendel's experiments and his conclusions about the inheritance of traits.

 Students can save their summaries in their portfolios.

Developing Hypotheses

Take a Class Survey

Preparing for Inquiry

Key Concept Humans traits are controlled by dominant and recessive alleles, causing many different combinations of traits among a group of people.

Skills Objectives Students will be able to
- develop hypotheses about whether traits controlled by dominant alleles are more common than traits controlled by recessive alleles;
- interpret data about certain traits controlled by dominant and recessive alleles in humans;
- draw conclusions about the frequency and the variation of certain traits in the class.

Time 40 minutes

Advance Planning Purchase PTC paper from a science supply house. Gather mirrors, or invite students to bring some from home. You might wish to make photocopies of the circle chart and the data table.

Alternative Materials If PTC paper is not available, this trait can be omitted. If you do not have mirrors, students can observe each other.

Guided Inquiry

Invitation Help students relate Mendel's conclusions to their own physical characteristics. Ask: **Why do you think people often look very similar to other family members, but also different?** *(Some students might realize that children inherit both dominant and recessive alleles from each parent. The combination of these alleles determines the child's physical appearance.)*

Introducing the Procedure
- Have students read through the entire procedure. Then review with them what each trait looks like. Refer students to the illustrations in the text, or find examples of each trait among the class. Explain that PTC paper tastes bitter to those who can taste it.

Take a Class Survey

In this lab, you'll explore how greatly traits can vary in a group of people—your classmates.

Problem

Are traits controlled by dominant alleles more common than traits controlled by recessive alleles?

Materials

mirror (optional)   PTC paper

Procedure

Part 1 Dominant and Recessive Alleles

1. Write a hypothesis reflecting your ideas about the problem question. Then copy the data table.
2. For traits A, B, C, D, and E, work with a partner to determine which trait you have. Circle that trait in your data table.

3. For trait F, wash and dry your hands. Taste the PTC paper your teacher gives you. Circle either "can taste PTC" or "cannot taste PTC" in your data table. **CAUTION:** *Never taste any substance in the lab unless directed to by your teacher.*

4. Count the number of students who have each trait. Record that number in your data table. Also record the total number of students.

DATA TABLE

Total Number _____

	Trait 1	Number	Trait 2	Number
A	Free ear lobes		Attached ear lobes	
B	Hair on fingers		No hair on fingers	
C	Widow's peak		No widow's peak	
D	Curly hair		Straight hair	
E	Cleft chin		Smooth chin	
F	Can taste PTC*		Cannot taste PTC*	

PTC stands for phenylthiocarbamide.

Free ear lobe

Attached ear lobe

Hair on fingers

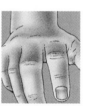
No hair on fingers

Widow's peak

No widow's peak

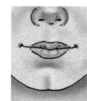
Cleft chin

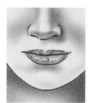
No cleft chin

Nontasters will not taste anything. Curly hair includes wavy hair or any hair that is not straight.
- Make sure students know how to use the circle of traits in Part 2. Point out how to use the color-coding, starting at the center of the circle.

Troubleshooting the Experiment
- Monitor students as they work to make sure they correctly identify each trait.
- The class can record their results on a large data table on the chalkboard by writing their initials in the appropriate columns.

Expected Outcome
Students will show a great variation in traits. Few, if any, will have the same number on the circle of traits.

Analyze and Conclude
1. Some traits controlled by dominant alleles that are usually more common include free earlobes and ability to taste PTC. Some traits

Part 2 Are Your Traits Unique?

5. Look at the circle of traits below. All the traits in your data table appear in the circle. Place the eraser end of your pencil on the trait in the small central circle that applies to you—either free ear lobes or attached ear lobes.

6. Look at the two traits touching the space your eraser is on. Move your eraser onto the next description that applies to you. Continue using your eraser to trace your traits until you reach a number on the outside rim of the circle. Share that number with your classmates.

Analyze and Conclude

1. The traits listed under Trait 1 in the data table are controlled by dominant alleles. The traits listed under Trait 2 are controlled by recessive alleles. Which traits controlled by dominant alleles were shown by a majority of students? Which traits controlled by recessive alleles were shown by a majority of students?

2. How many students ended up on the same number on the circle of traits? How many students were the only ones to have their number? What do the results suggest about each person's combination of traits?

3. **Think About It** Do your data support the hypothesis you proposed in Step 1? Explain your answer with examples.

Design an Experiment

Do people who are related to each other show more genetic similarity than unrelated people? Write a hypothesis. Then design an experiment to test your hypothesis.

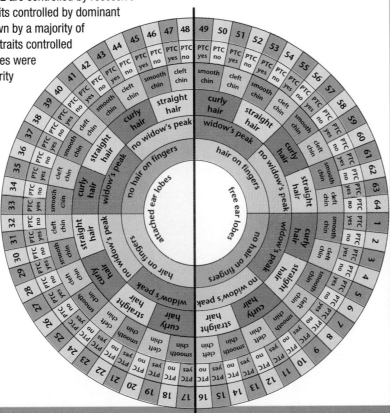

controlled by recessive alleles that are usually more common include smooth chin, straight hair, no widow's peak, and no mid-finger hair. However, any class's results may vary from the overall population patterns because of the small sample size.

2. Answers will vary, but usually few or no students have the same number when six traits are studied. As more traits are considered, the smaller the chance that any two people in a class will have the same number. Even siblings, except for identical twins, have different combinations of traits.

3. Answers will vary, but students should describe, using examples from the lab, that neither traits controlled by dominant alleles nor traits controlled by recessive alleles are automatically more common in a population.

Extending the Inquiry

Design an Experiment Students' hypotheses will vary. *Sample hypothesis: A group of related people will share more numbers on the circle of traits than a group of unrelated people.* Student experiments can follow the same procedure as this lab, except students observe the traits in family members.

Safety

Remind students to wash their hands before tasting the PTC paper. Caution them to never taste any substance in the lab unless you instruct them to. Review the safety guidelines in Appendix A.

SECTION 2 Probability and Genetics

Objectives

After completing the lesson, students will be able to

◆ describe the principles of probability and how Mendel applied them to inheritance;

◆ state how geneticists use Punnett squares;

◆ explain the meanings of the terms *phenotype, genotype, homozygous, heterozygous,* and *codominance.*

Key Terms probability, Punnett square, phenotype, genotype, homozygous, heterozygous, codominance

1 Engage/Explore

Activating Prior Knowledge

Invite students to describe situations in which they have used a coin toss to decide an issue. Ask: **Why did you toss a coin in these situations?** *(Students might mention that it was the fairest way to make a decision.)* **Why is a coin toss fair?** *(Each person has a 50–50 chance of winning.)*

⟨ DISCOVER ⟩

Skills Focus predicting
Materials *coin*
Time 15 minutes
Expected Outcome The actual outcome of the coin tosses will vary. The more data, the closer the outcome will be to the expected ratio of 1 head: 1 tail.
Think It Over For most students, their results were slightly different from their predictions. The combined class data should be closer to the expected ratio of 1 head to 1 tail. Students might infer that the difference is due to chance or that the more coin tosses they make, the closer they will come to the predicted outcome.

SECTION 2 Probability and Genetics

⟨ DISCOVER ⟩ ·················· ACTIVITY

What's the Chance?

1. Suppose you were to toss a coin 20 times. Predict how many times the coin would land "heads up" and how many times it would land "tails up."

2. Now test your prediction by tossing a coin 20 times. Record the number of times the coin lands heads up and the number of times it lands tails up.

3. Combine the data from the entire class. Record the total number of tosses, the number of heads, and the number of tails.

Think It Over

Predicting How did your results in Step 2 compare to your prediction? How can you account for any differences between your results and the class results?

⟨ GUIDE FOR READING ⟩

◆ How do the principles of probability help explain Mendel's results?

◆ How do geneticists use Punnett squares?

Reading Tip Before you read, rewrite the headings in the section as questions that begin with *how, what,* or *why.* As you read, look for answers to these questions.

The city of Portland, Oregon, was founded in the mid-1800s. Two men, Asa L. Lovejoy and Francis W. Pettygrove, owned the land on which the new city was built. Lovejoy, who was from Massachusetts, wanted to name the new town Boston. Pettygrove, however, thought the town should be named after his hometown, Portland, Maine. To settle the dispute, they decided to toss a coin. Pettygrove won, and the new town was named Portland.

What was the chance that Pettygrove would win the coin toss? To answer this question, you need to understand the principles of probability. **Probability** is the likelihood that a particular event will occur.

⟨ READING STRATEGIES ⟩

Reading Tip Students can write questions for both the major headings and the subheads in the section. Remind students to leave adequate space after each question to allow room for their answers. Encourage students to keep their questions nearby as they read the section so they can write the answers as they read. Students can use the questions and answers as study guides.

Vocabulary Show students that the term *homozygous* is made up of the Greek words *homos,* meaning "same," and *zygos,* meaning "yoked or paired." Taken together, these words describe a cell formed from two gametes that have the same genetic makeup. In *heterozygous, heteros* is the Greek word meaning "other or different." This word describes a cell formed from two gametes that have a different genetic makeup.

Principles of Probability

If you did the Discover activity, you used the principles of probability to predict the results of a particular event. Each time you toss a coin, there are two possible ways that the coin can land—heads up or tails up. Each of these two events is equally likely to occur. In mathematical terms, you can say that the probability that a tossed coin will land heads up is 1 in 2. There is also a 1 in 2 probability that the coin will land tails up. A 1 in 2 probability can also be expressed as the fraction $\frac{1}{2}$ or as a percent—50 percent.

If you tossed a coin 20 times, you might expect it to land heads up 10 times and tails up 10 times. However, you might not actually get these results. You might get 11 heads and 9 tails, or 8 heads and 12 tails. Remember that the laws of probability predict what is likely to occur, not necessarily what will occur. However, the more tosses you make, the closer your actual results will be to the results predicted by probability.

When you toss a coin more than once, the results of one toss do not affect the results of the next toss. Each event occurs independently. For example, suppose you toss a coin five times and it lands heads up each time. What is the probability that it will land heads up on the next toss? Because the coin landed heads up on the previous five tosses, you might think that it would be likely to land heads up on the next toss. However, this is not the case. The probability of the coin landing heads up on the next toss is still 1 in 2, or 50 percent. The results of the first five tosses do not affect the results of the sixth toss.

☑ **Checkpoint** *Why is there a 1 in 2 probability that a tossed coin will land heads up?*

Math TOOLBOX

Calculating Percent

One way you can express a probability is as a percent. A percent (%) is a number compared to 100. For example, 50% means 50 out of 100.

Suppose that 3 out of 5 tossed coins landed heads up. Here's how you can calculate what percent of the coins landed heads up.

1. Write the comparison as a fraction.

$$3 \text{ out of } 5 = \frac{3}{5}$$

2. Multiply the fraction by 100% to express it as a percent.

$$\frac{3}{5} \times \frac{100\%}{1} = 60\%$$

60% of the coins landed heads up.

Now, suppose 3 out of 12 coins landed tails up. How can you express this as a percent?

Figure 6 According to the laws of probability, there is a 50 percent probability that the coin will land heads up. *Calculating* What is the probability that the coin will land tails up?

Answers to Self-Assessment

☑ *Checkpoint*

There are two possible ways that the coin can land, and each one has an equal chance of occurring.

Caption Question

Figure 6 50%

2 Facilitate

Principles of Probability

Including All Students

Materials *4 pipe cleaners of different lengths, but all the same color* **ACTIVITY**

To help reinforce the concept of probability, challenge student pairs to use the pipe cleaners to illustrate the two principles of probability: each event has equal chance of occurring and each event occurs independently. Then ask: **What is the chance that the longest pipe cleaner will be chosen?** *(1 out of 4 or 25%)* **If the longest pipe cleaner is chosen the first time and is replaced, what is the chance that it will be chosen again?** *(Also 25%; each event occurs independently of the results of other events.)* **learning modality: kinesthetic**

Inquiry Challenge

Challenge small groups of students to create a game **ACTIVITY** that uses the principles of probability. Students may use coin tosses in the game, use a spinner, or anything else that gives players an equal chance at winning the game. Each group should write rules for its game and teach another group how to play the game. **cooperative learning**

Math TOOLBOX

Time 10 minutes
Tips Remind students that in fractions, the line separating the numbers stands for "divided by." For the problem, students should set up the fraction $\frac{3}{12}$, or calculate 3 "divided by" 12 to get 0.25. To calculate the percent, students should then multiply 0.25 by 100% to get 25%. **learning modality: logical/mathematical**

Ongoing Assessment

Oral Presentation Call on students at random to describe the two principles of probability using a coin toss as an example.

Mendel and Probability

Building Inquiry Skills: Calculating

Using the example from the text, have students calculate the probability that a cross between two hybrid tall pea plants *(Tt)* will produce tall offspring. *($\frac{3}{4} \times 100\% = 75\%$)* Ask: **What is the probability that such a cross will produce short offspring?** *($\frac{1}{4} \times 100\% = 25\%$)* Extend this by challenging students to calculate the probabilities of tall and short offspring from a cross between a purebred tall pea *(TT)* and a purebred short pea *(tt)*. *(100% of offspring will be tall; 0% will be short.)* **learning modality: logical/mathematical**

Punnett Squares

Using the Visuals: Figure 7

Have students identify in Figure 7 the two alleles that each parent could pass on to the offspring *(Tt)*. Make sure students understand how the alleles combine from each parent to form the different offspring classes. Emphasize that a cross between these two plants will produce more than just four offspring. The Punnett square simply identifies all the *possible* combinations of alleles. In this case, offspring will be either tall or short with three different allele combinations. Ask: **Which of these combinations is more likely to occur than others?** *(Tt)* **What percentage of the offspring will have that combination?** *(50%)* **learning modality: visual**

Inquiry Challenge

Materials *F_2 ear of corn with purple and yellow kernels*

Time 15 minutes

Challenge students to devise a Punnett square that illustrates the possible offspring in a cross between two plants that could produce corn with both purple (dominant allele) and yellow (recessive allele) kernels. *(Pp × Pp)* Then have students set up Punnett squares that show the possible offspring in a cross between a purebred yellow corn plant *(pp)* and a purebred purple corn plant *(PP)*. **learning modality: logical/ mathematical**

Mendel and Probability

How is probability related to genetics? To answer this question, think back to Mendel's experiments with peas. Remember that Mendel carefully counted the offspring from every cross that he carried out. When Mendel crossed two plants that were hybrid for stem height *(Tt)*, three fourths of the F_1 plants had tall stems. One fourth of the plants had short stems.

Each time Mendel repeated the cross, he obtained similar results. Mendel realized that the mathematical principles of probability applied to his work. He could say that the probability of such a cross producing a tall plant was 3 in 4. The probability of producing a short plant was 1 in 4. **Mendel was the first scientist to recognize that the principles of probability can be used to predict the results of genetic crosses.**

Punnett Squares

A tool that can help you understand how the laws of probability apply to genetics is called a Punnett square. A **Punnett square** is a chart that shows all the possible combinations of alleles that can result from a genetic cross. **Geneticists use Punnett squares to show all the possible outcomes of a genetic cross and to determine the probability of a particular outcome.**

The Punnett square in Figure 7 shows a cross between two hybrid tall pea plants *(Tt)*. Each parent can pass either of its alleles, *T* or *t*, to its offspring. The possible alleles that one parent can pass on are written across the top of the Punnett square. The possible alleles that the other parent can pass on are written down the left side of the Punnett square. The boxes in the Punnett square represent the possible combinations of alleles that the offspring can inherit. The boxes are filled in like a multiplication problem, with one allele contributed by each parent.

Using a Punnett Square You can use a Punnett square to calculate the probability that offspring with a certain combination of alleles will result. The allele that each parent will pass on is based on chance, just like the toss of a coin. Thus, there are four possible combinations of alleles that can result. The

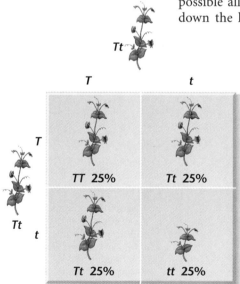

Figure 7 This Punnett square shows a cross between two hybrid tall pea plants. *Interpreting Charts Which allele combinations will result in tall offspring?*

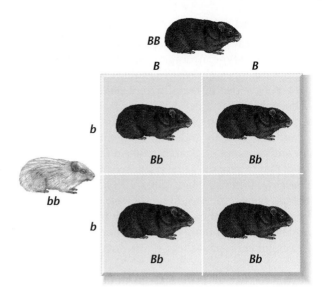

BB

B   B

b

b

Bb   *Bb*

Bb   *Bb*

bb

Figure 8 This Punnett square shows a cross between a black guinea pig (*BB*) and a white guinea pig (*bb*). *Calculating What is the probability that an offspring will have white fur?*

probability that an offspring will be *TT* is 1 in 4, or 25 percent. The probability that an offspring will be *tt* is also 1 in 4, or 25 percent. Notice, however, that the *Tt* allele combination appears in two boxes in the Punnett square. This is because there are two possible ways in which this combination can occur. The probability, then, that an offspring will be *Tt* is 2 in 4, or 50 percent.

Recall that when Mendel performed this cross, he discovered that about three fourths of the plants (75%) had tall stems. The remaining one fourth of the plants (25%) had short stems. Now you can understand why that was true. Plants with the *TT* allele combination would be tall. So too would those plants with the *Tt* allele combination. Remember that the dominant allele masks the recessive allele. Only those plants with the *tt* allele combination would be short.

Predicting Probabilities You can also use a Punnett square to predict probabilities. For example, Figure 8 shows a cross between a purebred black guinea pig and a purebred white guinea pig. The allele for black fur is dominant over the allele for white fur. Notice that only one allele combination is possible in the offspring—*Bb*. All of the offspring will inherit the dominant allele for black fur. Because of this, all of the offspring will have black fur. You can predict that there is a 100% probability that the offspring will have black fur.

☑ *Checkpoint* *If two guinea pigs with the alleles Bb are crossed, what is the probability that an offspring will have white fur?*

Coin Crosses

Here's how you can use coins to model Mendel's cross between two *Tt* pea plants.

1. Place a small piece of masking tape on each side of two coins.

2. Write a *T* (for tall) on one side of each coin and a *t* (for short) on the other.

3. Toss both coins together 20 times. Record the letter combinations that you obtain from each toss.

Interpreting Data How many of the offspring would be tall plants? (*Hint:* What different letter combinations would result in a tall plant?) How many would be short? Convert your results to percents. Then compare your results to Mendel's.

Demonstration

Materials *F₂ tobacco seeds that produce green (GG, Gg) and albino (gg) seedlings in a ratio of 3:1, seed starting soil, shallow pan, plastic wrap, water*

Advance Preparation Order the seeds from a science supply house in plenty of time. Plant the seeds 7 to 14 days in advance, or as directed on the seed packet.

Time 15 minutes

Explain that a cross between two hybrid green tobacco plants (*Gg* and *Gg*) produces both green and white offspring. Help students complete a Punnett square of this cross. Ask: **What percentage of seedlings will be green?** ($\frac{3}{4} \times 100\% = 75\%$) **What percentage will be white?** ($\frac{1}{4} \times 100\% = 25\%$) Then have students count the number of green and white seedlings from the F_2 seeds you planted. Have students compare the actual number of green and white seedlings to the amount predicted. **learning modality: logical/mathematical**

TRY THIS

Skills Focus interpreting data

Materials *2 coins, masking tape, scissors*

Time 15 minutes

Expected Outcome 5 *TT*, 10 *Tt*, 5 *tt*; All plants that are *TT* and *Tt* will be tall, approximately 15, or 75%. All *tt* plants will be short, approximately 5, or 25%. Some students might observe that their results are similar to Mendel's results, 75% tall and 25% short.

Extend Let students toss both coins another twenty times and observe whether or not their percentages are closer to Mendel's results. **learning modality: logical/mathematical**

Program Resources

◆ **Interdisciplinary Exploration Series** "The Power of Patterns," p. 42

Media and Technology

 Transparencies "Punnett Square— Pea Plants," Transparency 11

Answers to Self-Assessment

Caption Question

Figure 7 *TT* and *Tt*

Figure 8 0% white fur

☑ *Checkpoint*

25% probability of white fur

Ongoing Assessment

Drawing Have students draw a Punnett square for a cross between any two hybrids (*Aa* × *Aa*). They should include the probabilities of each offspring type.

C ◆ 91

Phenotypes and Genotypes

Including All Students

For students who need more help, explain that the terms *heterozygous* and *hybrid* are synonyms, as are *purebred* and *homozygous*. To help students remember the meanings of *genotype* and *phenotype*, explain that both *genotype* and *genetics* begin with the same prefix, *gen-*, and *physical* and *phenotype* both begin with *ph*. For *codominance*, tell students that the prefix *co-* means "jointly" or "together." **learning modality: verbal**

Building Inquiry Skills: Classifying

Have students make a chart in which they identify the genotypes and the phenotypes of the seven traits in garden peas that Mendel studied. Also have students include the genotypes and the phenotypes of any organisms from other teaching strategies that you might have used in the first two sections, such as the *Drosophila* body color, kernel color in corn, and the color of tobacco seedlings. In their charts, students should also identify the homozygous and the heterozygous genotypes. **learning modality: logical/mathematical**

Codominance

Addressing Naive Conceptions

Some students may have difficulty with the concept that alleles can be inherited in patterns other than in simple dominance, like Mendel studied in garden peas. One way to help students start thinking about different inheritance patterns is to challenge them to create patterns using two different colored pencils or markers. One pattern should represent the combinations of genotypes and phenotypes in simple dominance. The other pattern should represent the combination of genotypes and phenotypes in codominance. For ideas on creating these patterns, students can think about the expression of phenotypes in both kinds of inheritance, as well as the phenotypic and genotypic ratios. **learning modality: visual**

Phenotypes and Genotypes	
Phenotype	**Genotype**
Tall	*TT*
Tall	*Tt*
Short	*tt*

Figure 9 The phenotype of an organism is its physical appearance. Its genotype is its genetic makeup.

Phenotypes and Genotypes

Two useful terms that geneticists use to describe organisms are phenotype and genotype. An organism's **phenotype** (FEE noh typ) is its physical appearance, or its visible traits. For example, pea plants can have one of two different phenotypes for stem height—short or tall.

An organism's **genotype** (JEN uh typ) is its genetic makeup, or allele combinations. To understand the difference between phenotype and genotype, look at the table in Figure 9. Although all of the tall plants have the same phenotype (they are all tall), they can have two different genotypes—*TT* or *Tt*. If you were to look at the tall plants, you would not be able to tell the difference between those with the *TT* genotype and those with the *Tt* genotype. The short pea plants, on the other hand, would all have the same phenotype—short stems—as well as the same genotype—*tt*.

Geneticists use two additional terms to describe an organism's genotype. An organism that has two identical alleles for a trait is said to be **homozygous** (hoh moh ZY gus) for that trait. A tall pea plant that has the alleles *TT* and a short pea plant with the alleles *tt* are both homozygous. An organism that has two different alleles for a trait is said to be **heterozygous** (het ur oh ZY gus) for that trait. A tall pea plant with the alleles *Tt* is heterozygous. Mendel used the term *hybrid* to describe heterozygous pea plants.

☑ *Checkpoint* *If a pea plant's genotype is Tt, what is its phenotype?*

Codominance

For all of the traits that Mendel studied, one allele was dominant while the other was recessive. This is not always the case. For some alleles, an inheritance pattern called codominance exists. In **codominance,** the alleles are neither dominant nor recessive. As a result, neither allele is masked in the offspring.

Look at the Punnett square in Figure 11. Mendel's principle of dominant and recessive alleles does not explain why the heterozygous chickens have both black and white feathers. The alleles for feather color are

Figure 10 In Erminette chickens, the alleles for black feathers and white feathers are codominant.

Background

Facts and Figures Another pattern of inheritance is called incomplete dominance, in which neither allele is fully dominant. This is different from codominance in which both alleles are fully expressed, resulting in organisms that display the characteristics of both parents. Incomplete dominance results in organisms that have an intermediate phenotype. For example, in four o'clock flowers, a cross between a homozygous red-flowered plant and a homozygous white-flowered plant produces F_1 offspring with pink flowers. When the F_1 offspring are crossed, the F_2 offspring are in a ratio of 1 red : 2 pink : 1 white.

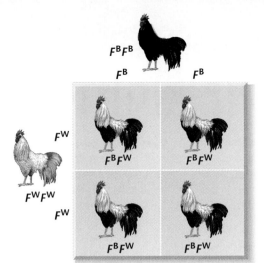

$F^B F^B$

F^B

F^B

F^W

$F^B F^W$

$F^B F^W$

$F^W F^W$

F^W

$F^B F^W$

$F^B F^W$

Figure 11 The offspring from the cross in this Punnett square will have both black and white feathers. *Classifying* Will the offspring be heterozygous or homozygous? Explain your answer.

codominant—neither dominant nor recessive. As you can see, neither allele is masked in the heterozygous chickens. Notice also that the codominant alleles are written as capital letters with superscripts—F^B for black feathers and F^W for white feathers. As the Punnett square shows, heterozygous chickens have the $F^B F^W$ allele combination.

Another example of codominance can be found in cattle. Red hair and white hair are codominant. Heterozygous cattle have coats with both white hairs and red hairs. From a distance, heterozygous cattle look pinkish brown, a color called roan.

Section 2 Review

1. What is meant by the term *probability*? How is probability related to genetics?
2. How are Punnett squares useful to geneticists?
3. What is the difference between a phenotype and a genotype? Give an example of each.
4. A white cow is crossed with a red bull. The calf is neither white nor red, but roan. Explain how this happens.
5. **Thinking Critically Problem Solving** In pea plants, the allele for round seeds (*R*) is dominant over the allele for wrinkled seeds (*r*). Construct a Punnett square that shows a cross between a heterozygous plant with round seeds (*Rr*) and a homozygous plant with wrinkled seeds (*rr*). What is the probability that an offspring will have wrinkled seeds?

Science at Home

Have a family member think of a number between 1 and 5. Then try to guess the number. Discuss the probability of guessing the correct number. Then repeat the guessing activity four more times. How did your success rate compare to the probability of guessing correctly? How can you account for any difference between your success rate and the results predicted by probability?

Program Resources

◆ **Teaching Resources** 3-2 Review and Reinforce, p. 77; 3-2 Enrich, p. 78

Media and Technology

 Interactive Student Tutorial CD-ROM C-3

Answers to Self-Assessment

☑ *Checkpoint*

It is tall.

Caption Question

Figure 11 Heterozygous; they have alleles for both white feathers and black feathers.

3 Assess

Section 2 Review Answers

1. Probability is the likelihood that a particular event will occur. It can be used to predict the results of genetic crosses.
2. Geneticists use Punnett squares to show all the possible genotypes of the offspring produced in a genetic cross and to help calculate the probability of each outcome.
3. Phenotype is the physical appearance, or visible traits of an organism. Example: tall stems. Genotype is the genetic makeup, or the combinations of alleles in an organism. Example: *Tt*.
4. The alleles for red hair and white hair are codominant. The calf is roan because it has both white and red hairs in its coat; it is heterozygous for coat color.
5.

	R	r
r	Rr	rr
r	Rr	rr

There is a 1 in 2 probability that an offspring will have wrinkled seeds (*rr*).

Science at Home

Tips Review how to calculate probabilities. Ask: **How would you calculate the probability of guessing a number between 1 and 5?** (*There is a 1 in 5 chance of guessing the right number, or $\frac{1}{5} \times 100\% = 20\%$*) Remind students of the coin tosses they made. Emphasize that the laws of probability predict what is *likely* to occur, not what *will* occur. Many students will find that their success rates are different from what the laws of probability predicted.

Performance Assessment

Skills Check Have students construct a Punnett square for a cross between two heterozygous Erminette chickens ($F^B F^W$) that shows all the possible genotypes and phenotypes of the offspring. Students should also calculate the probabilities of each genotype and phenotype. (*$F^B F^B$ 1 in 4; $F^B F^W$ 2 in 4; $F^W F^W$ 1 in 4*)

Make the Right Call!

Preparing for Inquiry

Key Concepts Punnett squares can predict the results of a genetic cross when the genotypes of both parents are known.

Skills Objectives Students will be able to
◆ model the combination of alleles in a genetic cross;
◆ predict the offspring of a genetic cross;
◆ analyze data from models of genetic crosses;
◆ compare actual data with predicted outcomes.

Time 40 minutes

Alternative Materials Marbles of other colors may be substituted, but use two easily distinguished colors. (Some students may be colorblind.) Other small colored objects that have the same shape and texture, such as buttons, can also be used.

Guiding Inquiry

Invitation Discuss circumstances in which students make predictions in their lives. Talk about the different evidence and ideas that lead to various predictions. Then ask: **Why is it helpful to scientists to make accurate predictions in their experiments?** *(Accurate predictions make scientists more confident that they are asking the right questions and correctly understanding the phenomena that they are studying; they also help scientists to better plan their experiments.)*

Introducing the Procedure

◆ Have students read the entire procedure. Then ask: **What do the marbles represent?** *(The alleles from each parent)* **Why should you not look inside the bag when you remove the marbles?** *(To make sure the allele combinations occur randomly)*
◆ Make sure students know the meanings of *homozygous* and *heterozygous*.

MAKE THE RIGHT CALL!

You know that making predictions is an important part of science. An accurate prediction can be a sign that you understand the event you are studying. In this lab, you will make predictions as you model the events involved in genetic crosses.

Problem

How can you predict the possible results of genetic crosses?

Materials

2 small paper bags
marking pen
3 blue marbles
3 white marbles

Procedure

1. Label one bag "Bag 1, Female Parent." Label the other bag "Bag 2, Male Parent." Then read over Part 1, Part 2, and Part 3 of this lab. Write a prediction about the kinds of offspring you expect from each cross.

Part 1 Crossing Two Homozygous Parents

2. Copy the data table and label it *Data Table Number 1*. Then place two blue marbles in Bag 1. This pair of marbles represents the female parent's alleles. Use the letter *B* to represent the dominant allele for blue color.

3. Place two white marbles in Bag 2. Use the letter *b* to represent the recessive allele for white color.

4. For Trial 1, remove one marble from Bag 1 without looking in the bag. Record the result in your data table. Return the marble to the bag. Again, without looking in the bag, remove one marble from Bag 2. Record the result in your data table. Return the marble to the bag.

5. In the column labeled *Offspring's Alleles*, write *BB* if you removed two blue marbles, *bb* if you removed two white marbles, or *Bb* if you removed one blue marble and one white marble.

6. Repeat Steps 4 and 5 nine more times.

DATA TABLE

Number _____

Trial	Allele From Bag 1 (Female Parent)	Allele From Bag 2 (Male Parent)	Offspring's Alleles
1			
2			
3			
4			
5			
6			

Troubleshooting the Experiment

◆ As students perform the different crosses, encourage them to discuss whether only one type of allele can be passed on by a parent or whether either of two alleles can be passed on.
◆ Monitor students to make sure they correctly identify the dominant and recessive alleles.

Expected Outcome

In the first cross ($BB \times bb$), students should observe that all offspring are *Bb*. In the second cross ($BB \times Bb$), all offspring are blue, but some are homozygous (*BB*) and some are heterozygous (*Bb*). In the third cross (*Bb* $\times$ *Bb*), some offspring are blue and some are white. All white offspring are homozygous (*bb*). Blue offspring are either homozygous (*BB*) or heterozygous (*Bb*).

Part 2 Crossing a Homozygous Parent With a Heterozygous Parent

7. Place two blue marbles in Bag 1. Place one white marble and one blue marble in Bag 2. Copy the data table again, and label it *Data Table Number 2*.

8. Repeat Steps 4 and 5 ten times.

Part 3 Crossing Two Heterozygous Parents

9. Place one blue marble and one white marble in Bag 1. Place one blue marble and one white marble in Bag 2. Copy the data table again and label it *Data Table Number 3*.

10. Repeat Steps 4 and 5 ten times.

Analyze and Conclude

1. Make a Punnett square for each of the crosses you modeled in Part 1, Part 2, and Part 3.

2. According to your results in Part 1, how many different kinds of offspring are possible when the homozygous parents (*BB* and *bb*) are crossed? Do the results you obtained using the marble model agree with the results shown by a Punnett square?

3. According to your results in Part 2, what percent of offspring are likely to be homozygous when a homozygous parent (*BB*) and a heterozygous parent (*Bb*) are crossed? What percent of offspring are likely to be heterozygous? Does the model agree with the results shown by a Punnett square?

4. According to your results in Part 3, what different kinds of offspring are possible when two heterozygous parents (*Bb* × *Bb*) are crossed? What percent of each type of offspring are likely to be produced? Does the model agree with the results of a Punnett square?

5. For Part 3, if you did 100 trials instead of 10 trials, would your results be closer to the results shown in a Punnett square? Explain.

6. **Think About It** How does the marble model compare with a Punnett square? How are the two methods alike? How are they different?

More to Explore

In peas, the allele for yellow seeds (*Y*) is dominant over the allele for green seeds (*y*). What possible crosses do you think could produce a heterozygous plant with yellow seeds (*Yy*)? Use the marble model and Punnett squares to test your predictions.

Punnett square for Part 3:

	B	b
B	BB	Bb
b	Bb	bb

2. Only heterozygous blue offspring (*Bb*) are possible. The Punnett square shows the same results.

3. Student results may produce slightly different answers. As the number of trials increases, the more closely it will show that 50 percent of the offspring are likely to be homozygous (*BB*), while 50 percent are likely to be heterozygous (*Bb*). The Punnett square shows that 50 percent will be homozygous and 50 percent will be heterozygous.

4. Student results may vary due to chance, but all should observe that three different kinds of offspring are possible: *BB*, *Bb*, and *bb*. From the Punnett square, students can predict that 25 percent are likely to be *BB*, 50 percent are likely to be *Bb*, and 25 percent are likely to be *bb*. The marble model will probably not totally agree with the Punnett square due to chance.

5. Probably, as the number of trials is increased, the results are more likely to match those predicted in a Punnett square because of chance.

6. The marble model and the Punnett square both show the genotypes of the parents and offspring and demonstrate how the parent can donate one of two possible alleles to the offspring. The Punnett square gives all the possible genotypes of the offspring and their probabilities of occurring. The model gives the genotypes of the offspring based on chance, much like the actual combining of alleles in a real genetic cross.

Extending the Inquiry

More to Explore Crosses that will produce a heterozygous plant (*Yy*) include *YY* × *yy*, *YY* × *Yy*, *Yy* × *Yy*, and *Yy* × *yy*.

Analyze and Conclude

1. Punnett square for Part 1:

	b	b
B	Bb	Bb
B	Bb	Bb

Punnett square for Part 2:

	B	b
B	BB	Bb
B	BB	Bb

Program Resources

◆ **Teaching Resources** Chapter 3 Skills Lab, pp. 89–91

Objectives

After completing the lesson, students will be able to
◆ describe the role of chromosomes in inheritance;
◆ identify and describe the events that occur during meiosis.

Key Term meiosis

1 Engage/Explore

Activating Prior Knowledge

Have students recall what they know about cells and cell structure. Based on their knowledge of cell structure, challenge them to predict the location of Mendel's hereditary factors, or genes, within the cell. You might wish to record students' predictions on the board and have the class evaluate them as you study the section.

········ DISCOVER ········

Skills Focus inferring
Materials *4 craft sticks, 3 pieces of paper, marking pen*
Time 10 minutes
Expected Outcome Students should realize that parents contribute only one of their two chromosomes to the offspring. The idea is to get students thinking about genes being carried on chromosomes and the cell has some kind of process to make sure only one allele of a gene is contributed to offspring.
Think It Over Students might infer that genes are located on chromosomes and chromosomes must divide and separate in a certain way so that the offspring get only one chromosome, or one allele, from each parent.

DISCOVER ········ ACTIVITY

Which Chromosome Is Which?

Mendel did not know that chromosomes play a role in genetics. Today we know that genes are located on chromosomes.

1. Label two craft sticks with the letter *A*. The craft sticks represent a pair of chromosomes in the female parent. Turn the sticks face down on a piece of paper.

2. Label two more craft sticks with the letter *a*. These represent a pair of chromosomes in the male parent. Turn the sticks face down on another piece of paper.

3. Turn over one craft stick "chromosome" from each piece of paper. Move both sticks to a third piece of paper. These represent a pair of chromosomes in the offspring. Note the allele combination that the offspring received.

Think It Over

Inferring Use this model to explain how chromosomes are involved in the inheritance of alleles.

GUIDE FOR READING

◆ What role do chromosomes play in inheritance?

◆ What events occur during meiosis?

Reading Tip Before you read, preview *Exploring Meiosis* on page 99. Predict what role chromosomes play in the inheritance of traits.

Sperm cells ▼

When Mendel's results were rediscovered in 1900, scientists around the world became excited about Mendel's principles of inheritance. They were eager to identify the structures inside of cells that carried Mendel's hereditary factors, or genes.

In 1903, Walter Sutton, an American geneticist, added an important piece of information to scientists' understanding of genetics. Sutton was studying the cells of grasshoppers. He was trying to understand how sex cells—sperm and egg—form. During his studies, Sutton examined sex cells in many different stages of formation. He became particularly interested in the movement of chromosomes during the formation of sex cells. Sutton hypothesized that chromosomes were the key to understanding how offspring come to have traits similar to those of their parents.

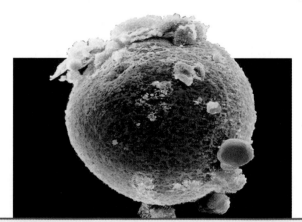

◄ **Egg cell**

96 ◆ C

READING STRATEGIES

Reading Tip Instruct students to record their predictions on a piece of paper and place that piece of paper in their books at the end of this section. When students have finished reading the section, have them review their predictions and revise them, if necessary. Explain that scientists make many predictions while setting up experiments and often revise them after completing the experiments.

Vocabulary While studying the process of meiosis, explain to students that the term *meiosis* is a Greek word that means "to diminish or make less." Discuss with students what objects are diminishing during the process of meiosis. *(the number of chromosomes)*

Figure 12 Grasshoppers have 24 chromosomes in each of their body cells. *Applying Concepts How many chromosomes did Sutton observe in the sperm cells and egg cells of grasshoppers?*

Chromosomes and Inheritance

Sutton knew that structures inside cells must be responsible for the inheritance of genes. He needed evidence to support his hypothesis that chromosomes were those structures. Sutton compared the number of chromosomes in a grasshopper's sex cells with the number of chromosomes in the other cells in the grasshopper's body. As you can see in Figure 12, the body cells of grasshoppers have 24 chromosomes. To his surprise, Sutton found that the grasshopper's sex cells have only 12 chromosomes. In other words, a grasshopper's sex cells have exactly half the number of chromosomes found in its body cells.

Sutton knew that he had discovered something important. He observed what happened when a sperm cell (with 12 chromosomes) and an egg cell (with 12 chromosomes) joined. The fertilized egg that formed had 24 chromosomes—the original number. As a result, the grasshopper offspring had exactly the same number of chromosomes in its cells as did each of its parents. The 24 chromosomes existed in 12 pairs. One chromosome in each pair came from the male parent, while the other chromosome came from the female parent.

Sutton concluded that the chromosomes carried Mendel's hereditary factors, or genes, from one generation to the next. In other words, genes are located on chromosomes. Sutton's idea came to be known as the chromosome theory of inheritance. **According to the chromosome theory of inheritance, genes are carried from parents to their offspring on chromosomes.**

☑ *Checkpoint* *How does the number of chromosomes in a grasshopper's sex cells compare to the number in its body cells?*

---

2 Facilitate

Chromosomes and Inheritance

Addressing Naive Conceptions

Students might have difficulty visualizing exactly where genes are located on chromosomes and how chromosomes fit inside cells. Review cell structure and encourage students to draw diagrams of the cell in which they show the chromosomes inside the cell nucleus. Until students learn the composition of chromosomes (in Section 4), it will be difficult for them to visualize what kind of structure a gene actually has. Explain that chromosomes are made up of many, many genes lined up one after the other. Genes are not separate structures "stuck to" chromosomes; rather chromosomes are long chains of genes. **learning modality: visual**

Inquiry Challenge

Challenge small groups of students to conclude **ACTIVITY** what might happen if sex cells did not have half the number of chromosomes as body cells. Groups should develop a model that illustrates their conclusions. Provide various art materials for students to use, or encourage them to bring materials from home. Have groups present their models to the class and explain why sex cells must have half the chromosomes as body cells. **learning modality: logical/mathematical**

Program Resources

◆ **Teaching Resources** 3-3 Lesson Plan, p. 79; 3-3 Section Summary, p. 80
Science Explorer Series *Human Biology and Health*, Chapter 8, gives more information about sex cells.

Media and Technology

🎧 **Audiotapes** English-Spanish Summary 3-3

Answers to Self-Assessment

Caption Question
Figure 12 12 chromosomes in each

☑ *Checkpoint*
The sex cells have exactly half the number of chromosomes as the body cells.

Ongoing Assessment

Drawing Have students draw a diagram of a grasshopper body cell and sex cell and show the number of chromosomes in each of these cells.

EXPLORING

Meiosis

Walk students through each stage in meiosis. Point out that before meiosis occurs, every chromosome is copied, so the cell actually has four copies of each chromosome. Emphasize that during Meiosis I, the chromosome pairs separate. The centromeres are still holding together the chromosome copies. When discussing Meiosis II, point out that this division is similar to the division that occurs during mitosis—the centromeres split and the chromosome copies separate. Ask: **How many sex cells are produced at the end of the meiosis?** *(four)* **How do the sex cells differ from the parent cell?** *(The sex cells have half the number of chromosomes of the parent cell.)* **learning modality: visual**

Building Inquiry Skills: Making Models

Materials *8 pipe cleaners—4 of one color and 4 of another, 4 beads*

Time 15 minutes

Challenge students to model the steps in meiosis using the pipe cleaners to represent two chromosomes in a cell. Students should use pipe cleaners of the same color to represent chromosome pairs, with different chromosome pairs having different colors. Monitor students to make sure they double each chromosome before meiosis begins. (They should add another pipe cleaner of the same color to each pipe cleaner chromosome.) Students can use beads to hold the chromosome copies together, or they can simply twist the pipe cleaners together at one point. Make sure students separate the chromosome pairs during Meiosis I and the chromosome copies during Meiosis II. **learning modality: kinesthetic**

Meiosis

How do sex cells end up with half the number of chromosomes as body cells? To answer this question, you need to understand the events that occur during meiosis. **Meiosis** (my OH sis) is the process by which the number of chromosomes is reduced by half to form sex cells—sperm and eggs.

You can trace the events of meiosis in *Exploring Meiosis.* In this example, each parent cell has four chromosomes arranged in two pairs. During meiosis, the chromosome pairs separate and are distributed to two different cells. The resulting sex cells have only half as many chromosomes as the other cells in the organism. In *Exploring Meiosis,* notice that the sex cells end up with only two chromosomes each—half the number found in the parent cell. Only one chromosome from each chromosome pair ends up in each sex cell.

When sex cells combine to produce offspring, each sex cell will contribute half the normal number of chromosomes. Thus, the offspring gets the normal number of chromosomes—half from each parent.

☑ *Checkpoint* What types of cells form by meiosis?

Meiosis and Punnett Squares

The Punnett squares that you learned about earlier in this chapter are actually a shorthand way to show the events that occur at meiosis. When the chromosome pairs separate into two different sex cells, so do the alleles carried on each chromosome. One allele from each pair goes to each sex cell. In Figure 13, you can see how the Punnett square accounts for the separation of alleles during meiosis.

As shown across the top of the Punnett square, half of the sperm cells from the male parent will receive the chromosome with the *T* allele. The other half of the sperm cells will receive the chromosome with the *t* allele. In this example, the same is true for the egg cells from the female parent, as shown down the left side of the Punnett square. Depending on which sperm cell combines with which egg cell, one of the allele combinations shown in the boxes will result.

Figure 13 This Punnett square shows how alleles separate when sex cells form during meiosis. It also shows the possible allele combinations that can result after fertilization occurs. *Interpreting Charts What is the probability that a sperm cell will contain a* T *allele?*

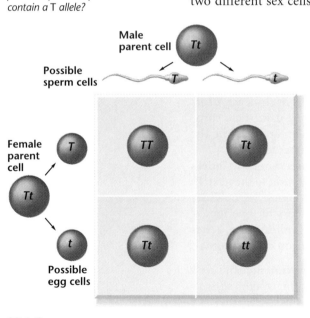

Male parent cell Tt

Possible sperm cells T   t

Female parent cell Tt

Possible egg cells T   t

| TT | Tt |
| Tt | tt |

Background

Facts and Figures Before the first division of meiosis occurs, an important event, called crossing over, occurs. In crossing over, corresponding segments of chromosome pairs exchange parts. In effect, the organism's maternal and paternal chromosomes exchange some alleles, producing some chromosomes that are genetically different from either parent of the organism. This increases the genetic diversity of a species.

Crossing over occurs randomly, but the farther apart genes are located on their chromosomes, the more often crossing over will occur between them. Geneticists use this principle to map the location of genes on chromosomes.

EXPLORING Meiosis

During meiosis, a cell undergoes two divisions to produce sex cells that have half the number of chromosomes.

1 Beginning of Meiosis
Before meiosis begins, every chromosome in the cell is copied. As in mitosis, centromeres hold the double-stranded chromosomes together.

2 Meiosis I
The chromosome pairs line up next to each other in the center of the cell. The pairs then separate from each other and move to opposite ends of the cell. Two cells form, each with half the number of chromosomes. Each chromosome is still double-stranded.

3 Meiosis II
The double-stranded chromosomes move to the center of the cell. The centromeres split and the two strands of each chromosome separate. The two strands move to opposite ends of the cell.

4 End of Meiosis
Four sex cells have been produced. Each cell has only half the number of chromosomes that the parent cell had at the beginning of meiosis. Each cell has only one chromosome from each original pair.

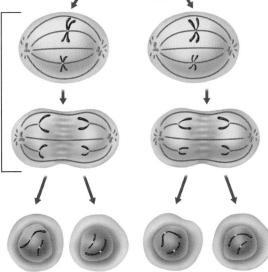

Media and Technology

 Transparency "Exploring Meiosis," Transparency 12

 Exploring Life Science Videodisc
Unit 5, Side 1, "The Chromosome Theory"
Chapter 3

Answers to Self-Assessment

☑ *Checkpoint*
Sex cells form by meiosis.

Caption Question
Figure 13 $\frac{1}{2} \times 100\% = 50\%$

Building Inquiry Skills: Observing

Materials *a set of prepared slides showing the stages of meiosis in animal cells, microscopes*

ACTIVITY

Set up microscope stations at which you place the prepared slides. Depending on the number of microscopes you have and the ability of your students to use microscopes, you could place a whole set of slides at each microscope and allow students to change the slides themselves, or you could place the microscopes in a row with individual slides from a set positioned and focused for students to simply look at. As students examine the slides, encourage them to compare the *Exploring Meiosis* diagram to what they see. Have students draw their observations, labeling the chromosomes. Emphasize that meiosis is a dynamic process. Each slide represents a snapshot in a continuous event, much like a photograph captures an instant of time in a parade or a soccer game.
learning modality: visual

Meiosis and Punnett Squares

Using the Visuals: Figure 13

Point out that like other Punnett squares they have studied, the one in Figure 13 also shows all possible allele combinations for the offspring. Make it clear that the cells inside the boxes of the Punnett square represent the body cells of the offspring. This Punnett square goes one step further in showing the genotypes of the parents' body cells. Ask: **What are the possible sex cells produced by each offspring?** *(TT would only produce sex cells with T; Tt would produce both T and t sex cells; and tt would produce only sex cells with t.)* **learning modality: visual**

Ongoing Assessment

Writing Have students write an outline of meiosis in which each major step is a main heading in the outline.
Portfolio Students can save their outlines in their portfolios.

C ◆ 99

Chromosomes

Including All Students

Give students who need more help craft sticks to make a model of a chromosome pair based on the diagram in Figure 14. Each chromosome model should have at least six different genes, either homozygous or heterozygous. **learning modality: kinesthetic**

ACTIVITY

3 Assess

Section 3 Review Answers

1. Chromosomes carry the information for the inheritance of traits.
2. Chromosome pairs separate to form sex cells with half the number of chromosomes in each.
3. Genes are located on chromosomes.
4. It shows how the alleles separate when sex cells form during meiosis.
5. 22 chromosomes

Check Your Progress

CHAPTER PROJECT 3

Students can choose mates for their pets based on phenotypes or by you randomly choosing names out of a hat for males and one for females. Suggest that students first toss the coin to determine the color of each offspring and cut out each offspring from paper of the appropriate color. Then students can determine the genotypes of the other traits and write the genotypes directly on the backs of each offspring.

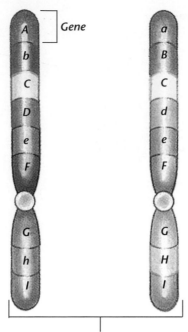

Gene

A chromosome pair

Figure 14 Genes are located on chromosomes. The chromosomes in a pair may have different alleles for some genes and the same alleles for others. *Classifying For which genes is this organism homozygous? For which genes is it heterozygous?*

Chromosomes

Since Sutton's time, scientists have studied the chromosomes of many different organisms. The body cells of humans, for example, contain 23 pairs, or 46 chromosomes. The body cells of dogs have 78 chromosomes, while the body cells of silkworms have 56 chromosomes. As you can see, larger organisms don't always have more chromosomes.

Chromosomes are made up of many genes joined together like beads on a string. Sutton reasoned that chromosomes must contain a large number of genes because organisms have so many traits. Although you have only 23 pairs of chromosomes, your body cells contain more than 60,000 genes. Each of the genes controls a particular trait.

Look at the pair of chromosomes in Figure 14. One chromosome in the pair came from the female parent. The other chromosome came from the male parent. Notice that each chromosome in the pair has the same genes. The genes are lined up in the same order from one end of the chromosome to the other. However, the alleles for some of the genes might be different. For example, the organism has the *A* allele on one chromosome and the *a* allele on the other. As you can see, this organism is heterozygous for some traits and homozygous for others.

Section 3 Review

1. Explain the role that chromosomes play in inheritance.
2. Briefly describe what happens to chromosomes during meiosis.
3. On what structures in a cell are genes located?
4. How is a Punnett square a model for what happens during meiosis?
5. **Thinking Critically Inferring** The body cells of hamsters have 44 chromosomes. How many chromosomes would the sex cells of a hamster have?

100 ◆ C

Check Your Progress

CHAPTER PROJECT 3

At this point, you should find a classmate with a paper pet of the opposite sex. Suppose the two pets were crossed and produced six offspring. For each trait, use coin tosses to determine which allele the offspring will inherit from each parent. Construct a paper pet for each offspring, showing the traits that each one has inherited. Write the genotype for each trait on their backs.

Performance Assessment

Drawing Have students make a Punnett square for a cross between two heterozygous black guinea pigs, *Bb* × *Bb*. Before they make the Punnett square, students should make a diagram similar to Figure 13, showing how the four sex cells formed for each parent.

Answers to Self-Assessment

Caption Question

Figure 14 The organism is homozygous for genes C, E, F, G, and I. The organism is heterozygous for genes A, B, D, and H.

Program Resources

◆ **Integrated Science Laboratory Manual** C-3, "Chromosomes and Inheritance"
◆ **Teaching Resources** 3-3 Review and Reinforce, p. 81; 3-3 Enrich, p. 82

SECTION 4 The DNA Connection

DISCOVER ••••••••••••••••••••••••• ACTIVITY

Can You Crack the Code?

A •–	N –•
B –•••	O –––
C –•–•	P •––•
D –••	Q ––•–
E •	R •–•
F ••–•	S •••
G ––•	T –
H ••••	U ••–
I ••	V •••–
J •–––	W •––
K –•–	X –••–
L •–••	Y –•––
M ––	Z ––••

1. Use the Morse code in the chart to decode the question in the message below. The letters are separated by slash marks.

•––/••••/•/•–•/•/–•–•/•/––•/•/–•/
•/•••/•–••/–––/–•–•/•/–/•/–••/

2. Write your answer to the question in Morse code.

3. Exchange your coded answer with a partner. Then decode your partner's answer.

Think It Over

Forming Operational Definitions Based on your results from this activity, write a definition of the word *code*. Then compare your definition to one in a dictionary.

A white buffalo calf was born on Childs Place Farm near Hanover, Michigan, in 1998. White buffaloes are extremely rare, occurring only once in every 10 million births. Why was this calf born with such an uncommon phenotype? To answer this question, you need to know how the genes on a chromosome control an organism's traits.

The Genetic Code

Today scientists know that the main function of genes is to control the production of proteins in the organism's cells. Proteins help to determine the size, shape, and many other traits of an organism.

Figure 15 The white color of this buffalo calf is very unusual. Both of the calf's parents had brown coats.

GUIDE FOR READING

◆ What is meant by the term "genetic code"?

◆ How does a cell produce proteins?

◆ How do mutations affect an organism?

Reading Tip As you read, create a flowchart that shows how a cell produces proteins.

Chapter 3 **C ◆ 101**

Program Resources

◆ **Teaching Resources** 3-4 Lesson Plan, p. 83; 3-4 Section Summary, p. 84

Media and Technology

 Audiotapes English-Spanish Summary 3-4

READING STRATEGIES

Reading Tip Student flowcharts should begin with genes on a chromosome in the nucleus of a cell. Next they should include the production of messenger RNA and its entrance into the cytoplasm to attach to a ribosome. Then transfer RNA brings the amino acid to the growing protein chain. Encourage students to illustrate their flowcharts, define terms, and explain processes that are new to them.

SECTION 4 The DNA Connection

Objectives

After completing the lesson, students will be able to

◆ explain the term "genetic code";

◆ describe the process by which a cell produces proteins;

◆ describe different types of mutations and how they affect an organism.

Key Terms messenger RNA, transfer RNA

1 Engage/Explore

Activating Prior Knowledge

Invite students to recall what they have learned about inheritance, DNA, and cell division up to this point. Then ask: **How do genes determine the traits of an organism?** (*Accept all answers without comment.*) Explain that students will learn more about this process in the section.

••••••••• DISCOVER •••••••••

Skills Focus forming operational definitions
Time 15 minutes
Expected Outcome The coded question is "Where are genes located?" The answer, "on chromosomes," is encoded below.

–––/–•/ / –••/•••/•••• / •–• / •––• / ––• / –•– / ––/
–––/ •••/ ––– / –– / •/•••/

Think It Over Students might define *code* as set of symbols with specific meanings used to send messages. Some dictionaries define *code* as a system of symbols, letters, or words given arbitrary meanings, used for transmitting messages requiring secrecy or brevity.

C ◆ 101

2 Facilitate

The Genetic Code

Using the Visuals: Figure 16

Have students trace the relationship between DNA and chromosomes in Figure 16. Explain that a gene is a segment of DNA with a specific sequence of nitrogen bases that codes for a certain protein. Remind students of DNA base pairing from Chapter 2. Ask: **Which nitrogen base always pairs with thymine?** *(adenine)* **Which always pairs with cytosine?** *(guanine)* Then start students thinking about protein synthesis by pointing out that although DNA is located in the cell nucleus, proteins are made in the cytoplasm.
learning modality: visual

Including All Students

To help students bring together everything they have studied so far, explain that the traits Mendel observed, such as tall plants and short plants, are the results of the action of proteins in an organism. Challenge students to draw a diagram or a concept map that shows the relationships among DNA, genes, proteins, genotypes, and phenotypes.
learning modality: visual

How Cells Make Proteins

Building Inquiry Skills: Inferring

Discuss the role of messenger RNA. Then ask: **Why do you think the cell sends a coded message for a gene into the cytoplasm instead of sending the gene itself?** *(Some students might infer that by using a coded message for a gene, the cell protects its DNA from possible damage, ensuring that it will always produce the proper proteins throughout its life.)*
learning modality: logical/ mathematical

Recall from Chapter 2 that chromosomes are composed mostly of DNA. In Figure 16, you can see the relationship between chromosomes and DNA. Notice that a DNA molecule is made up of four different nitrogen bases—adenine (A), thymine (T), guanine (G), and cytosine (C). These bases form the rungs of the DNA "ladder." A single gene on a chromosome may contain anywhere from several hundred to a million or more of these bases. The bases are arranged in a specific order—for example, ATGACGTAC.

The order of the nitrogen bases along a gene forms a genetic code that specifies what type of protein will be produced. In the genetic code, a group of three bases codes for the production of a specific amino acid. Amino acids are the building blocks of proteins. The order of the bases determines the order in which amino acids are put together to form a protein. You can think of the bases as three-letter code words. The code words tell the cell which amino acid to add to the growing protein chain.

☑ *Checkpoint* *What is the main function of genes?*

How Cells Make Proteins

The production of proteins is called protein synthesis. **During protein synthesis, the cell uses information from a gene on a chromosome to produce a specific protein.** Protein synthesis takes place on the ribosomes in the cytoplasm of the cell. As you know, the cytoplasm is outside the nucleus. The chromosomes, however, are found inside the nucleus. How, then, does the information needed to produce proteins get out of the nucleus and into the cytoplasm?

Figure 16 A chromosome contains thousands of genes along its length. The sequence of bases along a gene forms a code that tells the cell what protein to produce. *Interpreting Diagrams* *Where in the cell are the chromosomes located?*

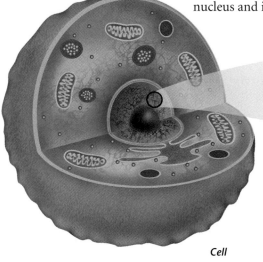

Cell

Chromosome

Facts and Figures *Transcription* is the process by which RNA is produced using a single-stranded DNA template. Messenger RNA, transfer RNA, and ribosomal RNA are all transcribed in the nuclei of eukaryotic cells and then pass into the cytoplasms. Ribosomal RNA and proteins make up the structures of ribosomes, the organelles where proteins are made.

Translation is the production of protein in the ribosomes. Often, several ribosomes are attached to the same messenger RNA molecule. The ribosome holds both the messenger RNA with its genetic information and the transfer RNAs with their attached amino acids in position to allow a specific protein chain to form.

The Role of RNA Before protein synthesis can take place, a "messenger" must first carry the genetic code from the DNA inside the nucleus into the cytoplasm. This genetic messenger is called ribonucleic acid, or RNA.

Although RNA is similar to DNA, the two molecules differ in some important ways. Unlike DNA, which looks like a twisted ladder, an RNA molecule looks like only one side, or strand, of the ladder. RNA also contains a different sugar molecule from the sugar found in DNA. Another difference between DNA and RNA is in their nitrogen bases. Like DNA, RNA contains adenine, guanine, and cytosine. However, instead of thymine, RNA contains uracil (YOOR uh sil).

There are several types of RNA involved in protein synthesis. **Messenger RNA** copies the coded message from the DNA in the nucleus, and carries the message into the cytoplasm. Another type of RNA, called **transfer RNA**, carries amino acids and adds them to the growing protein.

Translating the Code The process of protein synthesis is shown in *Exploring Protein Synthesis* on the next page. The first step is for a DNA molecule to "unzip" between its base pairs. Then one of the strands of DNA directs the production of a strand of messenger RNA. To form the RNA strand, RNA bases pair up with the DNA bases. Instead of thymine, however, uracil pairs with adenine. The messenger RNA then leaves the nucleus and attaches to a ribosome in the cytoplasm. There, molecules of transfer RNA pick up the amino acids specified by each three-letter code word. Each transfer RNA molecule puts the amino acid it is carrying in the correct order along the growing protein chain.

☑ *Checkpoint* *What is the function of transfer RNA?*

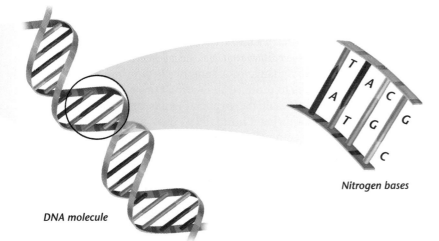

DNA molecule

Nitrogen bases

Sharpen your Skills

Predicting ACTIVITY

The following is a sequence of nitrogen bases on a DNA molecule.

Write out the sequence of RNA bases that would pair up with the DNA bases.

Sharpen your Skills

Predicting

Time 10 minutes ACTIVITY

Expected Outcome The sequence of RNA bases is U A C A G U C G.

Extend Ask students: **What is the DNA sequence that pairs to this DNA sequence?** *(T A C A G T C G. Uracil is present in RNA in place of thymine.)* **What RNA bases would pair up with the strand of DNA you just identified?** *(A U G U C A G C)* Point out that this is different from the RNA sequence they first identified. Explain that these two RNA sequences would code for different proteins. The cell uses only one of the two DNA strands to make a protein.
learning modality: logical/ mathematical

Inquiry Challenge

Materials *building blocks* ACTIVITY
Time 20 minutes

Construct a structure from building blocks in a place where students cannot see it. Then challenge student groups to build the same structure as yours with these stipulations: Only two people from each group may look at the structure, and they may look at it only once; no verbal communication is allowed between the group members who observe the structure and the rest of the group; only group members who did not see the structure may build it; all building blocks must be gathered from a central point. Suggest to students that they may use a code to communicate instructions on how to build the structure. When each group has completed its structure, bring your structure into view and allow students to make comparisons. Discuss the characteristics of a good "code" and what groups might have done to improve theirs. Then relate the activity to protein synthesis. Talk about the importance of the cell building perfect proteins.
cooperative learning

Ongoing Assessment

Writing Have students describe the role of RNA in making proteins.

Program Resources

 Science Explorer Series *Cells and Heredity,* Chapter 2 gives more information about DNA and nitrogen bases.

Media and Technology

Exploring Life Science Videodisc
Unit 5, Side 1, "DNA: The Double Helix"

Chapter 5

Answers to Self-Assessment

Caption Question

Figure 16 in the nucleus

☑ *Checkpoint*
(p. 102) To control the production of proteins
(p. 103) To carry amino acids and add them to the growing protein chain

EXPLORING

Protein Synthesis

Review each step in the process of protein synthesis using the Exploring. Emphasize in Step 1 that DNA always stays inside the cell nucleus. In Step 2, explain that the ribosome has special sites that hold messenger RNA as the ribosome moves along it. The ribosome also has special sites that hold transfer RNA so its amino acid can easily join the growing protein chain. In Step 3, explain that transfer RNA is made in the same way as messenger RNA, but has a region to which amino acids bond. In Step 4, explain that more than one ribosome can attach to a single messenger RNA at one time. **learning modality: visual**

Including All Students

Some students may have difficulty with the terms related to protein synthesis. Help students identify these words and have them add the words to the glossary of genetics terms that they began in Section 1. **learning modality: verbal**

EXPLORING Protein Synthesis

To make proteins, messenger RNA copies information from DNA in the nucleus. Transfer RNA then uses this information to produce proteins in the ribosomes.

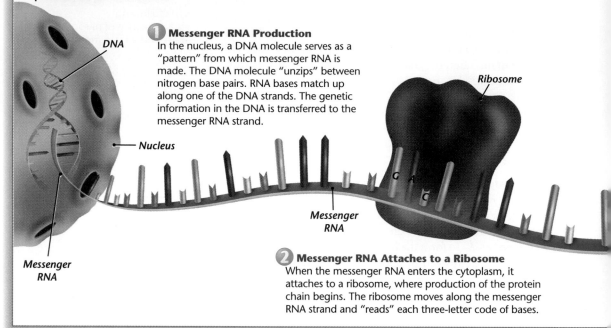

1 Messenger RNA Production
In the nucleus, a DNA molecule serves as a "pattern" from which messenger RNA is made. The DNA molecule "unzips" between nitrogen base pairs. RNA bases match up along one of the DNA strands. The genetic information in the DNA is transferred to the messenger RNA strand.

DNA

Ribosome

Nucleus

Messenger RNA

Messenger RNA

2 Messenger RNA Attaches to a Ribosome
When the messenger RNA enters the cytoplasm, it attaches to a ribosome, where production of the protein chain begins. The ribosome moves along the messenger RNA strand and "reads" each three-letter code of bases.

Mutations

Suppose that a mistake occurred in one gene of a chromosome. Instead of the base A, for example, the DNA molecule might have the base G. Such a mistake is one type of mutation that can occur in a cell's hereditary material. Recall from Chapter 2 that a mutation is any change in a gene or chromosome. Mutations can cause a cell to produce an incorrect protein during protein synthesis. As a result, the organism's traits, or phenotype, will be different from what it normally would have been. In fact, the term *mutation* comes from a Latin word that means "change."

Types of Mutations Some mutations are the result of small changes in an organism's hereditary material, such as the substitution of a single base for another. This type of mutation can occur during the DNA replication process. The white coat on the

Background

Facts and Figures Different types of changes in the base sequence of DNA affect the organism in different ways. If a base is inserted or deleted from a gene, the reading frame for three-letter base code, or codon, is shifted. The result of a frame-shift mutation is a nonfunctional protein.

A point mutation occurs when one base is substituted for another. This kind of mutation affects only one codon, which has variable affects on the protein product. Sometimes it has no effect because most amino acids are encoded by more than one codon. Sometimes the protein will have a reduced function because one amino acid is substituted for the correct one. Other times, the protein will not work at all, either because the codon has been changed to a stop codon or the amino acid that is substituted completely changes the nature of the protein.

3 Transfer RNA Attaches to Messenger RNA

Transfer RNA molecules carry specific amino acids to the ribosome. There they match up with three-letter codes of bases on the messenger RNA. The protein chain grows as each amino acid is attached in the correct sequence.

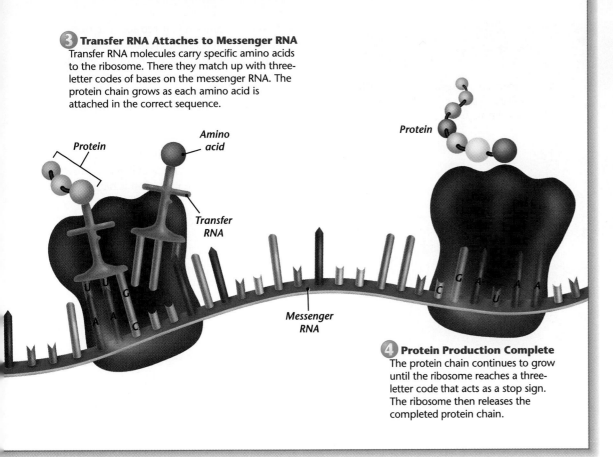

Protein

Amino acid

Transfer RNA

Messenger RNA

Protein

4 Protein Production Complete

The protein chain continues to grow until the ribosome reaches a three-letter code that acts as a stop sign. The ribosome then releases the completed protein chain.

buffalo calf you read about at the start of this section might have resulted from this type of mutation. Other mutations may occur when chromosomes don't separate correctly during meiosis. When this type of mutation occurs, a cell can end up with too many or too few chromosomes. The cell could also end up with extra segments of chromosomes.

If a mutation occurs in a body cell, such as a skin cell, the mutation will affect only the cell that carries it. If, however, a mutation occurs in a sex cell, the mutation can be passed on to an offspring and affect the offspring's phenotype.

The Effects of Mutations Because mutations can introduce changes in an organism, they can be a source of genetic variety. **Some of the changes brought about by mutations are harmful to an organism. Other mutations, however, are helpful, and still others are neither harmful nor helpful.** A mutation is

Mutations

Building Inquiry Skills: Making Models

Materials *beads of different colors, pipe cleaners*

Time 15 minutes

Challenge students to use the materials to model the two types of mutations described in the text: a point mutation, in which a single base is substituted for another, and a chromosomal mutation, in which chromosomes do not separate correctly during meiosis. The beads should represent nitrogen bases, and the pipe cleaners should be the chromosomes. Check students' models to make sure they are accurate. Remind students that organisms have two copies of each chromosome. You might also challenge students to model why mutations in body cells do not affect offspring. **learning modality: kinesthetic**

Addressing Naive Conceptions

Some students might think that mutations can only harm an organism. To help dispel this misconception, explain that mutations can also provide organisms a means to better adapt to their environment. Then display pictures of a monarch and a viceroy butterfly. Tell students that birds learn to avoid monarchs because of their bitter taste. Birds like the taste of viceroy butterflies, and many years ago, viceroys looked different from monarchs. However over time, various mutations in the appearance of viceroy butterflies have made them look similar to monarchs. Ask: **How have these mutations helped viceroys?** *(Birds also avoid viceroys because they associate their appearance with a bitter taste.)* **learning modality: visual**

Ongoing Assessment

Oral Presentation Call on students at random to explain what a mutation is and how mutations affect organisms.

Mutations, continued

Integrating Health

Ask students: **What is cancer?** (*A disease in which mutated body cells grow out of control*) Explain that the mutation that causes a particular cancer may occur either in a gene that causes cancer cells to grow or in a gene that prevents cancer cells from growing. Emphasize that one of the best ways to stop cancer is by prevention. Eating a healthful diet that is low in fat, high in fiber, and includes plenty of fruits and vegetables is one way to reduce the risk of cancer. Other ways include regular physical exams and cancer screenings and avoiding smoking, sunbathing, and alcohol. **learning modality: verbal**

3 Assess

Section 4 Answers

1. The order of the nitrogen bases forms a genetic code that specifies what type of protein will be produced. Groups of three bases code for specific amino acids, the building blocks of proteins.

2. First, messenger RNA is produced using a strand of DNA as a pattern. Messenger RNA moves into the cytoplasm where it attaches to a ribosome. The ribosome helps match the three-letter code of bases in the messenger RNA to the transfer RNA that carries the specified amino acid. The protein chain continues to grow until the ribosome comes to a stop signal, and then the completed protein chain is released.

3. Some mutations can be helpful to the organism, some are harmful, and others are neither helpful nor harmful.

4. in the cytoplasm

5. Only sex cells can pass on their chromosomes to the offspring. Body cells are not passed to offspring, they remain a part of the parent.

Figure 17 Mutations can affect an organism's traits, or phenotype. The unusually large strawberries on the left are the result of a mutation. The cells of these strawberries have extra sets of chromosomes.

harmful to an organism if it reduces the organism's chance for survival and reproduction.

Whether a mutation is harmful or not depends partly on the organism's environment. The mutation that led to the production of a white buffalo calf would probably be harmful to an organism in the wild. Its white color would make it more visible, and thus easier for predators to find. However, a white buffalo calf raised on a farm has the same chance for survival as a brown buffalo. On the farm, the mutation is neutral—it neither helps nor harms the buffalo.

 INTEGRATING HEALTH Some diseases in humans are caused by harmful mutations. For example, some forms of cancer are caused by mutations in an organism's body cells. Overexposure to the ultraviolet radiation in sunlight, for example, may lead to mutations that could cause skin cancer. In Chapter 4, you will learn more about other diseases that result from harmful mutations.

Helpful mutations, on the other hand, improve an organism's chances for survival and reproduction. For example, a gene mutation in potatoes led to the production of a new variety of potato called the Katahdin potato. This potato is resistant to some diseases that attack other varieties of potatoes. As a bonus for humans, it also looks and tastes better than other types of potatoes.

Section 4 Review

1. How do the nitrogen bases along a gene serve as a genetic code?
2. Briefly describe the process by which a cell produces proteins.
3. What possible effects can a mutation have on an organism?
4. Where in a cell does protein synthesis take place?
5. **Thinking Critically Relating Cause and Effect** Why are mutations that occur in an organism's body cells not passed on to its offspring?

106 ◆ C

 Check Your Progress

CHAPTER PROJECT 3

With your partner, plan a display of your pet's family. Label the parents the P generation. Label the offspring the F₁ generation. Construct a Punnett square for each trait to help explain the inheritance pattern in your pet's family. (*Hint: Attach your pets to the display in a way that lets viewers turn the pets over to read their genotypes.*)

Program Resources

◆ **Teaching Resources** 3-4 Review and Reinforce, p. 85; 3-4 Enrich, p. 86

Media and Technology

Interactive Student Tutorial CD-ROM C-3

SECTION 1 Mendel's Work

Key Ideas
- Gregor Mendel's work was the foundation for understanding why offspring have traits similar to those of their parents.
- Traits are controlled by alleles of genes. Organisms inherit one allele from each parent.
- Some alleles are dominant over others. A dominant allele is one whose trait always shows up in the organism when the allele is present. A recessive allele is masked whenever the dominant allele is present.

Key Terms
trait	allele
heredity	dominant allele
genetics	recessive allele
purebred	hybrid
gene	

SECTION 2 Probability and Genetics
INTEGRATING MATHEMATICS

Key Ideas
- Probability is the likelihood that a particular event will happen.
- Mendel was the first scientist to interpret his data using the principles of probability.
- Geneticists use Punnett squares to show all the possible outcomes of a genetic cross. Punnett squares allow a person to determine the probability of a particular outcome.
- An organism's phenotype is its physical appearance. An organism's genotype is its genetic makeup.

Key Terms
probability
Punnett square
phenotype
genotype
homozygous
heterozygous
codominance

SECTION 3 The Cell and Inheritance

Key Ideas
- According to the chromosome theory of inheritance, genes are carried from parents to their offspring on chromosomes.
- During meiosis, chromosome pairs separate to form sex cells. The sex cells have half the number of chromosomes as the body cells. Only one chromosome from each chromosome pair ends up in each sex cell.

Key Term
meiosis

SECTION 4 The DNA Connection

Key Ideas
- The nitrogen bases along a gene form a code that specifies the order in which amino acids will be put together to produce a protein.
- During protein synthesis, messenger RNA copies the coded message from the DNA in the nucleus and carries the message into the cytoplasm. Transfer RNA adds amino acids to the growing protein.
- A mutation is a change in a gene or chromosome. Some mutations are harmful, some are helpful, and some are neutral.

Key Terms
messenger RNA	transfer RNA

USING THE INTERNET

ACTIVITY

www.science-explorer.phschool.com

Check Your Progress
CHAPTER PROJECT 3

Give each student pair poster board on which they can display their pet family. If students don't understand the hint, show them how to attach the pets to the poster board by taping down the left side of the pet so people can easily turn over the pet to read their genotypes, much like turning the page in a book. Check Punnett squares to make sure students have correctly shown all the possible genotypes and phenotypes of the F_1 pets, based on the genotypes of the two parents. Each student pair should construct five Punnett squares, one for each trait—sex, body color, eye shape, nose shape, and teeth shape.

Program Resources

- **Teaching Resources** Chapter 3 Project Scoring Rubric, p. 70; Chapter 3 Performance Assessment, pp. 166–168; Chapter 3 Test, pp. 169–172

Media and Technology

Interactive Student Tutorial CD-ROM C-3

Computer Test Bank Test C-3

Performance Assessment

Drawing Have students draw a diagram that shows the process by which a cell produces proteins. In their diagrams, have students indicate where mistakes could occur, leading to mutations.

Portfolio Students can save their diagrams in their portfolios.

Reviewing Content:
Multiple Choice
1. a 2. c 3. b 4. a 5. c

True or False
6. true 7. phenotype 8. true
9. meiosis 10. cytoplasm

Checking Concepts
11. All the first generation offspring were tall.

12. There is a 1 in 2, or 50 percent chance that the coin will land heads up on the sixth toss because each coin toss is an independent event—the result of one toss does not affect the following coin tosses.

13. Punnett squares should look like the following:

	B	b
b	Bb	bb
b	Bb	bb

There is a 50 percent (2 in 4) chance that an offspring will have a white coat (bb).

14. Before meiosis begins, the chromosomes make copies of themselves. During Meiosis I, chromosome pairs separate from each other. In Meiosis II, the chromosome copies separate from each other to form four sex cells, each with half the number of chromosomes as the parent cell.

15. Transfer RNA carries the amino acid that corresponds to the code in the messenger RNA and adds it to the growing protein chain.

16. Student letters should describe Mendel's experiments as outlined in Section 1.

Thinking Visually
17. a.–d. adenine, thymine, guanine, cytosine e. one strand of the ladder f. carries the genetic code from the DNA inside the nucleus into the cytoplasm

Applying Skills
18. $\frac{9}{12} \times 100\% = 75\%$ green pods; $\frac{3}{12} \times 100\% = 25\%$ yellow pods
19. Yellow pods: gg; green pods: GG or Gg
20. Both parents are Gg. If both parents were GG, then none of the offspring would have yellow pods. If one parent

---

Reviewing Content
 For more review of key concepts, see the Interactive Student Tutorial CD-ROM.

Multiple Choice
Choose the letter of the best answer.

1. The different forms of a gene are called
   a. alleles.   b. chromosomes.
   c. phenotypes.   d. genotypes.

2. In a coin toss, the probability of the coin landing heads up is
   a. 100 percent.   b. 75 percent.
   c. 50 percent.   d. 25 percent.

3. An organism with two identical alleles for a trait is
   a. heterozygous.
   b. homozygous.
   c. recessive.
   d. dominant.

4. If the body cells of an organism have 10 chromosomes, then its sex cells would have
   a. 5 chromosomes.
   b. 10 chromosomes.
   c. 15 chromosomes.
   d. 20 chromosomes.

5. During protein synthesis, messenger RNA
   a. "reads" each three-letter code of bases.
   b. releases the completed protein chain.
   c. copies information from DNA in the nucleus.
   d. carries amino acids to the ribosome.

True or False
If the statement is true, write true. If it is false, change the underlined word or words to make the statement true.

6. The scientific study of heredity is called <u>genetics</u>.
7. An organism's physical appearance is its <u>genotype</u>.
8. In <u>codominance</u>, neither of the alleles is dominant or recessive.
9. <u>Heredity</u> is the process by which sex cells form.
10. Proteins are made in the <u>nucleus</u> of the cell.

Checking Concepts
11. Describe what happened when Mendel crossed purebred tall pea plants with purebred short pea plants.

12. You toss a coin five times and it lands heads up each time. What is the probability that it will land heads up on the sixth toss? Explain your answer.

13. In guinea pigs, the allele for black fur (B) is dominant over the allele for white fur (b). In a cross between a heterozygous black guinea pig (Bb) and a homozygous white guinea pig (bb), what is the probability that an offspring will have white fur? Use a Punnett square to answer the question.

14. In your own words, describe the sequence of steps in the process of meiosis.

15. Describe the role of transfer RNA in protein synthesis.

16. **Writing to Learn** Imagine that you are a student in the 1860s visiting Gregor Mendel in his garden. Write a letter to a friend describing Mendel's experiments with pea plants.

Thinking Visually
17. **Compare/Contrast Table** Copy the table comparing DNA and messenger RNA onto a separate sheet of paper. Then complete the table. (For more about compare/contrast tables, see the Skills Handbook.)

Characteristic	DNA	Messenger RNA
Nitrogen bases	a. ? b. ? c. ? d. ?	Adenine, uracil, guanine, cytosine
Structure	Twisted ladder	e. ?
Function	Forms a genetic code that specifies what type of protein will be produced	f. ?

---

were GG and the other were Gg, then, again, none of the offspring would have yellow pods. If both parents were gg, none of the offspring would have green pods.

Thinking Critically
21. The solid-colored parent must be homozygous for the recessive allele (ss), and the spotted parent must be homozygous for the dominant allele (SS). If the spotted parent were heterozygous (Ss), then 50% of the offspring would have been solid-colored.

22. The allele for the striped trait is dominant. If it were recessive, all of the offspring would have been solid green.

23. A thicker coat is a helpful mutation in a very cold environment, because it provides extra insulation to keep the mouse warm. It would be harmful in a very warm environment, because the mouse would not be able to easily lose heat.

Applying Skills

In peas, the allele for green pods (G) is dominant over the allele for yellow pods (g). The table shows the phenotypes of the offspring produced from a cross of two plants with green pods. Use the data to answer Questions 18–20.

Phenotype	Number of Offspring
Green pods	9
Yellow pods	3

18. **Calculating** Calculate what percent of the offspring have green pods. Calculate what percent have yellow pods.

19. **Inferring** What is the genotype of the offspring with yellow pods? What are the possible genotypes of the offspring with green pods?

20. **Drawing Conclusions** What are the genotypes of the parents? How do you know?

Thinking Critically

21. **Applying Concepts** In rabbits, the allele for a spotted coat is dominant over the allele for a solid-colored coat. A spotted rabbit was crossed with a solid-colored rabbit. The offspring all had spotted coats. What were the genotypes of the parents? Explain.

22. **Problem Solving** Suppose you are growing purebred green-skinned watermelons. One day you find a mutant striped watermelon. You cross the striped watermelon with a purebred green watermelon. Fifty percent of the offspring are striped, while fifty percent are solid green. Is the allele for the striped trait dominant or recessive? Explain your answer.

23. **Predicting** A new mutation in mice causes the coat to be twice as thick as normal. In what environment would this mutation be helpful? In what environment would it be harmful?

CHAPTER 3 REVIEW

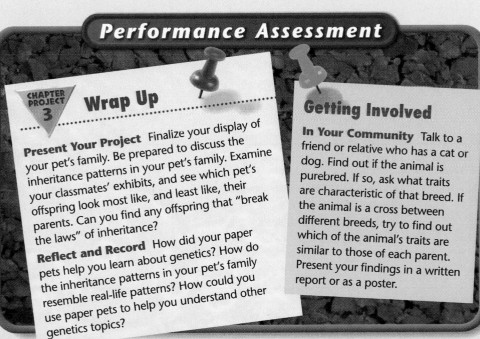

Performance Assessment

Wrap Up

CHAPTER PROJECT 3

Present Your Project Finalize your display of your pet's family. Be prepared to discuss the inheritance patterns in your pet's family. Examine your classmates' exhibits, and see which pet's offspring look most like, and least like, their parents. Can you find any offspring that "break the laws" of inheritance?

Reflect and Record How did your paper pets help you learn about genetics? How do the inheritance patterns in your pet's family resemble real-life patterns? How could you use paper pets to help you understand other genetics topics?

Getting Involved

In Your Community Talk to a friend or relative who has a cat or dog. Find out if the animal is purebred. If so, ask what traits are characteristic of that breed. If the animal is a cross between different breeds, try to find out which of the animal's traits are similar to those of each parent. Present your findings in a written report or as a poster.

Program Resources

◆ **Inquiry Skills Activity Book** Provides teaching and review of all inquiry skills

Performance Assessment

Present Your Project Make sure students understand that "breaking the laws" of inheritance refers to proposed inheritance patterns that violate the principles of heredity. This could happen, for example, when students propose that two homozygous recessive parents produce offspring with one or two dominant alleles. Students should review each other's Punnett squares to make sure that no offspring "break the inheritance laws."

CHAPTER PROJECT 3

Reflect and Record Students should record in their journals how their paper pets helped them understand specific concepts and principles of genetics. For example, students should describe how the inheritance patterns of their paper pets demonstrated the inheritance of dominant and recessive alleles, or showed the relationship between genotype and phenotype. They should also explain how paper pets could be used as models to study other topics in genetics.

Getting Involved

In Your Community If possible, have students photograph the cat or dog they are studying. Students can use an encyclopedia about dog breeds or cat breeds to learn the characteristics of a certain breed. If students do not know what the parents of a mixed breed animal are, challenge them to infer the breeds of the parents based on the characteristics of the animal. Allow time for students to report their findings to the class, or give them space to display their posters.

CHAPTER 4 Modern Genetics

Sections	Time	Student Edition Activities	Other Activities
CHAPTER PROJECT 4 **A Family Portrait** p. 111	Ongoing (2 weeks)	Check Your Progress, p. 118￼Check Your Progress, p. 123￼Wrap Up, p. 137	
1 Human Inheritance pp. 112–118 ◆ Explain what multiple alleles are.￼◆ Explain why some human traits show a large variety of phenotypes.￼◆ Explain how environmental factors can alter the effects of a gene.￼◆ Explain what determines sex and why some sex-linked traits are more common in males than in females.￼◆ Describe how geneticists use pedigrees.	2–3 periods/ 1–1½ blocks	**Discover** How Tall Is Tall?, p. 112￼**Try This** The Eyes Have It, p. 114￼**Try This** Girl or Boy?, p. 116	**TE** Including All Students, p 117￼**ISLM** C-4, "How Are Genes on Sex Chromosomes Inherited?"
2 Human Genetic Disorders pp. 119–125 ◆ Describe the causes and symptoms of four human genetic disorders.￼◆ Explain how genetic disorders are diagnosed.	3–4 periods/ 1½–2 blocks	**Discover** How Many Chromosomes?, p. 119￼**Real-World Lab: Careers in Science** Family Puzzles, pp. 124–125	**TE** Including All Students, p. 120￼**TE** Demonstration, p. 122
3 ◆ *INTEGRATING TECHNOLOGY* **Advances in Genetics** pp. 126–134 ◆ Describe three ways in which people have developed organisms with desired traits.￼◆ Explain how DNA fingerprinting is used.￼◆ State the goal of the Human Genome Project.	3–4 periods/ 1½–2 blocks	**Discover** What Do Fingerprints Reveal?, p. 126￼**Sharpen Your Skills** Communicating, p. 131￼**Science at Home,** p. 132￼**Real-World Lab: You Solve the Mystery** Guilty or Innocent?, p. 134	**TE** Real-Life Learning, p. 127￼**TE** Demonstration, p. 128￼**TE** Inquiry Challenge, p. 129
Study Guide/Chapter Review pp. 135–137	1 period/ ½ block		**ISAB** Provides teaching and review of all inquiry skills.

 For Standard or Block Schedule The Resource Pro® CD-ROM gives you maximum flexibility for planning your instruction for any type of schedule. Resource Pro® contains Planning Express®, an advanced scheduling program, as well as the entire contents of the Teaching Resources and the Computer Test Bank.

CHAPTER PLANNING GUIDE

Program Resources	Assessment Strategies	Media and Technology
TR Chapter 4 Project Teacher Notes, pp. 92–93 **TR** Chapter 4 Project Overview and Worksheets, pp. 94–97 **TR** Chapter 4 Project Scoring Rubric, p. 98	**SE** Performance Assessment: Chapter 4 Project Wrap Up, p. 137 **TE** Check Your Progress, pp. 118, 123 **TE** Performance Assessment: Chapter 4 Project Wrap Up, p. 137 **TR** Chapter 4 Project Scoring Rubric, p. 98	Science Explorer Internet Site
TR 4-1 Lesson Plan, p. 99 **TR** 4-1 Section Summary, p. 100 **TR** 4-1 Review and Reinforce, p. 101 **TR** 4-1 Enrich, p. 102 **SES** Book D, *Human Biology and Health,* Chapter 8	**SE** Section 1 Review, p. 118 **TE** Ongoing Assessment, pp. 113, 115, 117, **TE** Performance Assessment, p. 118 **TR** 4-1 Review and Reinforce, p. 101	Audiotapes, English-Spanish Summary 4-1 Transparencies 14, "Punnett Square—Male or Female?"; 15, "Exploring a Pedigree" Interactive Student Tutorial CD-ROM, C-4
TR 4-2 Lesson Plan, p. 103 **TR** 4-2 Section Summary, p. 104 **TR** 4-2 Review and Reinforce, p. 105 **TR** 4-2 Enrich, p. 106 **TR** Chapter 4 Real-World Lab, pp. 111–113 **SES** Book D, *Human Biology and Health,* Chapter 6	**SE** Section 2 Review, p. 123 **SE** Analyze and Conclude, p. 125 **TE** Ongoing Assessment, p. 121 **TE** Performance Assessment, p. 123 **TR** 4-2 Review and Reinforce, p. 105	Exploring Life Science Videodisc, Unit 5 Side 1, "An Unusual Mutation" Audiotapes, English-Spanish Summary 4-2 Interactive Student Tutorial CD-ROM, C-4
TR 4-3 Lesson Plan, p. 107 **TR** 4-3 Section Summary, p. 108 **TR** 4-3 Review and Reinforce, p. 109 **TR** 4-3 Enrich, p. 110 **TR** Chapter 4 Real-World Lab, pp. 114–115 **SES** Book A, *From Bacteria to Plants,* Chapter 2	**SE** Section 3 Review, p. 132 **SE** Analyze and Conclude, p. 134 **TE** Ongoing Assessment, pp. 127, 129, 131 **TE** Performance Assessment, p. 132 **TR** 4-3 Review and Reinforce, p. 109	Exploring Life Science Videodisc, Unit 5 Side 1, "Breeding for Dollars" Audiotapes, English-Spanish Summary 4-3 Transparency 16, "Exploring Genetic Engineering" Interactive Student Tutorial CD-ROM, C-4
TR Chapter 4 Performance Assessment, pp. 173–175 **TR** Chapter 4 Test, pp. 176–179	**SE** Chapter 4 Review, pp. 135–137 **TR** Chapter 4 Performance Assessment, pp. 173–175 **TR** Chapter 4 Test, pp. 176–179 **CTB** Test C-4	Interactive Student Tutorial CD-ROM, C-4 Computer Test Bank, Test C-4 Got It! Video Quizzes

Key: **SE** Student Edition **TE** Teacher's Edition **TR** Teaching Resources
 CTB Computer Test Bank **SES** Science Explorer Series Text **ISLM** Integrated Science Laboratory Manual
 ISAB Inquiry Skills Activity Book **PTA** Product Testing Activities by *Consumer Reports* **IES** Interdisciplinary Explorations Series

Meeting the National Science Education Standards and AAAS Benchmarks

National Science Education Standards	Benchmarks for Science Literacy	Unifying Themes
Science As Inquiry (Content Standard A) ◆ **Develop descriptions, explanations, predictions, and models using evidence** Students create a pedigree for an imaginary family, investigate inheritance patterns in families and model DNA fingerprinting. *(Chapter Project; Real-World Lab)* **Life Science** (Content Standard C) ◆ **Reproduction and heredity** Human traits can be controlled by single genes, multiple alleles, or many genes. A pedigree is used to trace the inheritance of traits. Genetic disorders are caused by mutations. People have used selective breeding, cloning, and genetic engineering to develop organisms with desirable traits. *(Chapter Project; Sections 1, 2, 3; Real-World Lab)* **Science and Technology** (Content Standard E) ◆ **Understandings about science and technology** Doctors use such tools as amniocentesis and karyotypes to help detect genetic disorders. In genetic engineering, genes from one organism are transferred into the DNA of another organism. DNA can be used to identify individuals. *(Sections 2, 3; Real-World Lab)* **Science in Personal and Social Perspectives** (Content Standard F) ◆ **Science and technology in society** Students examine the issue of who should have access to genetic test results. *(Science and Society)*	**1B Scientific Inquiry** Students create a pedigree for an imaginary family. Students investigate inheritance patterns in families. Students model DNA fingerprinting. *(Chapter Project; Real-World Lab)* **3A Technology and Science** Doctors use such tools as amniocentesis and karyotypes to help detect genetic disorders. In genetic engineering, genes from one organism are transferred into the DNA of another organism. DNA can be used to identify individuals. *(Sections 2, 3; Real-World Lab)* **3C Issues in Technology** Students examine the issue of who should have access to genetic test results. *(Science and Society)* **5B Heredity** Human traits can be controlled by single genes, multiple alleles, or many genes. A pedigree is used to trace the inheritance of traits. Genetic disorders are caused by mutations. People have used selective breeding, cloning, and genetic engineering to develop organisms with desirable traits. *(Chapter Project; Sections 1, 2, 3; Real-World Lab)* **12D Communication Skills** Students present their pedigrees and "photo" albums to the class. *(Chapter Project)*	◆ **Evolution** Geneticists use a pedigree to trace the inheritance of traits in humans. People have used selective breeding, cloning, and genetic engineering to develop organisms with desirable traits. *(Chapter Project; Sections 1, 3; Real-World Lab)* ◆ **Patterns of Change** The effects of genes are often altered by the environment. Genetic disorders are caused by mutations. Selective-breeding methods can be used to produce desired characteristics in plants and animals. *(Sections 1, 2, 3)* ◆ **Scale and Structure** The Y chromosome is much smaller than the X chromosome. The 23 pairs of human chromosomes that make up the human genome contain about 60,000 to 80,000 genes. *(Sections 1, 3)* ◆ **Stability** A clone is an organism that is genetically identical to the organism from which it was produced. *(Section 3)* ◆ **Systems and Interactions** Because males have only one X chromosome, males are more likely than females to inherit sex-linked traits controlled by recessive alleles. Doctors use tools such as amniocentesis and karyotypes to help detect genetic disorders. In genetic engineering, genes from one organism are transferred into the DNA of another organism. *(Sections 1, 2, 3)* ◆ **Unity and Diversity** Human traits can be controlled by single genes, multiple alleles, or many genes. A genetic disorder is an abnormal condition that a person inherits through genes or chromosomes. *(Sections 1, 2, 3; Real-World Lab)*

Media and Technology

Exploring Life Science Videodiscs
◆ **Section 2** "An Unusual Mutation" gives an in-depth view of sickle cell disease and the alleles that produce it.
◆ **Section 3** "Breeding for Dollars" discusses inbreeding, hybridization, and selective breeding.

Interactive Student Tutorial CD-ROM
◆ **Chapter Review** Interactive questions help students self-assess their mastery of key chapter concepts.

Student Edition Connection Strategies

◆ **Section 2** **Integrating Health,** p. 121
   Social Studies Connection, p. 121
   Integrating Technology, p. 122
◆ **Section 3** **Integrating Technology,** pp. 126–134
   Science and Society, p. 133

USING THE INTERNET
www.science-explorer.phschool.com

Visit the Science Explorer Internet site to find an up-to-date activity for Chapter 4 of *Cells and Heredity*.

ACTIVITY	Time (minutes)	Materials *Quantities for one work group*	Skills
Section 1			
Discover, p. 112	15	**Consumable** graph paper **Nonconsumable** tape measure	Inferring
Try This, p. 114	10	No special materials are required.	Designing Experiments
Try This, p. 116	10	**Nonconsumable** 2 paper bags, 3 red marbles, 1 white marble	Making Models
Section 2			
Discover, p. 119	10	No special materials are required.	Inferring
Real-World Lab, pp. 124–125	40	**Consumable** 12 index cards **Nonconsumable** scissors, marker	Interpreting Data, Drawing Conclusions
Section 3			
Discover, p. 126	15	**Consumable** plain white paper **Nonconsumable** ink pad, hand lens	Observing
Sharpen Your Skills, p. 131	15	No special materials are required.	Communicating
Science at Home, p. 132	home	No special materials are required.	Observing, Applying Concepts
Real-World Lab, p. 134	20	**Consumable** 4–6 bar codes	Observing, Making Models, Drawing Conclusions

A list of all materials required for the Student Edition activities can be found on pages T14–T15. You can order Materials Kits by calling 1-800-828-7777 or by accessing the Science Explorer Internet site at **www.science-explorer.phschool.com.**

A Family Portrait

In Chapter 4, students will learn more about human traits and how they are inherited. They also will learn how pedigrees can be used to trace the inheritance of traits in families. The Chapter 4 Project will give students an opportunity to use pedigrees to demonstrate different types of inheritance.

Purpose In the Chapter 4 Project, students will create a pedigree for an imaginary family and use it to show how two different traits have been passed from generation to generation within the family. Students also will create a family album showing how the traits appear in individual family members. Successfully completing the Chapter 4 Project will require students to understand different patterns of inheritance and the concepts of genotype and phenotype.

Skills Focus After completing the Chapter 4 Project, students will be able to
◆ create a model pedigree for an imaginary family;
◆ apply genetic concepts to show the inheritance of two different traits in the family's pedigree;
◆ predict phenotypes of individuals with different genotypes to create a family album;
◆ communicate their work in a class presentation.

Project Time Line The Chapter 4 Project will take about two weeks to complete. On the first day, launch the project and have students read about the project on page 111 in the text. Review the traits controlled by a single gene that are described in Chapters 3 and 4. Tell students to select two of the traits for the project. Distribute the Chapter 4 Project Overview, pages 94–95 in Teaching Resources, and give students a chance to read through it and ask questions.

The first day of the project is a good time to hand out the Chapter 4 Project Scoring Rubric, page 98 in Teaching Resources, so students will know how their work will be evaluated. If you want students to work in groups, assign them to groups at this time as well, and give groups a chance to meet and plan the project. Distribute Chapter 4 Project

CHAPTER 4 Modern Genetics

WHAT'S AHEAD

SECTION 1 Human Inheritance
Discover **How Tall Is Tall?**
Try This **The Eyes Have It**
Try This **Girl or Boy?**

SECTION 2 Human Genetic Disorders
Discover **How Many Chromosomes?**
Real-World Lab **Family Puzzles**

Integrating Technology
SECTION 3 Advances in Genetics
Discover **What Do Fingerprints Reveal?**
Sharpen Your Skills **Communicating**
Real-World Lab **Guilty or Innocent?**

110 ◆ C

Worksheet 1, page 96 in Teaching Resources, and instruct students to complete it before they begin their pedigrees.

Give students two or three days to create a pedigree for their imaginary families, following the specifications in *Exploring a Pedigree* on page 118 in their text. After students have completed their pedigrees, check them for errors. Then hand out Chapter 4 Project Worksheet 2, page 97 in Teaching Resources, and instruct students to complete the worksheet before they create their pedigrees for the two

traits. When students have finished their pedigrees, check their work before they begin their family albums.

Students may need several days to create their family albums, depending on how they choose to represent their selected traits. The more creative their approach, the more time they will probably need. Finally, set aside at least one class period at the end of the project for students to present their work to the rest of the class. Consider having students present their work in a poster-session format, where

PROJECT 4

A Family Portrait

A pedigree, or family tree, is a branched drawing that shows many generations of a family. In some cases, a pedigree may show centuries of a family's history.

In genetics, pedigrees are used to show how traits are passed from one generation to the next. In this project, you will create a genetic pedigree for an imaginary family. Although the family will be imaginary, your pedigree must show how real human traits are passed from parents to children.

Your Goal To create a pedigree for an imaginary family that shows the transfer of genetic traits from one generation to the next.

To complete the project you will

◆ choose two different genetic traits, and identify all the possible genotypes and phenotypes

◆ create pedigrees that trace each trait through three generations of your imaginary family

◆ prepare a family "photo" album to show what each family member looks like

Get Started With a partner, review the human traits described on page 86 in Chapter 3. List what you already know about human inheritance. For example, which human traits are controlled by dominant alleles? Which are controlled by recessive alleles? Then preview Section 1 of this chapter, and list the traits you'll be studying. Choose two traits that you would like to focus on in your project.

Check Your Progress You'll be working on this project as you study this chapter. To keep your project on track, look for Check Your Progress boxes at the following points.

Section 1 Review, page 118: Create a pedigree for the first trait you chose.

Section 2 Review, page 123: Create the second pedigree, and begin your family album.

Wrap Up At the end of the chapter (page 137), you will present your family's pedigrees and "photo" album to the class.

The children in this family have some traits like their mother's and some traits like their father's.

half the class at a time is available to discuss results and answer questions with the other half of the class.

For more detailed information on the chapter project, see Chapter 4 Project Teacher Notes, pages 92–93 in Teaching Resources.

Suggested Shortcuts Before students fill in the basic pedigree for specific traits, make sure it is accurate. Then have students make a photocopy of their pedigree. This will save them the time and effort of copying it over for the second trait.

Program Resources

◆ **Teaching Resources** Chapter 4 Project Teacher Notes, pp. 92–93; Chapter 4 Project Overview and Worksheets, pp. 94–97; Chapter 4 Project Scoring Rubric, p. 98

Another possible shortcut is to have each student choose just one trait. Also, instead of having students make oral presentations to the class, you can have them display their work on a bulletin board. Alternatively, you could select just a few students to present their pedigrees and family albums to the rest of the class. If this approach is taken, make sure a variety of traits with different patterns of inheritance are represented.

Possible Materials For their pedigrees, students can use large sheets of white paper or poster board. For their family albums, students can use a variety of different materials. The album itself may be a real photo album or scrapbook or a sheet of poster board. For pictures, students can use drawings or photographs from magazines or newspapers or sketches of their own. To show traits that are not visible, such as colorblindness or hemophilia, urge students to think of creative ways of depicting individuals with different phenotypes, such as fictitious newspaper articles or letters.

Launching the Project Introduce the project by calling students' attention to the family photograph on these pages and asking: **What are some traits that the children in this family appear to share with their parents?** *(Students are likely to name obvious physical traits such as hair color or nose shape.)* Point out that, in addition to traits such as these, children inherit thousands of other traits from their parents, including many traits that are not so apparent. Tell students that, in the Chapter 4 Project, they will create a family tree for an imaginary family and show how genetic traits pass from one generation to the next.

Performance Assessment

To assess students' performance in this project, use the Chapter 4 Project Scoring Rubric on page 98 of Teaching Resources. Students will be assessed on

◆ the accuracy of their pedigrees;

◆ how accurately and creatively they depict the phenotypes of the individuals in their family albums;

◆ how complete and prepared their class presentation is;

◆ their group participation, if they worked in groups.

Objectives

After completing the lesson, students will be able to

◆ explain what multiple alleles are;

◆ explain why some human traits show a large variety of phenotypes;

◆ explain how environmental factors can alter the effects of a gene;

◆ explain what determines sex and why some sex-linked traits are more common in males than in females;

◆ describe how geneticists use pedigrees.

Key Terms multiple alleles, sex-linked gene, carrier, pedigree

1 Engage/Explore

Activating Prior Knowledge

Help students think of examples of inherited traits by asking: **What are some traits that children may share with one or both of their parents?** (*Students are likely to identify traits such as hair color, nose shape, or eye color.*)

DISCOVER

Skills Focus inferring
Materials *metric ruler, graph paper*

Time 15 minutes
Tips If any students are in wheelchairs, you might want to have the class measure sitting height, which is the height from the base of the spine to the top of the head.
Expected Outcome The graph of students' heights is likely to include several bars, but not as many as there are students in the class.
Think It Over Students may infer that height in humans is controlled by more than one gene because the graph of students' heights has more bars than the two-bar graph Mendel would have drawn.

DISCOVER ·········· ACTIVITY

How Tall Is Tall?

1. Choose a partner. Measure each other's height to the nearest 5 centimeters. Record your measurements on the chalkboard.

2. Create a bar graph showing the number of students at each height. Plot the heights on the horizontal axis and the number of students on the vertical axis.

Think It Over
Inferring If Gregor Mendel had graphed the heights of his pea plants, the graph would have had two bars—one for tall stems and one for short stems. Do you think height in humans is controlled by a single gene, as it is in peas? Explain your answer.

GUIDE FOR READING

◆ Why do some human traits show a large variety of phenotypes?

◆ Why are some sex-linked traits more common in males than in females?

◆ How do geneticists use pedigrees?

Reading Tip Before you read, rewrite the headings in this section as *how, why,* or *what* questions. As you read, write answers to the questions.

Have you ever heard someone say "He's the spitting image of his dad" or "She has her mother's eyes"? Children often resemble their parents. The reason for this is that alleles for eye color, hair color, and thousands of other traits are passed from parents to their children. People inherit some alleles from their mother and some from their father. This is why most people look a little like their mother and a little like their father.

Traits Controlled by Single Genes

In Chapter 3, you learned that many traits in peas and other organisms are controlled by a single gene with two alleles. Often one allele is dominant, while the other is recessive. Many human traits are also controlled by a single gene with one dominant allele and one recessive allele. As with tall and short pea plants, these human traits have two distinctly different phenotypes, or physical appearances.

For example, a widow's peak is a hairline that comes to a point in the middle of the forehead. The allele for a widow's peak is dominant over the allele for a straight hairline. The Punnett square in Figure 1 illustrates a cross between two parents who are heterozygous for a widow's peak. Trace the possible combinations of alleles that a child may inherit. Notice that each child has a 3 in 4, or 75 percent, probability of having a widow's peak. There is only a 1 in 4, or 25 percent, probability that a child will have a straight hairline. Recall from Chapter 3 that when Mendel crossed peas that were heterozygous for a trait, he obtained similar percentages in the offspring.

READING STRATEGIES

Reading Tip *Sample questions:* What traits are controlled by single genes? What are multiple alleles? Which traits are controlled by many genes? How does the environment affect phenotypes? What determines whether you are male or female? How are sex-linked genes different from other genes? What is a pedigree? Advise students to save their questions and answers and use them to quiz themselves on the material when they prepare for assessments.

Study and Comprehension Before students begin the section, you may want to have them review several of the key terms from Chapter 3 that are important for understanding the concepts in this section. Have them find and read the definition of each of the following: *allele, dominant allele, recessive allele, phenotype, genotype,* and *codominance.*

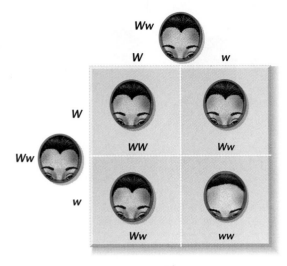

Figure 1 This Punnett square shows a cross between two parents with widow's peaks. *Interpreting Diagrams What are the possible genotypes of the offspring? What percent of the offspring will have each genotype?*

Do you have dimples when you smile? If so, then you have the dominant allele for this trait. Like having a widow's peak, having smile dimples is controlled by a single gene. People who have two recessive alleles do not have smile dimples.

Multiple Alleles

Some human traits are controlled by a single gene that has more than two alleles. Such a gene is said to have **multiple alleles**—three or more forms of a gene that code for a single trait. You can think of multiple alleles as being like flavors of pudding. Pudding usually comes in more flavors than just chocolate and vanilla!

Even though a gene may have multiple alleles, a person can carry only two of those alleles. This is because chromosomes exist in pairs. Each chromosome in a pair carries only one allele for each gene.

One human trait that is controlled by a gene with multiple alleles is blood type. There are four main blood types—A, B, AB, and O. Three alleles control the inheritance of blood types. The allele for blood type A and the allele for blood type B are codominant. The codominant alleles are written as capital letters with superscripts—I^A for blood type A and I^B for blood type B. The allele for blood type O—written i—is recessive. Recall that when two codominant alleles are inherited, neither allele is masked. A person who inherits an I^A allele from one parent and an I^B allele from the other parent will have type AB blood. Figure 2 shows the allele combinations that result in each blood type. Notice that only people who inherit two i alleles have type O blood.

☑ **Checkpoint** *If a gene has multiple alleles, why can a person only have two of the alleles for the gene?*

Blood Types	
Blood Type	**Combination of Alleles**
A	$I^A I^A$ or $I^A i$
B	$I^B I^B$ or $I^B i$
AB	$I^A I^B$
O	ii

Figure 2 Blood type is determined by a single gene with three alleles. This chart shows which combinations of alleles result in each blood type.

2 Facilitate

Traits Controlled by Single Genes

Addressing Naive Conceptions

Help students avoid the naive conception that the children in families always have genotypes that are in the ratios predicted by Punnett squares. Ask: **Could two parents with a widow's peak have three children without widow's peaks, and only one child with a widow's peak?** (*Students may say that three of the four children should have a widow's peak because the allele for the trait is dominant.*) Explain that three out of four children with a widow's peak is the most likely outcome for this mating. However, due to chance and the small number of offspring, any given family can deviate significantly from ratio determined by a Punnett square, as in the example given here. **learning modality: verbal**

Multiple Alleles

Using the Visuals: Figure 2

Make sure that students understand that the superscripts are not exponents but just labels used to distinguish the two codominant alleles, I^A and I^B. Then check that students understand the relationship between genotype and phenotype for traits controlled by multiple alleles, such as blood type, by asking: **Which column in the table lists the genotypes? Which lists the phenotypes?** (*The right column lists the genotypes; the left column the phenotypes.*) **Why are there more genotypes than phenotypes?** (*Because two different genotypes—$I^A I^A$ and $I^A i$—result in the A phenotype and two other genotypes—$I^B I^B$ and $I^B i$—result in the B phenotype.*) **learning modality: visual**

Ongoing Assessment

Drawing Have students draw a Punnett square that shows a cross between two heterozygotes for smile dimples (a trait controlled by a dominant allele).

Program Resources

◆ **Teaching Resources** 4-1 Lesson Plan, p. 99; 4-1 Section Summary, p. 100

Media and Technology

 Audiotapes English-Spanish Summary 4-1

Answers to Self-Assessment

Caption Question

Figure 1 The possible genotypes of the offspring are *WW*, *Ww*, and *ww*; 25% should have the *WW* genotype, 50% the *Ww* genotype, and 25% the *ww* genotype.

☑ Checkpoint

Chromosomes exist in pairs, and each chromosome in a pair carries only one allele for each gene.

Traits Controlled by Many Genes

Building Inquiry Skills: Calculating

Challenge students to identify all the possible genotypes for a hypothetical trait controlled by two genes, each having two alleles, with *A* and *a* representing the two alleles for one gene and *B* and *b* representing the two alleles for the other gene. Ask a volunteer to record students' responses on the chalkboard as they identify all the possible genotypes. *(The possible genotypes are AABB, AABb, AAbb, AaBB, AaBb, Aabb, aaBB, aaBb, and aabb.)* After the list is complete, ask: **How many more genotypes are there for a trait controlled by two genes than for a trait controlled by one gene, if each gene has two alleles?** *(Three times as many)* **learning modality: logical/mathematical**

The Effect of Environment

TRY THIS

Skills Focus designing experiments

Time 10 minutes

Tips Make sure students focus on an object that is at least a few meters away from them.

Expected Outcome Students should find that when they close one eye their finger appears to be stationary, but when they close the other eye their finger appears to move. For some students the finger will appear stationary when they look at it with their right eye, meaning their right eye is dominant. For other students the finger will appear stationary when they look at it with their left eye, meaning their left eye is dominant. To test the relationship between eye and hand dominance, students might determine eye and hand dominance for a large sample of people, and then inspect the data to see if a pattern emerges.

Extend Ask: **How is a dominant eye different than a dominant allele?** *(A dominant eye is a trait, whereas a dominant allele controls the inheritance of a trait.)* **learning modality: kinesthetic**

TRY THIS

The Eyes Have It

ACTIVITY

One inherited trait is eye dominance—the tendency to use one eye more than the other. Here's how you can test yourself for this trait.

1. Hold your hand out in front of you at arm's length. Point your finger at an object across the room.

2. Close your right eye. With only your left eye open, observe how far your finger appears to move.

3. Repeat Step 2 with the right eye open. With which eye did your finger seem to remain closer to the object? That eye is dominant.

Designing Experiments Is eye dominance related to hand dominance—whether a person is right-handed or left-handed? Design an experiment to find out. Obtain your teacher's permission before carrying out your experiment.

Figure 3 Skin color in humans is determined by three or more genes. Different combinations of alleles at each of the genes result in a wide range of possible skin colors.

Traits Controlled by Many Genes

If you did the Discover activity, you observed that height in humans has more than two distinct phenotypes. In fact, there is an enormous variety of phenotypes for height. What causes this wide range of phenotypes? **Some human traits show a large number of phenotypes because the traits are controlled by many genes. The genes act together as a group to produce a single trait.** At least four genes control height in humans, so there are many possible combinations of genes and alleles.

Like height, skin color is determined by many genes. Human skin color ranges from almost white to nearly black, with many shades in between. Skin color is controlled by at least three genes. Each gene, in turn, has at least two possible alleles. Various combinations of alleles at each of the genes determine the amount of pigment that a person's skin cells produce. Thus, a wide variety of skin colors is possible.

The Effect of Environment

The effects of genes are often altered by the environment—the organism's surroundings. For example, people's diets can affect their height. A diet lacking in protein, minerals, and vitamins can prevent a person from growing to his or her potential maximum height. Since the late 1800s, the average height of adults in the United States has increased by almost 10 centimeters. During that time, American diets have become more healthful. Other environmental factors, such as medical care and living conditions, have also improved since the late 1800s.

✓ *Checkpoint How can environmental factors affect a person's height?*

Background

History of Science The existence of sex chromosomes was discovered in the late 1800s by Hermann Henking. While studying wasp cells, Henking observed an "accessory chromosome" in each dividing cell that did not have a matching chromosome at prophase. He also noted that male wasps had an uneven number of chromosomes, but females had an even number.

In the early 1900s, the American zoologist Clarence McClung observed "accessory chromosomes" in cells of grasshoppers. McClung's work revealed the significance of the "accessory chromosome," the X chromosome, as a mechanism for the determination of an organism's sex.

Male or Female?

"Congratulations, Mr. and Mrs. Gonzales. It's a baby girl!" What factors determine whether a baby is a boy or a girl? As with other traits, the sex of a baby is determined by genes on chromosomes. Among the 23 pairs of chromosomes in each body cell is a single pair of chromosomes called the sex chromosomes. The sex chromosomes determine whether a person is male or female.

The sex chromosomes are the only pair of chromosomes that do not always match. If you are female, your two sex chromosomes match. The two chromosomes are called X chromosomes. If you are male, your sex chromosomes do not match. One of your sex chromosomes is an X chromosome. The other chromosome is a Y chromosome. The Y chromosome is much smaller than the X chromosome.

What happens to the sex chromosomes when egg and sperm cells form? As you know, each egg and sperm cell has only one chromosome from each pair. Since both of a female's sex chromosomes are X chromosomes, all eggs carry one X chromosome. Males, however, have two different sex chromosomes. This means that half of a male's sperm cells carry an X chromosome, while half carry a Y chromosome.

When a sperm cell with an X chromosome fertilizes an egg, the egg has two X chromosomes. The fertilized egg will develop into a girl. When a sperm with a Y chromosome fertilizes an egg, the egg has one X chromosome and one Y chromosome. The fertilized egg will develop into a boy. Thus it is the sperm that determines the sex of the child, as you can see in Figure 4.

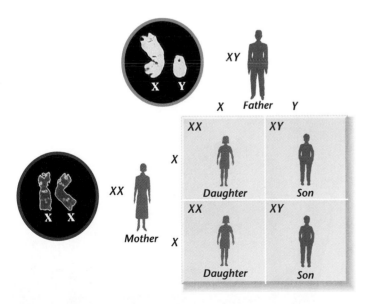

Figure 4 As this Punnett square shows, there is a 50 percent probability that a child will be a girl and a 50 percent probability that a child will be a boy. *Interpreting Diagrams What sex will the child be if a sperm with a Y chromosome fertilizes an egg?*

Chapter 4 **C ◆ 115**

Program Resources

 Science Explorer Series *Human Biology and Health*, Chapter 8, has more information about human reproduction.

Media and Technology

Transparencies "Punnett Square– Male or Female?," Transparency 14

Answers to Self-Assessment

☑ *Checkpoint*

Environmental factors such as a poor diet can affect a person's height by preventing the person from reaching his or her potential maximum height.

Caption Question
Figure 4 The child will be male.

Male or Female?

Building Inquiry Skills: Drawing Diagrams

Challenge students to draw two simple diagrams of meiosis, contrasting the formation of sex cells in males and females. Their drawings should show clearly which type of sex chromosome each of the sex cells contains. If students do not remember the details of meiosis, suggest that they refer to *Exploring Meiosis* on page 99, Chapter 3. Explain that the X and Y chromosomes pair up during meiosis. After students have finished their drawings, ask: **How do your drawings demonstrate that it is the father's sperm that determines the sex of a child?** (*The drawings should show that the sex cells produced by a male may contain either an X or a Y chromosome, whereas the sex cells produced by a female may contain only an X chromosome. Thus, the sex of a child is determined by whether an egg is fertilized by an X-bearing or a Y-bearing sperm produced by the father.*)
learning modality: kinesthetic

Using the Visuals: Figure 4

Use the visual to help students understand why an allele on a man's X chromosome cannot be inherited by his sons. Ask: **If the man in the figure had an allele *A* on his X chromosome, which of his offspring—his sons or his daughters— would inherit the allele?** (*The man's daughters*) **Why wouldn't his sons inherit the allele?** (*Because the man's sons inherit only the Y chromosome from their father.*)
learning modality: visual

Ongoing Assessment

Writing Have students explain, in their own words, why about half of all babies are boys and about half are girls. (*Sample answer: A baby's sex depends on whether it receives an X or a Y chromosome from the father. Half the sperm produced by males contain an X chromosome, and the other half contain a Y chromosome. Therefore, about half the time eggs are fertilized by Y-bearing sperm and about half the time they are fertilized by X-bearing sperm. This results in about half the babies being boys and about half being girls.*)

C ◆ 115

Male or Female?, continued

Skills Focus making models

Materials *two paper bags, three red marbles, one white marble*

Time 10 minutes

Tips Remind students to replace the two marbles in the correct bags each time before they make their next draw.

Expected Outcome About half the time students will draw two red marbles, representing a female, and about half the time they will draw one red and one white marble, representing a male. If you add up the numbers of females and males produced by the whole class, the totals are likely to be even closer to half female and half male.

Extend Ask: **How could you use the same setup to model the inheritance of a trait controlled by a single gene, such as widow's peak?** *(The most likely way is to assume that one color marble represents the dominant allele and the other color represents the recessive allele for the same gene. Students would draw one marble from each bag, as in the original activity.)*

learning modality: kinesthetic

Sex-Linked Genes

Building Inquiry Skills: Inferring

Challenge students to infer how the inheritance of a sex-linked trait controlled by a dominant allele would differ from the inheritance of a sex-linked trait controlled by a recessive allele. First, remind students that a sex-linked trait controlled by a recessive allele is more common in males because males need to inherit just one recessive allele to have the trait. Then ask: **If a sex-linked trait is controlled by a dominant allele, would the trait be more common in males than in females? Why or why not?** *(A trait controlled by a dominant allele would not be more common in males because females, like males, would need to inherit just one dominant allele to have the trait.)* **learning modality: logical/mathematical**

Girl or Boy?

You can model how the sex of an offspring is determined.

1. Label one paper bag "female." Label another paper bag "male."
2. Place two red marbles in the bag labeled "female." The red marbles represent X chromosomes.
3. Place one red marble and one white marble in the bag labeled "male." The white marble represents a Y chromosome.
4. Without looking, pick one marble from each bag. Two red marbles represent a female offspring. One red marble and one white marble represent a male offspring. Record the sex of the "offspring."
5. Put the marbles back in the correct bags. Repeat Step 4 nine more times.

Making Models How many males were produced? How many females? How close were your results to the expected probabilities for male and female offspring?

Program Resources

◆ **Integrated Science Laboratory Manual** C-4, "How Are Genes on Sex Chromosomes Inherited?"

Sex-Linked Genes

Some human traits occur more often in one sex than the other. The genes for these traits are often carried on the sex chromosomes. Genes on the X and Y chromosomes are often called **sex-linked genes** because their alleles are passed from parent to child on a sex chromosome. Traits controlled by sex-linked genes are called sex-linked traits.

Like other genes, sex-linked genes can have dominant and recessive alleles. Recall that females have two X chromosomes, whereas males have one X chromosome and one Y chromosome. In females, a dominant allele on one X chromosome will mask a recessive allele on the other X chromosome. The situation is not the same in males, however. In males, there is no matching allele on the Y chromosome to mask, or hide, the allele on the X chromosome. As a result, any allele on the X chromosome—even a recessive allele—will produce the trait in a male who inherits it. **Because males have only one X chromosome, males are more likely than females to have a sex-linked trait that is controlled by a recessive allele.**

One example of a sex-linked trait that is controlled by a recessive allele is red-green colorblindness. A person with red-green colorblindness cannot distinguish between red and green. A common test for red-green colorblindness is shown in Figure 5.

Many more males than females have red-green colorblindness. You can understand why this is the case by examining the Punnett square in Figure 6. Both parents in this example have normal color vision. Notice, however, that the mother is a carrier of colorblindness. A **carrier** is a person who has one recessive allele for a trait and one dominant allele. Although a carrier does not have the trait, the carrier can pass the recessive allele on to his or her offspring.

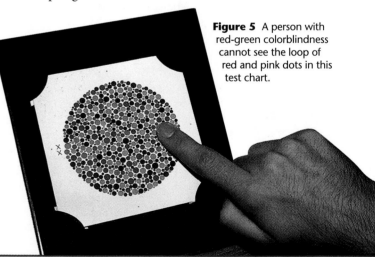

Figure 5 A person with red-green colorblindness cannot see the loop of red and pink dots in this test chart.

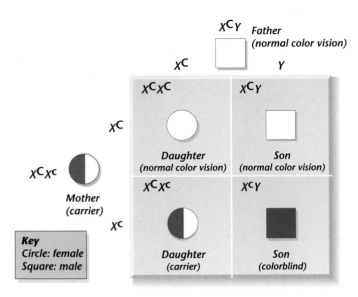

X^CY Father (normal color vision)

X^C / Y

X^C

X^CX^C Daughter (normal color vision)

X^CY Son (normal color vision)

X^CX^c Mother (carrier)

X^c

X^CX^c Daughter (carrier)

X^cY Son (colorblind)

Key
Circle: female
Square: male

Figure 6 Red-green color-blindness is a sex-linked trait. A girl who receives only one recessive allele (written X^c) for red-green colorblindness will not have the trait. However, a boy who receives one recessive allele will be colorblind. *Applying Concepts What allele combination would a daughter need to inherit to be colorblind?*

As you can see in Figure 6, there is a 25 percent probability that this couple will have a colorblind child. Notice that none of the couple's daughters will be colorblind. On the other hand, the sons have a 50 percent probability of being colorblind. For a female to be colorblind, she must inherit two recessive alleles for colorblindness, one from each parent. A male needs to inherit only one recessive allele. This is because there is no gene for color vision on the Y chromosome. Thus, there is no allele that could mask the recessive allele on the X chromosome.

Pedigrees

Imagine that you are a geneticist interested in studying inheritance patterns in humans. What would you do? You can't set up crosses with people as Mendel did with peas. Instead, you would need to trace the inheritance of traits through many generations in a number of families.

One important tool that geneticists use to trace the inheritance of traits in humans is a pedigree. A **pedigree** is a chart or "family tree" that tracks which members of a family have a particular trait. The trait recorded in a pedigree can be an ordinary trait such as widow's peak, or it could be a sex-linked trait such as colorblindness. In *Exploring a Pedigree* on page 118, you can trace the inheritance of colorblindness through three generations of a family.

 Checkpoint How is a pedigree like a "family tree"?

Chapter 4 **C ◆ 117**

C ◆ 117

3 Assess

Section 1 Review Answers

1. Such traits are controlled by many genes and influenced by environment.

2. It is controlled by a recessive allele on the X chromosome, and males need to inherit only one recessive allele to have the trait.

3. It is a chart that tracks which members of a family have a particular trait. They are used by geneticists as tools for tracing inheritance.

4. Yes, if both parents are heterozygous for widow's peak and the child inherits a recessive allele for straight hairline from each parent. No, because the parents each have two recessive alleles for straight hairline, so the child will inherit two recessive alleles.

> **Check Your Progress** CHAPTER PROJECT 4
>
> Check that students' pedigrees cover at least three generations and that the second generation consists of five children. Make sure the pedigrees do not contain any errors before students start using them to show inheritance patterns. Also check that students have chosen traits controlled by single genes to represent in their pedigrees.

Performance Assessment

Drawing Have students draw a pedigree showing the inheritance of a single recessive allele, starting with first generation genotypes of *Aa* × *Aa* and continuing for three generations.

EXPLORING *a Pedigree*

This pedigree traces the occurrence of colorblindness in three generations of a family. Colorblindness is a sex-linked trait that is controlled by a recessive allele. Notice that specific symbols are used in pedigrees to communicate genetic information.

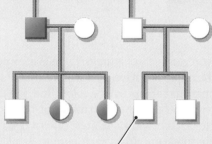
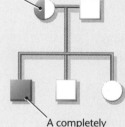

A circle represents a female.

A square represents a male.

A horizontal line connecting a male and female represents a marriage.

A vertical line and a bracket connect the parents to their children.

A half-shaded circle or square indicates that a person is a carrier of the trait.

A completely shaded circle or square indicates that a person has the trait.

A circle or square that is not shaded indicates that a person neither has the trait nor is a carrier of the trait.

 ## Section 1 Review

1. Why do human traits such as height and skin color have many different phenotypes?

2. Explain why red-green colorblindness is more common in males than in females.

3. What is a pedigree? How are pedigrees used?

4. **Thinking Critically Predicting** Could two people with widow's peaks have a child with a straight hairline? Could two people with straight hairlines have a child with a widow's peak? Explain.

> **Check Your Progress** CHAPTER PROJECT 4
>
> By now, you should be creating your pedigree for the first trait you chose. Start with one couple, and show two generations of offspring. The couple should have five children. It is up to you to decide how many children each of those children has. Use Punnett squares to make sure that your imaginary family's inheritance pattern follows the laws of genetics.

Background

Facts and Figures Traits controlled by sex-linked recessive alleles are unique in appearing to skip generations in a pedigree. Such traits do not pass from a man to his sons. Instead they pass from a man through his daughters, who do not have the trait but are carriers, to his grandsons. When a trait shows this inheritance pattern, it is likely to be controlled by a sex-linked recessive allele.

Program Resources

◆ **Teaching Resources** 4-1 Review and Reinforce, p. 101; 4-1 Enrich, p. 102

Media and Technology

 Interactive Student Tutorial CD-ROM C-4

SECTION
2 Human Genetic Disorders

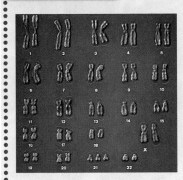

DISCOVER

How Many Chromosomes?

The photo at the left shows the chromosomes from a cell of a person with Down syndrome, a genetic disorder. The chromosomes have been sorted into pairs.

1. Count the number of chromosomes in the photo.
2. How does the number of chromosomes compare to the usual number of chromosomes in human cells?

Think It Over

Inferring How do you think a cell could have ended up with this number of chromosomes? (*Hint:* Think about the events that occur during meiosis.)

The air inside the stadium was hot and still. The crowd cheered loudly as eight runners approached the starting blocks. The runners shook out their arms and legs to loosen up their muscles and calm their jitters. When the starter raised the gun, all eyes focused on the runners. At the crack of the starter's gun, the runners leaped into motion and sprinted down the track.

Seconds later, the race was over. The runners, bursting with pride, hugged each other and their coaches. It didn't matter where each of the runners placed. All that mattered was that they had finished the race and done their best. These athletes were running in the Special Olympics, a competition for people with disabilities.

Many of the athletes who compete in the Special Olympics have disabilities that result from genetic disorders. A **genetic disorder** is an abnormal condition that a person inherits through genes or chromosomes. **Genetic disorders are caused by mutations, or changes in a person's DNA.** In some cases, a mutation occurs when sex cells form during meiosis. In other cases, a mutation that is already present in a parent's cells is passed on to the offspring. In this section, you will learn about some common genetic disorders.

GUIDE FOR READING

◆ What causes genetic disorders?

◆ How are genetic disorders diagnosed?

Reading Tip As you read, make a list of different types of genetic disorders. Write a sentence about each disorder.

A runner at the Special Olympics ▶

Chapter 4 **C ◆ 119**

SECTION
2 Human Genetic Disorders

Objectives

After completing the lesson, students will be able to
◆ describe the causes and symptoms of four human genetic disorders;
◆ explain how genetic disorders are diagnosed.

Key Terms genetic disorder, amniocentesis, karyotype

1 Engage/Explore

Activating Prior Knowledge

Introduce human genetic disorders by asking: **What do you think is a genetic disorder?** (*An abnormal condition that is inherited*) **What are some genetic disorders you have heard about?** (*Accept all student responses without comment at this time.*) Write students' suggestions of genetic disorders on the board, so students can reevaluate the list at the end of the section.

DISCOVER

Skills Focus inferring
Time 10 minutes
Tips Provide any students who have vision problems with a hand lens for examining the photo.
Expected Outcome Students should count 47 chromosomes in the photo, or one more than the 46 chromosomes normally found in human cells, because there is an extra copy of chromosome 21.
Think It Over Students may correctly say that the extra chromosome is due to failure of the chromosomes to separate during meiosis.

Program Resources

◆ **Teaching Resources** 4-2 Lesson Plan, p. 103; 4-2 Section Summary, p. 104

Media and Technology

 Audiotapes English-Spanish Summary 4-2

READING STRATEGIES

Vocabulary Students may find several terms in this section difficult to spell and pronounce. Before students read the section, write the following terms on the board: *cystic fibrosis, sickle-cell, hemophilia, amniocentesis,* and *karyotype.* Pronounce each term clearly, and have students repeat it after you. Also have students write and rewrite each term until they can spell it correctly.

2 Facilitate

Cystic Fibrosis

Building Inquiry Skills: Relating Cause and Effect

Point out that cystic fibrosis, like most genetic disorders, can be treated but not cured. Then ask: **What is the difference between a treatment and a cure for a disease like cystic fibrosis?** *(A cure eliminates the disease, and therefore the symptoms, whereas a treatment controls the symptoms without eliminating the disease.)* **What are some ways that cystic fibrosis can be treated?** *(Possible ways include drugs to prevent infections and physical therapy to break up mucus in the lungs.)* **How could a genetic disorder like cystic fibrosis be cured?** *(By changing or replacing the gene that causes the symptoms)* **learning modality: verbal**

Sickle-Cell Disease

Including All Students

Materials *poster board, marker*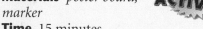
Time 15 minutes

Reinforce the concept of codominance for hands-on learners by having them draw a two-generation pedigree for sickle-cell disease, starting with the genotypes of *Ss* × *Ss*. Remind students to include a key indicating which individuals in the pedigree have normal hemoglobin, one sickle-cell allele, and sickle-cell disease. Invite students to share their pedigrees with the rest of the class. Follow up by asking: **In terms of the genetics, why is having one sickle-cell allele different from being a carrier of cystic fibrosis?** *(People with one sickle-cell allele have both normal hemoglobin and sickle-cell hemoglobin because the allele for abnormal hemoglobin is codominant with the allele for normal hemoglobin. In contrast, people who are carriers of cystic fibrosis have no signs or symptoms of cystic fibrosis because the allele for cystic fibrosis is recessive to the normal allele.)* **learning modality: logical/mathematical**

Figure 7 Cystic fibrosis is a genetic disorder that causes thick mucus to build up in a person's lungs and intestines. This patient is inhaling a fine mist that will help loosen the mucus in her lungs.

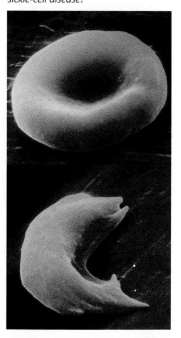

Figure 8 Normally, red blood cells are shaped like round disks (top). In a person with sickle-cell disease, red blood cells can become sickle-shaped (bottom). *Relating Cause and Effect What combination of alleles leads to sickle-cell disease?*

Cystic Fibrosis

Cystic fibrosis is a genetic disorder in which the body produces abnormally thick mucus in the lungs and intestines. The thick mucus fills the lungs, making it hard for the affected person to breathe. Bacteria that grow in the mucus can cause infections and, eventually, lung damage. In the intestines, the mucus makes it difficult for digestion to occur.

The mutation that leads to cystic fibrosis is carried on a recessive allele. The cystic fibrosis allele is most common among people whose ancestors are from Northern Europe. Every day in this country, four babies are born with cystic fibrosis.

Currently there is no cure for cystic fibrosis. Medical treatments include drugs to prevent infections and physical therapy to break up mucus in the lungs. Recent advances in scientists' understanding of the disease may lead to better treatments and longer lifespans for people with cystic fibrosis.

☑ *Checkpoint* *What are some symptoms of cystic fibrosis?*

Sickle-Cell Disease

Sickle-cell disease is a genetic disorder that affects the blood. The mutation that causes the disorder affects the production of an important protein called hemoglobin. Hemoglobin is the protein in red blood cells that carries oxygen. People with sickle-cell disease produce an abnormal form of hemoglobin. When oxygen concentrations are low, their red blood cells have an unusual sickle shape, as you can see in Figure 8.

Sickle-shaped red blood cells cannot carry as much oxygen as normal-shaped cells. Because of their shape, the cells become stuck in narrow blood vessels, blocking them. People with sickle-cell disease suffer from lack of oxygen in the blood and experience pain and weakness.

Background

Integrating Science Another example of a genetic disorder controlled by a recessive allele is Tay-Sachs disease, found primarily in Jews from central or eastern Europe. People with Tay-Sachs disease are missing an enzyme needed to break down fats in the brain. As a result, fatty substances accumulate in the brain, leading to blindness, deafness, and paralysis. Death usually occurs by age four or five.

The allele for the sickle-cell trait is most common in people of African ancestry. About 9 percent of African Americans carry the sickle-cell allele. The allele for the sickle-cell trait is codominant with the normal allele. A person with two sickle-cell alleles will have the disease. A person with one sickle-cell allele will produce both normal hemoglobin and abnormal hemoglobin. This person usually will not have symptoms of the disease.

Currently, there is no cure for sickle-cell disease. People with sickle-cell disease are given drugs to relieve their painful symptoms and to prevent blockages in blood vessels. As with cystic fibrosis, scientists are hopeful that new, successful treatments will soon be found.

Hemophilia

Hemophilia is a genetic disorder in which a person's blood clots very slowly or not at all. People with the disorder do not produce one of the proteins needed for normal blood clotting. A person with hemophilia can bleed to death from a minor cut or scrape. The danger of internal bleeding from small bumps and bruises is also very high.

Hemophilia is an example of a disorder that is caused by a recessive allele on the X chromosome. Because hemophilia is a sex-linked disorder, it occurs more frequently in males than in females. 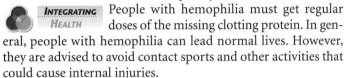 **INTEGRATING HEALTH** People with hemophilia must get regular doses of the missing clotting protein. In general, people with hemophilia can lead normal lives. However, they are advised to avoid contact sports and other activities that could cause internal injuries.

Hemophilia has affected European history. Queen Victoria of England had a son and three grandsons with hemophilia. Victoria, at least two of her daughters, and four of her granddaughters were carriers of the disease.

As Victoria's descendants passed the hemophilia allele to their offspring, hemophilia spread through the royal families of Europe. For example, Princess Alexandra, Queen Victoria's granddaughter, married the Russian Czar Nicholas II in 1894. Alexandra, a carrier of hemophilia, passed the disease to her son Alexis, who was heir to the throne.

A monk named Rasputin convinced Alexandra that he could cure Alexis. As a result of his control over Alexandra, Rasputin was able to control the Czar as well. The people's anger at Rasputin's influence may have played a part in the Russian Revolution of 1917, in which the Czar was overthrown.

In Your Journal

Imagine that you are Princess Alexandra. Write a diary entry expressing your feelings and unanswered questions about Alexis's condition.

Figure 9 Princess Alexandra of Russia (center row, left) passed the allele for hemophilia to her son Alexis (front).

Chapter 4 **C ◆ 121**

Answers to Self-Assessment

Caption Question

Figure 8 The combination of two recessive alleles leads to sickle-cell disease.

✓ Checkpoint

Some symptoms of cystic fibrosis are difficulty breathing, frequent infections, and difficulty digesting food.

Hemophilia

Integrating Health

Give a group of students who need extra challenges a chance to research and create a flowchart showing how blood clots form. Each group member should research at least one source. Group members should then compile their information and collaborate on creating the flowchart. Have one or more group members explain the flowchart to the rest of the class. Then ask: **How does the hemophilia allele interfere with blood clotting?** *(By leading to the lack of a protein, which is essential for blood to clot)* Challenge group members to point out this step in the flowchart. **cooperative learning**

Social Studies CONNECTION

Provide background for the feature by informing students that the presence of the hemophilia allele in Queen Victoria is believed to have been created by a new mutation. This is based on the fact that neither Victoria's husband nor any of her male relatives in earlier generations had the disorder.

In Your Journal

Help students put themselves in Alexandra's place by urging them to imagine what it was like for a child to live with hemophilia, especially in the late 1800s before the development of blood transfusions and blood-clotting proteins. Every cut or nosebleed could cause a life-threatening loss of blood. Ask: **How do you think her son's hemophilia might have affected the princess' relationship with him?** *(The princess might have been overly protective of her son and very focused on caring for his health and safety.)* Point out that this could have made Alexandra fall more easily under the influence of Rasputin. **learning modality: verbal**

Ongoing Assessment

Skills Check Have students create a table comparing and contrasting cystic fibrosis, sickle-cell disease, and hemophilia.

Down Syndrome

Demonstration

Materials *colored chalk*
Time 10 minutes

Demonstrate with a simple drawing how the production of sex cells with an abnormal number of chromosomes can lead to genetic disorders like Down syndrome. Use circles to represent cells and short lines to represent chromosomes. Start with one parent cell containing two colored X's to represent a pair of chromosomes that has replicated. Illustrate these chromosomes as the cell goes through Meiosis I and Meiosis II, as shown in *Exploring Meiosis* on page 99. Point out that the chromosome pairs can fail to separate correctly in either stage. Then draw four smaller circles to represent four sex cells. Distribute the colored chromosomes among the sex cells unequally, so that one of the sex cells contains two chromosomes and one contains none. Beside each sex cell, draw another small circle containing one white line, to represent a normal sex cell with one chromosome from the other parent. Finally, draw four circles to represent the possible individuals formed when sex cells unite. Two individuals should be normal, one should contain only one white chromosome, and one should contain one white and two colored chromosomes. Ask: **Which individual will have Down syndrome?** *(The one with three chromosomes)* **learning modality: visual**

Diagnosing Genetic Disorders

Integrating Technology

Tell students that amniocentesis is not performed routinely in every pregnancy because there are risks involved. Amniocentesis often is recommended for older mothers because they have a substantially greater risk of having babies with Down syndrome. Ask: **For what other women do you think amniocentesis is recommended?** *(Women who have, or whose husbands have, a family history of genetic disorders.)* **learning modality: logical/mathematical**

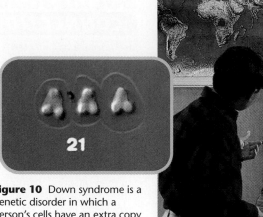

Figure 10 Down syndrome is a genetic disorder in which a person's cells have an extra copy of chromosome 21. Although people with Down syndrome have some mental and physical limitations, they can lead active, productive lives.

Down Syndrome

Some genetic disorders are the result of too many or too few chromosomes. In one such disorder, called Down syndrome, a person's cells have an extra copy of chromosome 21. The extra chromosome is the result of an error during meiosis. Recall that in meiosis, cells divide and chromosomes separate to produce sex cells with half the normal chromosome number. Down syndrome most often occurs when chromosomes fail to separate properly during meiosis.

People with Down syndrome have a distinctive physical appearance, and have some degree of mental retardation. Heart defects are also common, but can be treated. Despite their limitations, many people with Down syndrome lead full, active lives.

Diagnosing Genetic Disorders

INTEGRATING TECHNOLOGY Years ago, doctors had only Punnett squares and pedigrees to help them predict whether a child might have a genetic disorder. **Today doctors use tools such as amniocentesis and karyotypes to help detect genetic disorders.**

Before a baby is born, doctors can use a procedure called **amniocentesis** (am nee oh sen TEE sis) to determine whether the baby will have some genetic disorders. During amniocentesis, a doctor uses a very long needle to remove a small amount of the fluid that surrounds the developing baby. The fluid contains cells from the baby.

Background

Facts and Figures In addition to Down syndrome, there are a number of other syndromes caused by too many chromosomes. Edwards syndrome is caused by an extra copy of chromosome 18. It occurs about once in every 8,000 live births. Symptoms include mental retardation and malformations of the head, heart, and kidneys. Death usually occurs in the first year. Patau syndrome is caused by an extra copy of chromosome 13. It occurs about once in every 20,000 live births. Symptoms include mental retardation and defects of the hands, heart, and genitals. Death typically occurs by age one. Klinefelter's syndrome is caused by an extra X chromosome in males. It occurs about once in every 500 male live births. Symptoms may include feminine features, sterility, and behavioral problems.

The doctor then examines the chromosomes from the cells. To do this, the doctor creates a karyotype. A **karyotype** (KA ree uh typ) is a picture of all the chromosomes in a cell. The chromosomes in a karyotype are arranged in pairs. A karyotype can reveal whether a developing baby has the correct number of chromosomes in its cells and whether it is a boy or a girl. If you did the Discover activity, you saw a karyotype from a girl with Down syndrome.

Genetic Counseling

A couple that has a family history or concern about a genetic disorder may turn to a genetic counselor for advice. Genetic counselors help couples understand their chances of having a child with a particular genetic disorder. Genetic counselors use tools such as karyotypes, pedigree charts, and Punnett squares to help them in their work.

Suppose, for example, that a husband and wife both have a history of cystic fibrosis in their families. If they are considering having children, they might seek the advice of a genetic counselor. The genetic counselor might order a test to determine whether they are carriers of the allele for cystic fibrosis. The genetic counselor would then apply the same principles of probability that you learned about in Chapter 3 to calculate the couple's chances of having a child with cystic fibrosis.

Figure 11 Couples may meet with a genetic counselor and their doctor in order to understand their chances of having a child with a genetic disorder.

Section 2 Review

1. Explain how genetic disorders occur in humans. Give two examples of genetic disorders.
2. Describe two tools that doctors use to detect genetic disorders.
3. How do the cells of people with Down syndrome differ from those of others? How might this difference arise?
4. **Thinking Critically Problem Solving** A couple with a family history of hemophilia is about to have a baby girl. What information about the parents would you want to know? How would this information help you determine whether the baby will have hemophilia?

Check Your Progress
CHAPTER PROJECT 4
At this point, you should begin to trace the inheritance of another trait through the same family members that are in your first pedigree. Also, start making your family "photo" album. Will you use drawings or some other method to show what the family members look like? (*Hint:* Photo albums show phenotypes. Remember that more than one genotype can have the same phenotype.)

Program Resources

◆ **Teaching Resources** 4-2 Review and Reinforce, p. 105; 4-2 Enrich, p. 106

Media and Technology

 Interactive Student Tutorial CD-ROM C-4

Inquiry Challenge

Challenge students to assume they are genetic counselors who must determine the chance of a couple having a child with cystic fibrosis, when both husband and wife are carriers. (*Students should draw a Punnett square for two heterozygotes. The Punnett square should show that 25% of the couple's children would be likely to inherit two recessive alleles.*) Ask: **If the couple already has three normal children, what is the chance that their fourth child will have cystic fibrosis?** (*25%; each child has a 25% chance of having cystic fibrosis.*) **learning modality: logical/mathematical**

3 Assess

Section 2 Review Answers

1. Genetic disorders occur when mutations cause changes in DNA. Cystic fibrosis, sickle-cell disease, hemophilia
2. In amniocentesis, cells are removed from the fluid surrounding the baby; in karyotypes, a picture of the chromosomes is analyzed for abnormal chromosomes.
3. They have an extra copy of chromosome 21, which might arise if the chromosomes fail to separate properly during meiosis.
4. You would want to know if the parents have hemophilia or are carriers. This would help you predict the chances of their baby girl having hemophilia.

Check Your Progress
CHAPTER PROJECT 4
By now students should be working on their pedigrees for the second trait. Remind them to use the same basic pedigree as they did for the first trait. Ask students how they plan to show individuals in the family album.

Performance Assessment

Skills Check Have students explain how amniocentesis and a karyotype can be used to determine whether a developing baby will have Down syndrome.

Family Puzzles

Preparing for Inquiry

Key Concept By analyzing pedigrees, you can determine the pattern of inheritance of a trait and the chance of any given individual inheriting specific alleles.

Skills Objectives Students will be able to
◆ interpret data on phenotypes to construct family pedigrees;
◆ draw conclusions from the pedigrees about the type of alleles controlling the traits and the chances of given individuals inheriting specific alleles for the traits.

Time 40 minutes

Advance Planning To save time, you can cut and label the index cards for students before class begins.

Alternative Materials Instead of index cards to represent alleles, students can use marbles, game chips, beads, or other similar objects, with different colors representing the two different alleles in each case study.

Guiding Inquiry

Invitation Before students begin, draw a simple pedigree on the chalkboard showing a wife with a genetic disorder and a healthy husband who have an affected daughter and a healthy son. Ask: **Can you tell if the trait shown in this pedigree is controlled by a dominant or recessive allele?** *(No, there isn't enough information.)* Extend the pedigree back one generation by adding two healthy parents for the wife. Then ask: **Now can you tell if the trait is controlled by a dominant or recessive allele?** *(The trait must be controlled by a recessive allele; otherwise, at least one of the wife's parents would also have the trait.)* Point out to students that the more generations there are in a pedigree, the more obvious the pattern of inheritance becomes, as they will see when the do this lab.

Introducing the Procedure

◆ Check that students remember how to draw pedigrees. For example, ask: **How do you show in a pedigree that**

a man and woman are married? *(By linking their symbols with a horizontal line)* If necessary, suggest students review *Exploring a Pedigree* on page 118.

Troubleshooting the Experiment

◆ Before students answer the questions, check that they have drawn their pedigrees correctly and labeled each individual with the appropriate genotype(s). You may want to have pairs of students compare pedigrees to detect any errors.

I magine that you are a genetic counselor. Two couples come to you for advice. Their family histories are summarized in the boxes labeled *Case Study 1* and *Case Study 2*. They want to understand the probability that their children might inherit certain genetic disorders. In this lab, you will find answers to their questions.

Problem

How can you investigate inheritance patterns in families?

Materials

12 index cards
scissors
marker

Procedure

Part 1 Investigating Case Study 1

1. Read over Case Study 1. In your notebook, draw a pedigree that shows all the family members. Use circles to represent the females, and squares to represent the males. Shade in the circles or squares representing the individuals who have cystic fibrosis.

Case Study 1: Joshua and Bella

◆ Joshua and Bella have a son named Ian. Ian has been diagnosed with cystic fibrosis.
◆ Joshua and Bella are both healthy.
◆ Bella's parents are both healthy.
◆ Joshua's parents are both healthy.
◆ Joshua's sister, Sara, has cystic fibrosis.

---

2. You know that cystic fibrosis is controlled by a recessive allele. To help you figure out Joshua and Bella's family pattern, create a set of cards to represent the alleles. Cut each of six index cards into four smaller cards. On 12 of the small cards, write *N* to represent the dominant normal allele. On the other 12 small cards, write *n* for the recessive allele.

3. Begin by using the cards to represent Ian's alleles. Since he has cystic fibrosis, what alleles must he have? Write in this genotype next to the pedigree symbol for Ian.

4. Joshua's sister, Sara, also has cystic fibrosis. What alleles does she have? Write in this genotype next to the pedigree symbol that represents Sara.

◆ Tell students they will need to draw Punnett squares to find the answers to Questions 2 and 4.

Expected Outcome

Students should be able to use the data provided to construct a pedigree for each family. From the pedigrees, students should be able to determine the type of allele controlling the skin condition and the probability of particular individuals inheriting each condition.

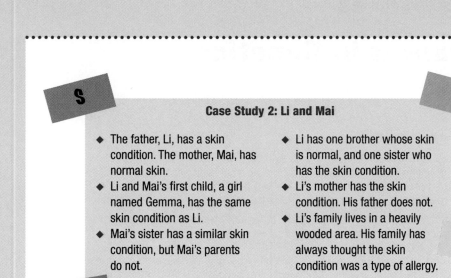

Case Study 2: Li and Mai

- The father, Li, has a skin condition. The mother, Mai, has normal skin.
- Li and Mai's first child, a girl named Gemma, has the same skin condition as Li.
- Mai's sister has a similar skin condition, but Mai's parents do not.
- Li has one brother whose skin is normal, and one sister who has the skin condition.
- Li's mother has the skin condition. His father does not.
- Li's family lives in a heavily wooded area. His family has always thought the skin condition was a type of allergy.

5. Now use the cards to figure out what genotypes Joshua and Bella must have. Write their genotypes next to their symbols in the pedigree.

6. Work with the cards to figure out the genotypes of all other family members. Fill in each person's genotype next to his or her symbol in the pedigree. If more than one genotype is possible, write in both genotypes.

Part 2 Investigating Case Study 2

7. Read over Case Study 2.

8. You suspect that Gemma and Li's skin condition is caused by an inherited recessive allele. Begin to investigate this possibility by drawing a family pedigree in your notebook. Use shading to indicate which individuals have the skin condition.

9. Fill in the genotype *ss* beside each individual who has the skin condition. Then use cards as you did in Case Study 1 to figure out each family member's genotype. If more than one genotype is possible, fill in both genotypes.

Analyze and Conclude

1. In Case Study 1, what were the genotypes of Joshua's parents? What were the genotypes of Bella's parents?

2. In Case Study 1, Joshua also has a brother. What is the probability that he has cystic fibrosis? Explain.

3. Can you conclude that the skin condition in Case Study 2 is most likely an inherited trait controlled by a recessive allele? Explain.

4. What is the probability that Mai and Li's next child will have the skin condition? Explain.

5. **Apply** Why do genetic counselors need information about many generations of a family in order to draw conclusions about a hereditary condition?

More to Explore

Review the two pedigrees that you just studied. What data suggests that the traits are not sex-linked? Explain.

---

condition is controlled by a recessive allele. At least one of Mai's parents would have the skin condition if the allele were dominant, but both of the parents have normal skin.

4. Because one of the parents is heterozygous *(Ss)* and one is homozygous *(ss)* for the skin condition, there is a 50 percent chance of each child inheriting two *s* alleles and having the skin condition.

5. Genetic counselors cannot usually draw firm conclusions about a hereditary condition with information about just one or two generations, because more than one inheritance pattern may explain the facts when the information is so limited. For example, if the only information in Case Study 2 were the phenotypes of Li, Mai, and Gemma, sex-linked inheritance could not be ruled out.

Extending the Inquiry

More to Explore Data showing that the traits are not sex-linked include the observation that the traits affect males and females about equally. If the skin condition in Case Study 2 were sex-linked, Li's brother also would have inherited the condition from their mother, but he did not. If cystic fibrosis in Case Study 1 were sex-linked, Ian would have inherited the disorder from his mother's side of the family, not his father's side of the family, as appears to have been the case.

Case Study 1: Joshua and Bella

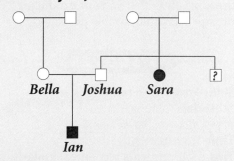

Case Study 2: Li and Mai

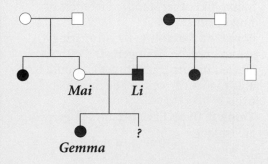

Analyze and Conclude

1. Joshua's parents are both heterozygous *(Nn)*. The genotypes of Bella's parents cannot be determined for certain, but at least one must be heterozygous; the other could be either heterozygous or homozygous *(NN)*.

2. Because both parents are heterozygous *(Nn)*, there is a 25 percent chance of each child inheriting two *n* alleles and having cystic fibrosis.

3. All the evidence in the family's pedigree supports the conclusion that the skin

Program Resources

◆ **Teaching Resources** Chapter 4 Real-World Lab, pp. 111–113

SECTION 3 Advances in Genetics

Objectives

After completing the lesson, students will be able to
◆ describe three ways in which people have developed organisms with desired traits;
◆ explain how DNA fingerprinting is used;
◆ state the goal of the Human Genome Project.

Key Terms selective breeding, inbreeding, hybridization, clone, genetic engineering, gene therapy, genome

1 Engage/Explore

Activating Prior Knowledge

Introduce the section by helping students appreciate the variation that has been selectively bred into dogs. Ask: **What are some breeds of dogs that have very different characteristics?** *(Possible answers might include dachshund, Chihuahua, and Great Dane.)* Explain that the different breeds were produced by mating animals that have certain desirable traits. In this section, students will learn about selective breeding and other ways of producing organisms with desirable traits.

DISCOVER

Skills Focus observing
Materials *plain white paper, ink pad, hand lens*
Time 15 minutes
Tips Help students recognize similarities and differences among the fingerprints by pointing out examples of whirls, loops, and other standard features of fingerprints.
Expected Outcome By comparing a group's unlabeled fingerprint with its labeled fingerprints, students should be able to identify who made the unlabeled print.
Think It Over Each person's fingerprints are unique.

SECTION 3 Advances in Genetics

DISCOVER .... ACTIVITY

What Do Fingerprints Reveal?

1. Label a sheet of paper with your name. Then roll one of your fingers from side to side on an ink pad. Make a fingerprint by carefully rolling your inked finger from side to side on the paper.

2. Divide into groups. Each group should choose one member to use the same finger to make a second fingerprint on a sheet of paper. Leave the paper unlabeled.

3. Exchange your group's fingerprints with those from another group. Compare each labeled fingerprint with the fingerprint on the unlabeled paper. Decide whose fingerprint it is.

4. Wash your hands after completing this activity.

Think It Over
Observing Why are fingerprints a useful tool for identifying people?

GUIDE FOR READING

◆ What are three ways in which an organism's traits can be altered?

◆ What is the goal of the Human Genome Project?

Reading Tip As you read, make a concept map of the methods used to produce organisms with desirable traits. Include at least one example of each technique.

Dolly ▼

In the summer of 1996, a lamb named Dolly was born in Scotland. Dolly was an ordinary lamb in every way except one. The fertilized cell that developed into Dolly was produced in a laboratory by geneticists using experimental techniques. You will learn more about the techniques used by the geneticists later in the section.

Although the techniques used to create Dolly are new, the idea of producing organisms with specific traits is not. For thousands of years, people have tried to produce plants and animals with desirable traits. **Three methods that people have used to develop organisms with desirable traits are selective breeding, cloning, and genetic engineering.**

Selective Breeding

More than 5,000 years ago, people living in what is now central Mexico discovered that a type of wild grass could be used as food. They saved the seeds from those plants that produced the best food, and planted them to grow new plants. By repeating this process over many generations of plants, they developed an early variety of the food crop we now call corn. The process of selecting a few organisms with desired traits to serve as parents of the next generation is called **selective breeding.**

People have used selective breeding with many different plants and animals. Breeding programs usually focus on increasing the value of the plant or animal to people. For

---

READING STRATEGIES

Reading Tip Students' concept maps should show that inbreeding and hybridization are two types of selective breeding and that cloning and genetic engineering are additional methods used to produce organisms with desirable traits.

Study and Comprehension Before students read the section, suggest that they make an outline using the boldfaced headings and subheadings. Then, as students read the section, urge them to add a sentence or two under each heading to summarize the main points. Encourage visual learners to preview the section by looking at the figures and reading the captions.

Vocabulary Help students understand the technical material presented in the section by having them write definitions of the bold-faced terms as they read.

example, dairy cows are bred to produce larger quantities of milk. Many varieties of fruits and vegetables are bred to resist diseases and insect pests.

Inbreeding One useful selective breeding technique is called inbreeding. **Inbreeding** involves crossing two individuals that have identical or similar sets of alleles. The organisms that result from inbreeding have alleles that are very similar to those of their parents. Mendel used inbreeding to produce purebred pea plants to use in his experiments.

One goal of inbreeding is to produce breeds of animals with specific traits. For example, by only crossing horses with exceptional speed, breeders can produce purebred horses that can run very fast. Purebred dogs, such as Labrador retrievers and German shepherds, were produced by inbreeding.

Unfortunately, because inbred organisms are genetically similar, inbreeding reduces an offspring's chances of inheriting new allele combinations. Inbreeding also increases the probability that organisms may inherit alleles that lead to genetic disorders. For example, inherited hip problems are common in many breeds of dogs.

Hybridization Another selective breeding technique is called hybridization. In **hybridization** (hy brid ih ZAY shun), breeders cross two genetically different individuals. The hybrid organism that results is bred to have the best traits from both parents. For example, a farmer might cross corn that produces many kernels with corn that is resistant to disease. The result might be a hybrid corn plant with both of the desired traits. Today, most crops grown on farms and in gardens were produced by hybridization.

Figure 12 For thousands of years, people have used selective breeding to produce plants and animals with desirable traits. *Making Generalizations What are some traits for which corn may be bred?*

---

2 *Facilitate*

Selective Breeding

Cultural Diversity

Provide students with additional information about selective breeding to help them appreciate its significance throughout human history. For example, thousands of years ago, Some Native Americans began domesticating plant species. They genetically changed plant species by cross-pollinating plants with desired traits. Eventually, more than 100 different species of plants were domesticated, of which maize, or corn, is probably the most important. Maize was selectively bred by Native Americans to have larger, more numerous kernels. Conclude by asking: **How do you think the selective breeding of plants such as maize would have affected the people who depended on the plants for food?** *(It would have increased the amount of food available, so people could have been better fed or more people could have been fed.)* **learning modality: verbal**

Real-Life Learning

Materials *seed catalogs*
Time 10 minutes

Help students appreciate the importance of hybridization in real life by giving them an opportunity to examine seed catalogs and read about hybrid varieties of flowers, vegetables, and fruits that have been developed by plant breeders. Ask: **What are some traits for which hybrids have been bred?** *(Students might name rapid growth or improved flavor, among many other possible traits.)* **learning modality: verbal**

Ongoing Assessment

Drawing Have students draw two Punnett squares, one to represent inbreeding and one to represent hybridization. *(To represent inbreeding, students should show a cross between individuals with the same genotype, such as* AA $\times$ AA. *To represent hybridization, students should show a cross between individuals with different genotypes, such as* AA $\times$ aa.)

Media and Technology

 Audiotapes English-Spanish Summary 4-3

 Exploring Life Science Videodisc Unit 5, Side 1, "Breeding for Dollars"   Chapter 2

Answers to Self-Assessment

Caption Question

Figure 12 Some traits include resistance to disease and the production of ears with many kernels.

Program Resources

◆ **Teaching Resources** 4-3 Lesson Plan, p. 107; 4-3 Section Summary, p. 108

Cloning

Demonstration

Materials *coleus plant,* *scissors, rooting solution, plant pot, vermiculite, water*

Time 5 minutes; 5 minutes two weeks later

Demonstrate how a plant can be cloned. Take a small cutting from a coleus plant, dip the cut end of the stem in rooting solution, and place the cutting in a pot of vermiculite. Keep the vermiculite moist, and after about two weeks gently pull the cutting out of the pot. Let students observe the tiny roots that have started to grow, and ask: **How is the new plant that grew from the cutting like the original plant from which the cutting was taken?** *(It is genetically identical to the original plant.)* **learning modality: visual**

Integrating Social Studies

Inform students that the cloning of Dolly the sheep raised the possibility of large-scale animal cloning, and that this, in turn, raised many ethical issues. Challenge students to use the Internet or other resources to learn more about animal cloning by finding answers to such questions as: **Is animal cloning unnatural? Would it narrow genetic diversity too much? What are some of its possible uses?** Encourage students to form their own opinions on the subject and share their findings in an oral report to the class. **learning modality: verbal**

Genetic Engineering

Addressing Naive Conceptions

The term *genetic engineering* may conjure up images of mad scientists and Frankenstein-type monsters. Address this naive conception by describing one or more real-life examples of genetic engineering, such as the production of bacteria that can manufacture human insulin or corn plants that can resist disease. Then ask: **Why do you think people hold naive conceptions about genetic engineering?** *(Because of fictional accounts in movies and books or lack of knowledge)* **learning modality: verbal**

Figure 13 Plants can be easily cloned by making a cutting. Once the cutting has grown roots, it can be planted and will grow into a new plant. *Applying Concepts* Why is the new plant considered to be a clone of the original plant?

Cloning

One problem with selective breeding is that the breeder cannot control whether the desired allele will be passed from the parent to its offspring. This is because the transmission of alleles is determined by probability, as you learned in Chapter 3. For some organisms, another technique, called cloning, can be used to produce offspring with desired traits. A **clone** is an organism that is genetically identical to the organism from which it was produced. This means that a clone has exactly the same genes as the organism from which it was produced. Cloning can be done in plants and animals, as well as other organisms.

Cloning Plants One way to produce a clone of a plant is through a cutting. A cutting is a small part of a plant, such as a leaf or a stem, that is cut from the plant. The cutting can grow into an entire new plant. The new plant is genetically identical to the plant from which the cutting was taken.

Cloning Animals Producing a clone of an animal is much more difficult than producing a clone of a plant. It isn't possible to use a cutting from a cow to produce a new cow. However, scientists have been experimenting with various techniques to produce clones of animals. Remember Dolly, the lamb described at the beginning of this section? Dolly was the first clone of an adult mammal ever produced.

To create Dolly, researchers first removed an egg cell from one sheep. The cell's nucleus was replaced with the nucleus from a cell of a six-year-old sheep. The egg was then implanted into the uterus of a third sheep. Five months later, Dolly was born. Dolly is genetically identical to the six-year-old sheep that supplied the cell nucleus. Dolly is a clone of that sheep.

Checkpoint How can a clone of a plant be produced?

Genetic Engineering

In the past few decades, geneticists have developed another powerful technique for producing organisms with desired traits. In this process, called **genetic engineering,** genes from one organism are transferred into the DNA of another organism. Genetic engineering is sometimes called "gene splicing" because a DNA molecule is cut open and a gene from another organism is spliced into it. Researchers use genetic engineering to produce medicines, to improve food crops, and to try to cure human genetic disorders.

Background

History of Science Since the structure of DNA was discovered in 1953, genetic research has advanced significantly. In 1959, Down syndrome was traced to the presence of an extra 21st chromosome, making it the first documented example of a genetic disorder. Geneticists successfully spliced together DNA segments from a toad cell and a bacterial cell, giving rise to the science of genetic engineering in 1973. In 1982,

scientists inserted rat growth hormone genes into some fertilized mouse eggs. The eggs developed into mice that grew nearly twice as large as mice without the gene for rat growth hormone. In 1990, researchers successfully inserted a gene needed for the functioning of the human immune system into a patient with ADA, a fatal immune system disorder.

EXPLORING Genetic Engineering

Scientists use genetic engineering to create bacterial cells that produce important human proteins, such as insulin.

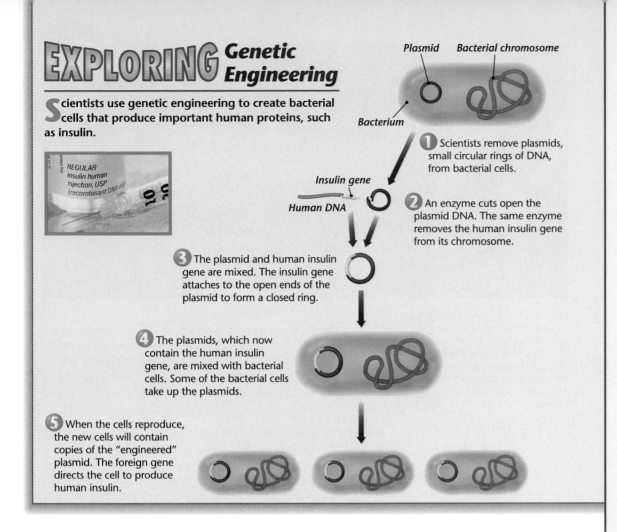

Plasmid   Bacterial chromosome

Bacterium

1 Scientists remove plasmids, small circular rings of DNA, from bacterial cells.

Insulin gene

Human DNA

2 An enzyme cuts open the plasmid DNA. The same enzyme removes the human insulin gene from its chromosome.

3 The plasmid and human insulin gene are mixed. The insulin gene attaches to the open ends of the plasmid to form a closed ring.

4 The plasmids, which now contain the human insulin gene, are mixed with bacterial cells. Some of the bacterial cells take up the plasmids.

5 When the cells reproduce, the new cells will contain copies of the "engineered" plasmid. The foreign gene directs the cell to produce human insulin.

Genetic Engineering in Bacteria Researchers had their first successes with genetic engineering when they inserted DNA from other organisms into bacteria. Recall that the single DNA molecule of bacterial cells is found in the cytoplasm. Some bacterial cells also contain small circular pieces of DNA called plasmids.

In *Exploring Genetic Engineering,* you can see how scientists insert a human gene into the plasmid of a bacterium. Once the DNA is spliced into the plasmid, the bacterial cell and all its offspring will contain this human gene. As a result, the bacteria produce the protein that the human gene codes for, in this case insulin. Because bacteria reproduce quickly, large amounts of insulin can be produced in a short time. The insulin can be collected and used to treat people with diabetes, a disorder in which the body does not produce enough of this protein.

Program Resources

Science Explorer Series *From Bacteria to Plants,* Chapter 2, has more information about bacteria.

Media and Technology

Transparencies "Genetic Engineering," Transparency 16

Answers to Self-Assessment
Caption Question
Figure 13 The new plant is genetically identical to the original plant.

☑ *Checkpoint*
By growing a cutting of the original plant

EXPLORING
Genetic Engineering

Provide students with background information about diabetes so they can appreciate the importance of genetically engineering bacteria to produce human insulin. Insulin is a hormone that cells need to absorb sugar from the blood for energy. People with diabetes cannot produce insulin. As a result, their cells are unable to absorb sugar from the blood, and the sugar level in their blood can become dangerously high. Taking insulin helps people with diabetes control the level of sugar in their blood, which helps prevent life-threatening complications of the disease.

Guide students who need more help by asking questions that will require them to read the captions carefully. For example, ask: **What is a plasmid, and where is it found?** (*A small circular ring of DNA in a bacterial cell*) **Why are the bacteria in Step 5 able to produce human insulin?** (*Because they contain copies of the human insulin gene.*)
limited English proficiency

Inquiry Challenge
Materials *two pieces of yarn of different colors, blunt scissors, tape*
Time 10 minutes

Challenge students to create a simple model of DNA with yarn and then to use the model to simulate gene splicing, as illustrated in *Exploring Genetic Engineering.* (*The most likely way is to arrange a piece of yarn of one color in a circle to represent a bacterial plasmid and to use the piece of yarn of the other color to represent a small section of human DNA. Gene splicing can be simulated by cutting both pieces of yarn, taping a piece of the "DNA" yarn to the piece of "plasmid" yarn, and reforming the circle.*) Ask: **What do the scissors represent in your model?** (*The enzyme that cuts the DNA*)
learning modality: kinesthetic

Ongoing Assessment

Skills Check Have students compare and contrast cloning and genetic engineering.

Genetic Engineering, continued

Inquiry Challenge

Challenge students to think of ways that plants could be genetically engineered to increase the production of food. Ask: **How could you genetically engineer a fruit, vegetable, or other food plant so that it would be more likely to survive and thrive?** *(Ways that food plants actually have been genetically engineered include making plants that are able to tolerate poor soil or resist disease.)* **learning modality: logical/mathematical**

Real-Life Learning

Point out that genetic engineering, particularly of food plants, has led to public concern about the potential consequences to consumers and the environment. Urge students who need extra challenges to learn more about the issues and form their own opinions. Then call on these students to debate the issues, with students on one side arguing that the genetic engineering of food plants should be unregulated and students on the other side arguing that the genetic engineering of food plants should be closely regulated or even outlawed. The debate should address such questions as: **What are the potential dangers of genetically engineered foods?** *(Potential dangers include the short and long term human health risks and the ecological impact that genetically engineered foods might have.)* **What are the potential benefits?** *(Foods might be more nutritious, keep longer, or be easier to transport. Also plants and animals can be genetically engineered to be raised under a wider range of conditions.)* After the debate, encourage the rest of the class to comment on which side was more convincing and why. **cooperative learning**

Figure 14 Scientists created this new variety of tomatoes using genetic engineering. The tomatoes taste better and keep longer than other varieties. *Making Judgments What other traits would be desirable in tomatoes?*

Today, many human proteins are produced in genetically engineered bacteria. For example, human growth hormone is a protein that controls the growth process in children. Children whose bodies do not produce enough human growth hormone can be given injections of the hormone. Today, an unlimited supply of the hormone exists, thanks to genetically engineered bacteria.

Genetic Engineering in Other Organisms Genetic engineering has also been used to insert genes into the cells of other organisms. Scientists have inserted genes from bacteria into the cells of tomatoes, wheat, rice, and other important crops. Some of the genes enable the plants to survive in colder temperatures or in poor soil conditions, and to resist insect pests.

Genetic engineering techniques can also be used to insert genes into animals, which then produce important medicines for humans. For example, scientists can insert human genes into the cells of cows. The cows then produce the human protein for which the gene codes. Scientists have used this technique to produce the blood clotting protein needed by people with hemophilia. The protein is produced in the cows' milk, and can easily be extracted and used to treat people with the disorder.

Gene Therapy Researchers are also using genetic engineering to try to correct some genetic disorders. This process, called **gene therapy,** involves inserting working copies of a gene directly into the cells of a person with a genetic disorder. For example, people with cystic fibrosis do not produce a protein that is needed for proper lung function. Both copies of the gene that codes for the protein are defective in these people.

Background

Facts and Figures Two major problems must be solved in developing gene therapy for a particular genetic disorder. The first problem is finding the best way to correct the genetic defect that is causing the disorder. Options may include correcting or increasing the defective cell product, making diseased cells weaker or more vulnerable, or blocking the operation of diseased cells. The other problem that must be solved is finding a way to carry the genetically engineered DNA to target cells. Because of their ability to infect living cells, viruses make excellent candidates for this role. However, before a virus can be used safely, the viral DNA must be genetically engineered to make the virus harmless to the human patient.

Scientists can insert working copies of the gene into harmless viruses. The "engineered" viruses can then be sprayed into the lungs of patients with cystic fibrosis. Researchers hope that the working copies of the gene in the viruses will function in the patient to produce the protein. Gene therapy is still an experimental method for treating genetic disorders. Researchers are working hard to improve this promising technique.

DNA Fingerprinting

In courtrooms across the country, a genetic technique called DNA fingerprinting is being used to help solve crimes. If you did the Discover activity, you know that fingerprints can help to identify people. No two people have the same fingerprints. Detectives routinely use fingerprints found at a crime scene to help identify the person who committed the crime. In a similar way, DNA from samples of hair, skin, and blood can also be used to identify a person. No two people, except for identical twins, have the same DNA.

In DNA fingerprinting, enzymes are used to cut the DNA in the sample found at a crime scene into fragments. An electrical current then separates the fragments by size to form a pattern of bands, like the ones you see in Figure 15. Each person's pattern of DNA bands is unique. The DNA pattern can then be compared to the pattern produced by DNA taken from people suspected of committing the crime.

☑ *Checkpoint* *In what way is DNA like fingerprints?*

Figure 15 This scientist is explaining how DNA fingerprinting can be used to help solve crimes. DNA from blood or other substances collected at a crime scene can be compared to DNA from a suspect's blood.

Chapter 4 **C ♦ 131**

Addressing Naive Conceptions

Students may develop the naive conception that all genetic disorders will soon be cured with gene therapy. Point out that gene therapy is unlikely to be developed, at least not any time soon, for diabetes, heart disease, or most types of cancer, because these diseases are also influenced by the environment. Conclude by asking: **Besides cystic fibrosis, which genetic disorders are good candidates for gene therapy?** (*Students' responses should reflect their understanding that gene therapy is most likely to lead to cures for genetic disorders caused by single genes, such as hemophilia or sickle-cell disease.*) **learning modality: logical/mathematical**

DNA Fingerprinting

Sharpen your Skills

Communicating

Time 15 minutes
Tips Advise students to **ACTIVITY** pretend they are explaining DNA fingerprinting to a friend who has no knowledge of genetics.
Expected Outcome Students should write a paragraph explaining the process of DNA fingerprinting in simple terms. Their paragraph should make it clear that each cell contains a complete set of a person's DNA and that each person, with the exception of identical twins, has DNA that is unique.
Extend Tell students that before DNA fingerprinting was developed, blood typing often was used for identification purposes. Ask: **Why is blood typing a less accurate way of identifying an individual?** (*Because many people have the same blood type*) **learning modality: verbal**

Answers to Self-Assessment

Caption Question

Figure 14 Other traits might include deep red color, large size, and firmness.

☑ *Checkpoint*

DNA, like fingerprints, is unique to each person, except for identical twins.

The Human Genome Project

Building Inquiry Skills: Communicating

Give students who need extra challenges a chance to learn more about the Human Genome Project and communicate what they learn in a report to the class. Students can get up-to-date information on the project from the following Internet site: **www.ornl.gov/TechResources/ Human_Genome/ learning modality: verbal**

3 Assess

Section 3 Review Answers

1. Inbreeding, hybridization, and cloning
2. To learn what makes the body work and what causes things to go wrong
3. The process of transferring genes from one organism into the DNA of another organism; produce medicines, improve food crops, treat human genetic disorders
4. It is produced by cutting the DNA from a sample of hair, skin, or blood into fragments and separating the fragments by size to form a pattern of bands. It can reveal who committed a crime by identifying the person who left the sample at the crime scene.
5. Answers may vary. Make sure students give logical, well-founded reasons to support their position.

Science at Home

Tips Other vegetables and fruits that students might focus on because of their variety are squash and pears. Suggest that students ask the store's produce manager what traits each variety is known for.

Performance Assessment

Skills Check Have students infer how the completion of the Human Genome Project might lead to advances in gene therapy.

Figure 16 The Human Genome Project is an attempt to identify the sequence of every DNA base pair in the human genome.

The Human Genome Project

Imagine trying to crack a code that is 3 billion characters long. Then imagine working with people all over the world to accomplish this task. That's exactly what scientists working on the Human Genome Project are doing. A **genome** is all the DNA in one cell of an organism. Researchers estimate that the 23 pairs of chromosomes that make up the human genome contain about 60,000 to 80,000 genes—or about 3 billion DNA base pairs.

The main goal of the Human Genome Project is to identify the DNA sequence of every gene in the human genome. When the Human Genome Project is completed, an encyclopedia of genetic information about humans will be available. Scientists will know the DNA sequence of every human gene, and thus the amino acid sequence of every protein.

With the information from the Human Genome Project, researchers may gain a better understanding of how humans develop from a fertilized egg to an adult. They may also learn what makes the body work, and what causes things to go wrong. New understandings may lead to new treatments and prevention strategies for many genetic disorders and for diseases such as cancer.

Section 3 Review

1. Name three techniques that people have used to produce organisms with desired traits.
2. Why do scientists want to identify the DNA sequence of every human gene?
3. What is genetic engineering? Describe three possible benefits of this technique.
4. Explain how a DNA fingerprint is produced. What information can a DNA fingerprint reveal?
5. **Thinking Critically Making Judgments** Do you think there should be any limitations on genetic engineering? Give reasons to support your position.

Science at Home

With a parent or other adult family member, go to a grocery store. Look at the different varieties of potatoes, apples, and other fruits and vegetables. Discuss how these varieties were created by selective breeding. Then chose one type of fruit or vegetable and make a list of different varieties. If possible, find out what traits each variety was bred for.

Background

Facts and Figures The Human Genome Project was started in 1990. By early 1999, about 480 million of the 3 billion base pairs in the human genome, or about 10 percent, had been sequenced. When completed, a listing of all the base pairs in the human genome will fill many volumes of an encyclopedia.

Program Resources

◆ **Teaching Resources** 4-3 Review and Reinforce, p. 109; 4-3 Enrich, p. 110

Media and Technology

 Interactive Student Tutorial CD-ROM C-4

Who Should Have Access to Genetic Test Results?

Scientists working on the Human Genome Project have identified many alleles that put people at risk for certain diseases, such as breast cancer and Alzheimer's disease. Through techniques known as genetic testing, people can have their DNA analyzed to find out whether they have any of these alleles. If they do, they may be able to take steps to prevent the illness or to seek early treatment.

Some health insurance companies and employers want access to this type of genetic information. However, many people believe that genetic testing results should be kept private.

The Issues

Why Do Insurance Companies Want Genetic Information? Health insurance companies set their rates based on a person's risk of health problems. To determine a person's insurance rate, insurance companies often require that a person have a physical examination. If the examination reveals a condition such as high blood pressure, the company may charge that person more for an insurance policy. This is because he or she would be more likely to need expensive medical care.

Insurance companies view genetic testing as an additional way to gather information about a person's health status. Insurers argue that if they were unable to gather this information, they would need to raise rates for everyone. This would be unfair to people who are in good health.

Why Do Employers Want Genetic Information? Federal laws forbid employers with 15 or more workers from choosing job applicants based on their health status. These laws do not apply to smaller companies, however. Employers may not want to hire employees with health problems because they often miss more work time than other employees. In addition, employers who hire people with health problems may be charged higher health insurance rates. Many small companies cannot afford to pay these higher rates.

Should Genetic Information Be Kept Private? Some people think that the government should prohibit all access to genetic information. Today, some people fear that they will be discriminated against as a result of genetic test results. Because of this fear, some people avoid genetic testing—even though testing might allow them to seek early treatment for a disorder. These people want tighter control of genetic information. They want to be sure that insurers and employers will not have access to genetic test results.

You Decide

1. Identify the Problem
In your own words, explain the problem of deciding who should have access to genetic test results.

2. Analyze the Options
Examine the pros and cons of keeping genetic test results private. List reasons to maintain privacy. List reasons why test results should be shared.

3. Find a Solution
Create a list of rules to control access to genetic information. Who should have access, and under what circumstances? Explain your reasoning.

SCIENCE AND SOCIETY

Who Should Have Access to Genetic Test Results?

Purpose To provide students with an introduction to the ethical problems raised by genetic testing.

Panel Discussion

Time a day to prepare; 30 minutes for panel discussion

Choose students to play the following roles in a panel discussion: the CEO of a health insurance company, the president of an association of small business owners, the doctor who presides over the American Medical Association, the spokesperson for a patients' rights group, the director of a diabetes foundation, and the president of a worker's union. Urge each panel member to take the point of view they believe the person they represent would actually take on issues relating to genetic testing. Other students should take notes during the discussion and ask questions afterward. The panel discussion should begin with each panel member briefly stating his or her position regarding who should have access to genetic test results. Then panel members should take turns presenting arguments in support of their statements.
Extend Challenge students to find out more about genetic testing by interviewing a lab technician, nurse, or doctor. Suggest that they ask such questions as: **What genetic tests are commonly performed today? What are some reasons genetic testing is done?**

You Decide

Help students keep to the point by challenging them to explain the problem in a single sentence. Reasons for sharing genetic test results can be found in the first two paragraphs. Reasons for keeping genetic test results private can be found in the last paragraph. In addition, encourage students to think of reasons of their own. If students are having difficulty creating a list of rules, suggest that they first decide what they believe are acceptable uses for genetic information. This will help them decide who should control it and under what circumstances.

Guilty or Innocent?

Preparing for Inquiry

Key Concept A person's DNA forms a unique pattern of bands that can be used to identify the person.

Skills Objectives Students will be able to
- use bar codes as models of DNA fingerprints;
- observe similarities and differences in the patterns of bands on the bar codes;
- draw conclusions about which suspect was present at the crime scene based on the comparisons.

Time 20 minutes

Advance Planning Remove bar codes from commercial products and cut the numbers from them. Each students' set of bar codes should contain one that is identical to the bar code from the crime scene. You could mount the bar codes on heavy paper so they can be reused.

Alternative Materials If you can obtain actual DNA fingerprints, the lab will be more realistic. Provide a hand lens for any student who has vision problems.

Guiding Inquiry

Troubleshooting the Experiment
- Advise students to examine the patterns of bands very carefully, because the differences may be minor and easily overlooked.

Expected Outcome
Students should find that one of the suspect DNA samples is identical to the DNA sample from the crime scene.

Analyze and Conclude
1. The suspect whose DNA sample matches the DNA sample from the crime scene must have been present at the crime scene.
2. DNA patterns differ so greatly because no two people, except for identical twins, have the same sequence of bases in their DNA.
3. The twin's DNA pattern would be identical to the suspect's, making it impossible to conclude which individual

---

Guilty or Innocent?

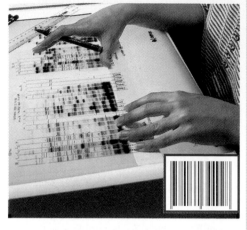

In this lab, you will investigate how DNA fingerprinting can be used to provide evidence related to a crime.

Problem

How can DNA be used to identify individuals?

Skills Focus

observing, making models, drawing conclusions

Materials

4–6 bar codes

Procedure

1. Look at the photograph of DNA band patterns shown at right. Each person's DNA produces a unique pattern of these bands.
2. Now look at the Universal Product Code, also called a bar code, shown below the DNA bands. A bar code can be used as a model of a DNA band pattern. Compare the bar code with the DNA bands to see what they have in common. Record your observations.
3. Suppose that a burglary has taken place, and you're the detective leading the investigation. Your teacher will give you a bar code that represents DNA from blood found at the crime scene. You arrange to have DNA samples taken from several suspects. Write a sentence describing what you will look for as you try to match each suspect's DNA to the DNA sample from the crime scene.
4. You will now be given bar codes representing DNA samples taken from the suspects. Compare those bar codes with the bar code that represents DNA from the crime scene.

5. Use your comparisons to determine whether any of the suspects was present at the crime scene.

Analyze and Conclude

1. Based on your findings, were any of the suspects present at the crime scene? Support your conclusion with specific evidence.
2. Why do people's DNA patterns differ so greatly?
3. How would your conclusions be affected if you learned that the suspect whose DNA matched the evidence had an identical twin?
4. **Apply** In everyday life, do you think that DNA evidence is enough to determine that a suspect committed the crime? Explain.

More to Explore

Do you think the DNA fingerprints of a parent and a child would show any similarities? Draw what you think they would look like. Then explain your thinking.

---

had been at the crime scene.

4. Students may say that DNA evidence alone is not enough, because it only identifies who was at the crime scene and not who actually committed the crime. Students also may say that errors can be made in analyzing the DNA evidence.

Extending the Inquiry

More to Explore The DNA fingerprints of a parent and a child should look more similar than the DNA fingerprints of unrelated people, because parents and children share many of the same genes.

Program Resources

- **Teaching Resources** Chapter 4 Real-World Lab, pp. 114–115

SECTION 1 — Human Inheritance

Key Ideas

◆ Some human traits are controlled by a single gene that has multiple alleles—three or more forms.

◆ Some human traits show a wide range of phenotypes because these traits are controlled by many genes. The genes act together as a group to produce a single trait.

◆ Traits are often influenced by the organism's environment.

◆ Males have one X chromosome and one Y chromosome. Females have two X chromosomes. Males are more likely than females to have a sex-linked trait controlled by a recessive allele.

◆ Geneticists use pedigrees to trace the inheritance pattern of a particular trait through a number of generations of a family.

Key Terms

multiple alleles   carrier
sex-linked gene   pedigree

SECTION 2 — Human Genetic Disorders

Key Ideas

◆ Genetic disorders are abnormal conditions that are caused by mutations, or DNA changes, in genes or chromosomes.

◆ Common genetic disorders include cystic fibrosis, sickle-cell disease, hemophilia, and Down syndrome.

◆ Amniocentesis and karyotypes are tools used to diagnose genetic disorders.

◆ Genetic counselors help couples understand their chances of having a child with a genetic disorder.

Key Terms

genetic disorder   karyotype
amniocentesis

SECTION 3 — Advances in Genetics

INTEGRATING TECHNOLOGY

Key Ideas

◆ Selective breeding is the process of selecting a few organisms with desired traits to serve as parents of the next generation.

◆ Cloning is a technique used to produce genetically identical organisms.

◆ Genetic engineering can be used to produce medicines and to improve food crops. Researchers are also using genetic engineering to try to cure human genetic disorders.

◆ DNA fingerprinting can be used to help determine whether material found at a crime scene came from a particular suspect.

◆ The goal of the Human Genome Project is to identify the DNA sequence of every gene in the human genome.

Key Terms

selective breeding
inbreeding
hybridization
clone
genetic engineering
gene therapy
genome

USING THE INTERNET

www.science-explorer.phschool.com

Program Resources

◆ **Teaching Resources** Chapter 4 Project Scoring Rubric, p. 98; Chapter 4 Performance Assessment, pp. 173–175; Chapter 4 Test, pp. 176–179

Media and Technology

Interactive Student Tutorial CD-ROM C-4

Computer Test Bank Test C-4

Reviewing Content
Multiple Choice
1. b 2. c 3. a 4. d 5. c

True or False
6. true 7. female 8. pedigree
9. Inbreeding 10. true

Checking Concepts
11. The four or more genes that control height determine the maximum height that a person can attain. The environment, particularly diet, medical care, and living conditions, determines whether or not the person reaches the potential maximum height.
12. Traits controlled by recessive alleles on the X chromosome are more common in males than in females because males need to inherit just one allele to have the trait, whereas females need to inherit two alleles.
13. Sickle-cell disease is a genetic disorder in which red blood cells contain an abnormal form of hemoglobin. People who have the disease inherit a copy of the affected allele from each parent.
14. In amniocentesis, a doctor removes fluid surrounding a growing baby so that the baby's chromosomes can be analyzed. Down syndrome is present if there is an extra copy of chromosome 21.
15. The horse breeder would mate only horses that have golden coats.
16. To treat hemophilia with gene therapy, doctors would give the person with hemophilia a virus containing the normal gene for the missing blood-clotting protein. The viral DNA would infect the person's cells and lead to the production of the missing protein.
17. Students should identify the genetic disorder they chose and then describe its symptoms, how it is inherited, and how it is treated. Check that students' answers accurately reflect the information provided in the text.

Thinking Visually
18. a. Single genes b. Many genes
c. Blood type d. Colorblindness (or Hemophilia) *Sample title:* The Inheritance of Human Traits

Reviewing Content

 For more review of key concepts, see the Interactive Student Tutorial CD-ROM.

Multiple Choice
Choose the letter of the best answer.

1. A human trait that is controlled by multiple alleles is
   a. dimples.   b. blood type.
   c. height.   d. skin color.
2. A genetic disorder caused by a sex-linked gene is
   a. cystic fibrosis.
   b. sickle-cell disease.
   c. hemophilia.
   d. Down syndrome.
3. Sickle-cell disease is characterized by
   a. abnormally shaped red blood cells.
   b. abnormally thick body fluids.
   c. abnormal blood clotting.
   d. an extra copy of chromosome 21.
4. Inserting a human gene into a bacterial plasmid is an example of
   a. inbreeding.
   b. selective breeding.
   c. DNA fingerprinting.
   d. genetic engineering.
5. DNA fingerprinting is a way to
   a. clone organisms.
   b. breed organisms with desirable traits.
   c. identify people.
   d. map and sequence human genes.

True or False
If the statement is true, write true. If it is false, change the underlined word or words to make the statement true.

6. A <u>widow's peak</u> is a human trait that is controlled by a single gene.
7. A person who inherits two X chromosomes will be <u>male</u>.
8. A <u>karyotype</u> is a chart that shows the relationships between the generations of a family.
9. <u>Hybridization</u> is the crossing of two genetically similar organisms.
10. A <u>clone</u> is an organism that is genetically identical to another organism.

Checking Concepts
11. Explain how both genes and the environment determine how tall a person will be.
12. Explain why traits controlled by recessive alleles on the X chromosome are more common in males than in females.
13. What is sickle-cell disease? How is this disorder inherited?
14. How can amniocentesis be used to detect a disorder such as Down syndrome?
15. Explain how a horse breeder might use selective breeding to produce horses that have golden coats.
16. Describe how gene therapy might be used in the future to treat a person with hemophilia.
17. **Writing to Learn** As the webmaster for a national genetics foundation, you must create a Web site to inform the public about genetic disorders. Choose one human genetic disorder discussed in this chapter. Write a description of the disorder that you will use for the Web site.

Thinking Visually
18. **Concept Map** Copy the concept map about human traits onto a separate sheet of paper. Then complete it and add a title. (For more on concept maps, see the Skills Handbook.)

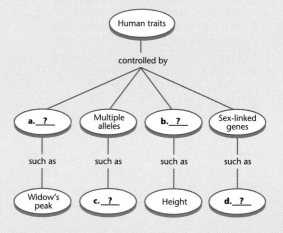

Applying Skills
19. The top row of the pedigree should show a half-shaded circle (Helen) connected with a half-shaded square (Bob), indicating that both parents are carriers for albinism. The second row should show two unshaded circles (the two daughters) and a shaded square (the affected son).
20. Albinism must be controlled by a recessive allele, because otherwise either Bob or Helen also would have the condition.
21. Both Bob and Helen must be carriers of the albinism allele in order to have an affected child, so there is a 25 percent chance that any child would have albinism.

Thinking Critically
22. Selective breeding is based on phenotypes. Therefore, ancient people could selectively breed corn without knowing about genes and inheritance by using seeds only from the plants that had the traits they desired.
23. If the mother is a carrier of hemophilia, one of her X chromosomes has the allele for

Applying Skills

A genetic counselor has gathered the information listed below. Use the information to answer Questions 19–21.

- Bob and Helen have three children.
- Bob and Helen have one son who has albinism, an inherited condition in which the skin does not have brown pigments.
- Bob and Helen have two daughters who do not have albinism.
- Neither Bob nor Helen has albinism.
- Albinism is neither sex-linked nor codominant.

19. Interpreting Data Use the information to construct a pedigree. If you don't know whether someone is a carrier, leave their symbol empty. If you decide later that a person is a carrier, change your pedigree.

20. Drawing Conclusions Is albinism controlled by a dominant allele or by a recessive allele? Explain your answer.

21. Predicting Suppose Bob and Helen were to have another child. What is the probability that the child will have albinism? Explain.

Thinking Critically

22. Inferring How could ancient people selectively breed corn if they didn't know about genes and inheritance?

23. Calculating If a mother is a carrier of hemophilia, what is the probability that her son will have the trait? Explain your answer.

24. Comparing and Contrasting How are selective breeding and genetic engineering different? How are they similar?

25. Applying Concepts Why can a person be a carrier of a trait caused by a recessive allele but not of a trait caused by a dominant allele?

26. Problem Solving A woman with normal color vision has a colorblind daughter. What are the genotypes and phenotypes of both parents?

CHAPTER 4 REVIEW

Performance Assessment

CHAPTER PROJECT 4

Wrap Up

Present Your Project Before displaying your project, exchange your pedigrees and photo album with another group to check each other's work. Make any necessary corrections, and then display your materials to the class. Be ready to explain the inheritance patterns shown in your pedigrees.

Reflect and Record In your journal, describe what you learned by creating the pedigrees. Which part of this project was the most challenging for you? Why? What questions do you have as a result of the project?

Getting Involved

In Your Community With your teacher's permission, invite a doctor, nurse, or genetic counselor to speak about some of the genetic disorders discussed in the chapter. Prepare a list of questions for the speaker. After the speaker's talk, write a short summary of what you learned.

Chapter 4 C ◆ 137

---

normal clotting and the other X chromosome has the allele for hemophilia. The son has a 50 percent chance of inheriting an X chromosome that carries the allele for hemophilia, and therefore of having hemophilia.

24. Both selective breeding and genetic engineering are ways of producing organisms with desirable traits. Selective breeding involves restricting matings to those individuals who have the desirable traits. Genetic engineering involves inserting genes for the desirable traits into an individual's genome.

25. A person can be a carrier of a trait caused by recessive allele because two alleles are needed for the trait to be expressed. If the person has only one recessive allele for the trait, he or she will not have the trait, but will be a carrier. However, a person cannot be a carrier of a trait caused by a dominant allele because

Program Resources

- **Inquiry Skills Activity Book** Provides teaching and review of all inquiry skills

---

if the person has only one dominant allele, he or she will have the trait.
26. The mother has normal color vision but is a carrier of the colorblindness allele. Her genotype is $X^C X^c$. The father is colorblind. His genotype is $X^c Y$.

Performance Assessment

CHAPTER PROJECT 4

Wrap Up
Present Your Project
Before students make their presentations, give them a chance to exchange their pedigrees and family albums with other students for feedback and to make any corrections or other changes. Have each student trace each of their family's traits through the pedigree from generation to generation and point out individuals in the family album with each possible phenotype for the two traits. Make sure that the family album is consistent with the information in the pedigrees.
Reflect and Record After all the students have presented their projects, encourage students to compare the different patterns of inheritance shown in the pedigrees. Challenge them to identify ways that the patterns differ. Conclude by saying that detecting such patterns in pedigrees is how geneticists have determined which type of gene controls different traits.

Getting Involved

In Your Community Advise students to take into account the speaker's area of expertise when preparing their questions. For example, a genetic counselor is likely to know more about how a genetic disorder is inherited, whereas a doctor is likely to know more about the symptoms and treatment of the disorder. Make sure the speaker has been provided with a list of genetic disorders that are covered in the chapter. If students cannot identify a suitable speaker, suggest that they contact the local branch of the March of Dimes Birth Defects Foundation and ask for recommendations.

CHAPTER 5 Changes Over Time

Sections	Time	Student Edition Activities	Other Activities
CHAPTER PROJECT 5 **Life's Long Calendar** pp. 139	Ongoing (2 weeks)	Check Your Progress, p. 150 Check Your Progress, p. 163 Wrap Up, p. 167	
1 Darwin's Voyage pp. 140–150 ◆ State how Darwin explained variations among similar species. ◆ Explain how natural selection leads to evolution and the role of genes in evolution. ◆ Describe how new species form.	4–5 periods/ 2–2½ blocks	**Discover** How Do Living Things Vary?, p. 140 **Try This** Bird Beak Adaptations, p. 143 **Sharpen Your Skills** Inferring, p. 145 **Skills Lab: Making Models** Nature at Work, pp. 146–147	TE Demonstration, p. 141 TE Building Inquiry Skills: Observing, p. 142 TE Inquiry Challenge, p. 148 ISLM C-5, "Variation in a Population"
2 **INTEGRATING EARTH SCIENCE** **The Fossil Record** pp. 151–158 ◆ Describe how most fossils form. ◆ Explain how a scientist determines a fossil's age. ◆ Describe the main events of the Geologic Time Scale. ◆ Describe two theories of how fast evolution occurs.	2–3 periods/ 1–1½ blocks	**Discover** What Can You Learn From Fossils?, p. 151 **Try This** Preservation in Ice, p. 153 **Sharpen Your Skills** Calculating, p. 154 **Science at Home,** p. 158	TE Demonstration, p. 152 TE Including All Students, p. 152 TE Inquiry Challenge, p. 157 TE Including All Students, p. 157 IES "The Glory of Ancient Rome," pp. 26–27
3 Other Evidence for Evolution pp. 159–164 ◆ State evidence from modern-day organisms that scientists use to determine evolutionary relationships among groups. ◆ Describe how scientists classify organisms and place them on branching trees.	2–3 periods/ 1–1½ blocks	**Discover** How Can You Classify Species?, p. 159 **Sharpen Your Skills** Drawing Conclusions, p. 160 **Skills Lab: Interpreting Data** Telltale Molecules, p. 164	TE Building Inquiry Skills: Observing, p. 160 TE Inquiry Challenge, p. 161 TE Building Inquiry Skills: Interpreting Data, p. 162
Study Guide/Chapter Review pp.165–167	1 period/ ½ block		ISAB Provides teaching and review of all inquiry skills

For Standard or Block Schedule The Resource Pro® CD-ROM gives you maximum flexibility for planning your instruction for any type of schedule. Resource Pro® contains Planning Express®, an advanced scheduling program, as well as the entire contents of the Teaching Resources and the Computer Test Bank.

CHAPTER PLANNING GUIDE

Program Resources	Assessment Strategies	Media and Technology
TR Chapter 5 Project Teacher Notes, pp. 116–117 **TR** Chapter 5 Project Overview and Worksheets, pp. 118–121 **TR** Chapter 5 Project Scoring Rubric, p. 122	**SE** Performance Assessment: Chapter 5 Project Wrap Up, p. 167 **TE** Check Your Progress, pp. 150, 153 **TE** Performance Assessment: Chapter 5 Project Wrap Up, p. 167 **TR** Chapter 5 Project Scoring Rubric, p.122	Science Explorer Internet Site
TR 5-1 Lesson Plan, p. 123 **TR** 5-1 Section Summary, p. 124 **TR** 5-1 Review and Reinforce, p. 125 **TR** 5-1 Enrich, p. 126 **TR** Chapter 5 Skills Lab, pp. 135–137 **SES** Book F, *Inside Earth,* Chapter 1	**SE** Analyze and Conclude, p. 147 **SE** Section 1 Review, p. 150 **TE** Ongoing Assessment, pp. 141, 143, 145, 149 **TE** Performance Assessment, p. 150 **TR** 5-1 Review and Reinforce, p. 125	Exploring Earth Science Videodisc, Unit 4 Side 2, "Hot, Cold, Wet, Dry" Exploring Life Science Videodisc, Unit 5 Side 2, "The Drifters" Audiotapes: English-Spanish Summary 5-1 Interactive Student Tutorial CD-ROM, C-5
TR 5-2 Lesson Plan, p. 127 **TR** 5-2 Section Summary, p. 128 **TR** 5-2 Review and Reinforce, p. 129 **TR** 5-2 Enrich, p. 130 **SES** Book A, *From Bacteria to Plants,* Chapter 1 **SES** Book G, *Earth's Changing Surface,* Chapter 4	**SE** Section 2 Review, p. 158 **TE** Ongoing Assessment, pp. 153, 155, 157 **TE** Performance Assessment, p. 158 **TR** 5-2 Review and Reinforce, p. 129	Exploring Life Science Videodisc, Unit 5 Side 2, "Fossils" Exploring Life Science Videodisc, Unit 5 Side 2, "The Earth Library" Exploring Life Science Videodisc, Unit 5 Side 2, "Extinction" Exploring Life Science Videodisc, Unit 5 Side 2, "Geologic Time" Audiotapes: English-Spanish Summary 5-2 Transparencies 17, "How Fossils Form"; 18, "Exploring Life's History (1)"; 19, "Exploring Life's History (2)" Interactive Student Tutorial CD-ROM, C-5
TR 5-3 Lesson Plan, p. 131 **TR** 5-3 Section Summary, p. 132 **TR** 5-3 Review and Reinforce, p. 133 **TR** 5-3 Enrich, p. 134 **TR** Chapter 5 Skills Lab, pp. 138–139 **SES** Book B, *Animals,* Chapter 3	**SE** Section 3 Review, p. 163 **SE** Analyze and Conclude, p. 164 **TE** Ongoing Assessment, pp. 161 **TE** Performance Assessment, p. 163 **TR** 5-3 Review and Reinforce, p. 133	Audiotapes: English-Spanish Summary 5-3 Transparency 20, "Homologous Structures" Interactive Student Tutorial CD-ROM, C-5
TR Chapter 5 Performance Assessment, pp. 180–182 **TR** Chapter 5 Test, pp. 183–186	**SE** Chapter 5 Review, pp. 165–167 **TR** Chapter 5 Performance Assessment, pp. 180–182 **TR** Chapter 5 Test, pp. 183–186 **CTB** Test C-5	Interactive Student Tutorial CD-ROM, C-5 Computer Test Bank, Test C-5 Got It! Video Quizzes

Key: **SE** Student Edition   **TE** Teacher's Edition   **TR** Teaching Resources
      CTB Computer Test Bank   **SES** Science Explorer Series Text   **ISLM** Integrated Science Laboratory Manual
      ISAB Inquiry Skills Activity Book   **PTA** Product Testing Activities by *Consumer Reports*   **IES** Interdisciplinary Explorations Series

Meeting the National Science Education Standards and AAAS Benchmarks

National Science Education Standards	Benchmarks for Science Literacy	Unifying Themes
Science As Inquiry (Content Standard A) ◆ **Develop descriptions, explanations, predictions, and models using evidence** Students create time lines of Earth's history. Students model how natural selection leads to changes in a species over time. Students compare the structure of a protein in several animals to determine their evolutionary relationships. *(Chapter Project; Skills Lab; Skills Lab)* **Life Science** (Content Standard C) ◆ **Diversity and adaptations of organisms** Over a long period of time, natural selection can lead to evolution. A species is extinct if no members of that species are still alive. Scientists compare body structures, early development, and DNA sequences to determine evolutionary relationships. *(Sections 1, 2, 3; Skills Lab; Skills Lab)* **Earth and Space Science** (Content Standard D) ◆ **Earth's history** The fossil record provides clues about how and when new groups of organisms evolved. *(Chapter Project; Section 2)* **History and Nature of Science** (Content Standard G) ◆ **History of science** Charles Darwin explained that evolution occurs by means of natural selection. *(Section 1)*	**1B Scientific Inquiry** Students create time lines of Earth's history. Students model how natural selection leads to changes in a species over time. Students compare the structure of a protein in several animals to determine their evolutionary relationships. *(Chapter Project; Skills Lab; Skills Lab)* **1C The Scientific Enterprise** Charles Darwin explained that evolution occurs by means of natural selection. *(Section 1)* **4C Processes that Shape the Earth** Most fossils form when organisms that die become buried in sediments. *(Section 2)* **5A Diversity of Life** Any difference between individuals of the same species is called a variation. *(Section 1)* **5F Evolution of Life** Over a long period of time, natural selection can lead to evolution. The fossil record provides clues about how and when new groups of organisms evolved. Scientists compare body structures, early development, and DNA sequences to determine the evolutionary relationships among organisms. *(Chapter Project, Sections 1, 2, 3; Skills Lab; Skills Lab)*	◆ **Evolution** Over a long period of time, natural selection can lead to evolution. The fossil record provides clues about how and when new groups of organisms evolved. Scientists compare body structures, early development, and DNA sequences to determine evolutionary relationships. *(Chapter Project, Sections 1, 2, 3; Skills Lab; Skills Lab)* ◆ **Patterns of Change** A new species can form when a group of individuals is isolated from the rest of the species. Most fossils form when organisms that die become buried in sediments. *(Sections 1, 2)* ◆ **Scale and Structure** Scientists can determine a fossil's age through relative dating and absolute dating. Similar structures that related species have inherited from a common ancestor are called homologous structures. Protein structures can reveal evolutionary relationships among organisms. *(Sections 2, 3; Skills Lab)* ◆ **Stability** Natural selection is the survival and reproduction of those organisms best adapted to their environment. The half-life of a radioactive element is the time it takes for half of the atoms in a sample to decay. *(Sections 1, 2)* ◆ **Unity and Diversity** A species is a group of similar organisms that can mate and produce fertile offspring. Two theories of how quickly evolution occurs are gradualism and punctuated equilibria. *(Sections 1, 2)*

Media and Technology

Exploring Earth Science Videodiscs

◆ **Section 1** "Hot, Cold, Wet, Dry" explores climatic conditions.

Exploring Life Science Videodiscs

◆ **Section 1** "The Drifters" gives evidence for continental drift.

◆ **Section 2** "Fossils" illustrates the formation and use of fossils. "The Earth Library" shows how layers of rock reflect Earth's history. "Extinction" discusses extinction and the evolution of new species. "Geologic Time" illustrates Earth's geologic history.

Interactive Student Tutorial CD-ROM

◆ **Chapter Review** Interactive questions help students self-assess their mastery of key chapter concepts.

Student Edition Connection Strategies

◆ **Section 1 Social Studies Connection,** p. 148

◆ **Section 2 Integrating Earth Science,** pp. 151–158
   Integrating Chemistry, p. 154

◆ **Section 3 Integrating Technology,** p. 162

USING THE INTERNET

www.science-explorer.phschool.com

Visit the Science Explorer Internet site to find an up-to-date activity for Chapter 5 of *Cells and Heredity*.

ACTIVITY	Time (minutes)	Materials *Quantities for one work group*	Skills
Section 1			
Discover, p. 140	15	**Consumable** 10 sunflower seeds **Nonconsumable** metric ruler, hand lens	Classifying
Try This, p. 143	10	**Consumable** bird seed, paper plate, 20 raisins, paper cup **Nonconsumable** tweezers, hair clips, hairpins, clothespins, stopwatch	Inferring
Sharpen Your Skills, p. 145	10	**Consumable** large sheet of plain white paper **Nonconsumable** 15 black buttons, 15 white buttons, stopwatch	Inferring
Skills Lab, p. 146–147	40	**Consumable** 2 colors of construction paper **Nonconsumable** scissors, marking pen	Making Models, Observing, Predicting
Section 2			
Discover, p. 151	5	No special materials are required.	Inferring
Try This, p. 153	10	**Consumable** fresh fruit, water **Nonconsumable** 2 plastic containers	Inferring
Sharpen Your Skills, p. 154	10	**Nonconsumable** calculator	Calculating
Science at Home, p. 158	home	**Consumable** mud **Nonconsumable** shallow, flat-bottomed pan	Making Models
Section 3			
Discover, p. 159	10	**Nonconsumable** 6-8 pens	Classifying
Sharpen Your Skills, p. 160	5	No special materials are required.	Drawing Conclusions
Skills Lab, p. 164	30	No special materials are required.	Interpreting Data, Comparing and Contrasting, Drawing Conclusions

A list of all materials required for the Student Edition activities can be found on pages T14–T15. You can order Materials Kits by calling 1-800-828-7777 or by accessing the Science Explorer Internet site at **www.science-explorer.phschool.com.**

Life's Long Calendar

Understanding evolution through natural selection requires an appreciation for the great age of Earth and for the vast spans of time involved in the development of Earth's diverse species. The Chapter 5 Project is designed to help students understand the large numbers involved in geologic time and place significant evolutionary events within an accurate model of Earth's history: a time line drawn to scale. The project works best as a small-group activity.

Sometimes illustrations of the history of life on Earth, including the main section on pages 156–157 of this book, are not drawn to scale. (The time line that runs across the top of the spread *is* drawn to scale.) Illustrations that are not drawn to scale do not give an accurate image of the relative amounts of time occupied by different eras and periods in geologic history. However, a single time line to scale would devote most of the line to the Precambrian and squeeze the evolution of all plants and animals into a very small portion. To avoid this problem, students will make two time lines in this project: one showing Earth's history from 5 billion years ago to the present, and the other from 600 million years ago to the present. Students will then be able to see the relative sizes of time spans and the comparative placement of events in Earth's evolutionary history.

Purpose Students will construct scale models of Earth's history by converting geological units of millions of years to more familiar and manageable units of either length or time. Students will mark both lines to show important events in Earth's history.

Skills Focus After completing the Chapter 5 Project, students will be able to
◆ calculate the scale of a model;
◆ make scale models representing the history of life on Earth, with major evolutionary events included;
◆ communicate the model-making procedures and results to others.

Project Time Line The Chapter 5 Project requires about two weeks to complete, depending on how detailed

you want the time lines to be. If students label only the major evolutionary events shown on the textbook's time line, less than two weeks should be sufficient. If you want students to add other important events, allow additional time.

Possible Materials
◆ Students could use calculators to determine the scale of each model and the placement of each evolutionary event.
◆ Meter sticks and metric tape measures will be needed to construct all models that use units

of length to represent millions of years.
◆ Other materials will vary depending on the formats that students choose.
◆ If you want students to research additional evolutionary events to include in their time lines, provide a variety of source materials.

Launching the Project Invite students to read the project description on page 139 and examine the time line on pages 156–157. Then draw a long line across the board, and label the left end *Beginning of Earth* and the right end *Present.* Ask: **How long ago did Earth begin?**

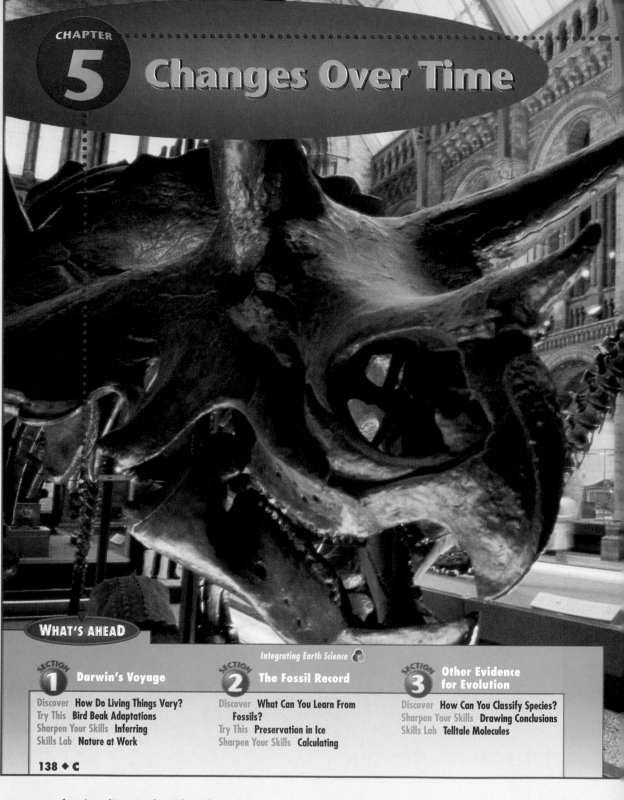

CHAPTER 5 Changes Over Time

WHAT'S AHEAD

Integrating Earth Science

SECTION 1 Darwin's Voyage

Discover **How Do Living Things Vary?**
Try This **Bird Beak Adaptations**
Sharpen Your Skills **Inferring**
Skills Lab **Nature at Work**

SECTION 2 The Fossil Record

Discover **What Can You Learn From Fossils?**
Try This **Preservation in Ice**
Sharpen Your Skills **Calculating**

SECTION 3 Other Evidence for Evolution

Discover **How Can You Classify Species?**
Sharpen Your Skills **Drawing Conclusions**
Skills Lab **Telltale Molecules**

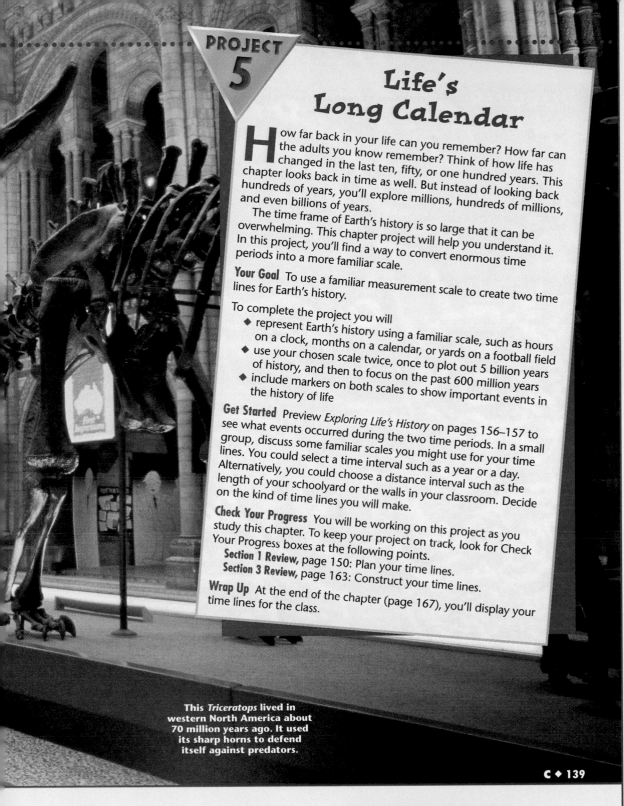

Life's Long Calendar

How far back in your life can you remember? How far can the adults you know remember? Think of how life has changed in the last ten, fifty, or one hundred years. This chapter looks back in time as well. But instead of looking back hundreds of years, you'll explore millions, hundreds of millions, and even billions of years.

The time frame of Earth's history is so large that it can be overwhelming. This chapter project will help you understand it. In this project, you'll find a way to convert enormous time periods into a more familiar scale.

Your Goal To use a familiar measurement scale to create two time lines for Earth's history.

To complete the project you will
◆ represent Earth's history using a familiar scale, such as hours on a clock, months on a calendar, or yards on a football field
◆ use your chosen scale twice, once to plot out 5 billion years of history, and then to focus on the past 600 million years
◆ include markers on both scales to show important events in the history of life

Get Started Preview *Exploring Life's History* on pages 156–157 to see what events occurred during the two time periods. In a small group, discuss some familiar scales you might use for your time lines. You could select a time interval such as a year or a day. Alternatively, you could choose a distance interval such as the length of your schoolyard or the walls in your classroom. Decide on the kind of time lines you will make.

Check Your Progress You will be working on this project as you study this chapter. To keep your project on track, look for Check Your Progress boxes at the following points.
Section 1 Review, page 150: Plan your time lines.
Section 3 Review, page 163: Construct your time lines.

Wrap Up At the end of the chapter (page 167), you'll display your time lines for the class.

This *Triceratops* lived in western North America about 70 million years ago. It used its sharp horns to defend itself against predators.

C ◆ 139

(4.6 billion years ago) Write *4,600,000,000* on the board. **When did the first animals appear on Earth?** *(600 million years ago)* Write *600,000,000* below the first number with the place values aligned. Ask: **Where should the line be marked to show when the first animals appeared on Earth?** Have a volunteer mark the line. *(The mark should be close to the "Present" end of the line. If it is not, ask the rest of the class to comment on the mark's placement.)* Point out that if students made only one time line to scale, all the events that

happened from the beginning of the Paleozoic Era to the present would have to be crowded into a very small section of the line. Explain that this is the reason they will make two time lines in this project.

Distribute the Chapter 5 Project Overview on pages 118–119 of Teaching Resources, and have students review the project rules and procedures. Invite questions and comments. Then divide the class into groups of three or four students each, and let the groups meet to discuss the types of time lines they could make.

When students are ready to make the first time line at the end of Section 1, distribute Worksheet 1 on page 120 of Teaching Resources. This worksheet will provide practice in making a time line to scale. At the end of Section 3, distribute Worksheet 2, on page 121 in Teaching Resources. This worksheet lists other evolutionary events that could be included in the time lines.

Additional information on guiding the project is provided in Chapter 5 Project Teacher Notes on pages 116–117 of Teaching Resources.

Program Resources

◆ **Teaching Resources** Chapter 5 Project Teacher Notes, pp. 116–117; Chapter 5 Project Overview and Worksheets, pp. 118–121; Chapter 5 Project Scoring Rubric, p. 122

Performance Assessment

The Chapter 5 Project Scoring Rubric on page 122 in Teaching Resources will help you evaluate how well students complete the Chapter 5 Project. You may want to share the scoring rubric with students so they are clear about what will be expected of them. Students will be assessed on
◆ their accuracy in calculating the scales for the two models;
◆ their ability to construct two scale models of Earth's history with important evolutionary events accurately marked;
◆ their effectiveness in communicating the model-making process and results to others;
◆ their participation in their groups.

C ◆ 139

Objectives

After completing the lesson, students will be able to

◆ state how Darwin explained variations among similar species;

◆ explain how natural selection leads to evolution and the role of genes in evolution;

◆ describe how new species form.

Key Terms species, adaptation, evolution, scientific theory, natural selection, variation

1 Engage/Explore

Activating Prior Knowledge

Most students will have read articles or seen television specials about Darwin or the Galapagos Islands. Help them recall what they know by asking: **Who was Charles Darwin?** (*A scientist who came up with the idea of evolution by natural selection*) **What is special about the Galapagos Islands?** (*They have a lot of unusual organisms, such as giant lizards and tortoises.*)

DISCOVER · · · · · · · · ·

Skills Focus classifying **ACTIVITY**
Materials *metric ruler, 10 sunflower seeds, hand lens*
Time 15 minutes
Tips Tell students that differences among seeds in their sample may be slight and hard to detect, so they should examine the seeds very carefully.
Expected Outcome Students should observe that the seeds in their sample differ in such traits as size, shape, color, or number of stripes.
Think It Over The seeds in each sample may differ in some traits and be similar in others. Depending on the makeup of their sample, students may group together seeds that are similar in size, shape, color, number of stripes, or other traits.

140 ◆ C

DISCOVER · **ACTIVITY** · · · ·

How Do Living Things Vary?

1. Use a ruler to measure the length and width of 10 sunflower seeds. Record each measurement.

2. Now use a hand lens to carefully examine each seed. Record each seed's shape, color, and number of stripes.

Think It Over

Classifying In what ways are the seeds in your sample different from one another? In what ways are they similar? How could you group the seeds based on their similarities and differences?

GUIDE FOR READING

◆ How did Darwin explain the differences between species on the Galapagos Islands and on mainland South America?

◆ How does natural selection lead to evolution?

◆ How do new species form?

Reading Tip As you read, make a list of main ideas and supporting details about evolution.

I n December 1831, the British naval ship HMS *Beagle* set sail from England on a five-year-long trip around the world. On board was a 22-year-old named Charles Darwin. Darwin eventually became the ship's naturalist—a person who studies the natural world. His job was to learn as much as he could about the living things he saw on the voyage.

During the voyage, Darwin observed plants and animals he had never seen before. He wondered why they were so different from those in England. Darwin's observations led him to develop one of the most important scientific theories of all time: the theory of evolution by natural selection.

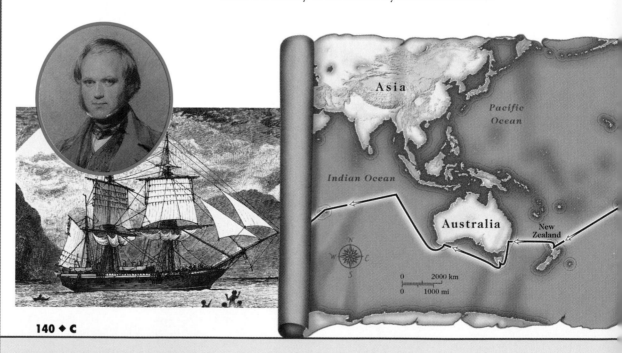

140 ◆ C

READING STRATEGIES

Reading Tip Help students find the main ideas by advising them to try to answer the Guide for Reading questions as they read the section.

Vocabulary Students may think that the term *species* is plural and that the singular form is *specie*. Explain that the term *species* is both singular and plural. Then use the word in a sentence to illustrate. For

example, say: "All humans belong to one species, but humans and chimpanzees belong to two different species."

Study and Comprehension As students read the section, have them rewrite as a question each of the boldfaced statements and the statements defining key terms. After students have finished reading the section, have pairs of students exchange and answer each other's questions.

Darwin's Observations

One of the *Beagle's* first stops was the coast of South America. In Brazil, Darwin saw insects that looked like flowers, and ants that marched across the forest floor like huge armies. In Argentina, he saw armadillos—burrowing animals covered with small, bony plates. He also saw sloths, animals that moved very slowly and spent much of their time hanging upside down in trees.

Darwin was amazed by the tremendous diversity, or variety, of living things he saw. Today scientists know that living things are even more diverse than Darwin could ever have imagined. Scientists have identified more than 2.5 million species of organisms on Earth. A **species** is a group of similar organisms that can mate with each other and produce fertile offspring.

Darwin saw something else in Argentina that puzzled him: the bones of animals that had died long ago. From the bones, Darwin inferred that the animals had looked like the sloths he had seen. However, the bones were much larger than those of the living sloths. He wondered why only smaller sloths were alive today. What had happened to the giant creatures from the past?

In 1835, the *Beagle* reached the Galapagos Islands, a group of small islands in the Pacific Ocean off the west coast of South America. It was on the Galapagos Islands that Darwin observed some of the greatest diversity of life forms. The giant tortoises, or land turtles, he saw were so tall that they could look him in the eye. There were also seals covered with fur, and lizards that ate nothing but tough, prickly cactus plants.

Figure 1 Charles Darwin sailed on HMS *Beagle* from England to South America and then to the Galapagos Islands. He saw many unusual organisms on the Galapagos Islands.

Galapagos hawk ▼

▲ *Giant tortoise*

▲ *Sally light-foot crab*

◀ *Blue-footed booby*

Chapter 5 **C ◆ 141**

2 Facilitate

Darwin's Observations

Using the Visuals: Figure 1

Have students trace on the map with their finger the route that Darwin took on his voyage. When they have traced Darwin's route as far as the Galapagos Islands, ask: **About how far are the Galapagos Islands from mainland South America?** *(About 1,000 km)* Help students appreciate how far away from the mainland that is, and therefore how isolated the islands are, by equating the distance to a distance with which they are more familiar, such as from Seattle to Sacramento, Detroit to Boston, or Indianapolis to Washington, D.C. **learning modality: kinesthetic**

Demonstration

Materials *taxonomic chart*
Time 10 minutes

ACTIVITY

Show students a taxonomic chart, either a chart from a biology book or encyclopedia or a simple chart that you have drawn on the chalkboard. Point out that the taxonomic categories group together organisms based on the degree to which they are similar, with the largest, most inclusive category being the kingdom. Explain that humans belong to the animal kingdom, because, like other animals, humans are multicellular and do not make their own food. Ask: **What other organisms are in the animal kingdom?** *(Accept any type of animal in response, and use students' responses to illustrate how diverse the animal kingdom is.)* Then point out that at the other end of the taxonomy is the species, the smallest, most exclusive category, containing only those organisms that can reproduce together. **learning modality: visual**

Ongoing Assessment

Writing Have students describe in their own words the insights Darwin's voyage gave him into the nature of living things.

Similarities and Differences

Building Inquiry Skills: Observing

Materials *drawings of related bird species from a field identification guide*

Time 10 minutes

Point out to students that much of Darwin's time during the voyage of the *Beagle* was spent observing and comparing different organisms. Add that Darwin was a keen observer, and he noticed many details that other people might overlook. Give students a chance to see how difficult Darwin's job was, as well as to improve their own observation skills. Provide students with drawings from a field guide that show several related species of birds, such as several species of ducks, warblers, herons, or woodpeckers. Have students examine the drawings carefully and make lists of all the similarities and differences they observe among the species pictured. Then, have pairs of students compare lists. Emphasize that being a good observer requires care and skill. Be sensitive to visually-challenged students by asking: **What are some other ways these birds might be similar or different that you cannot observe visually?** *(Possible ways include their songs and the texture of their feathers.)* **learning modality: visual**

Using the Visuals: Figure 2

Call students' attention to the figure and have them answer the caption question. Most students will respond that one way the two species differ is in color. Point out that variations in a trait such as this may make organisms better suited for their environment. Ask: **What difference in the environment do you think might explain the difference in color between the two species of iguanas?** *(Students may say the colors in the environment: the green iguana's color helps it blend in with its leafy environment, and the marine iguana's color helps it blend in with its rocky environment.)* **learning modality: logical/mathematical**

Similarities and Differences

Darwin was surprised that many of the plants and animals on the Galapagos Islands were similar to organisms on mainland South America. For example, many of the birds on the islands, including hawks, mockingbirds, and finches, resembled those on the mainland. Many of the plants were also similar to plants Darwin had collected on the mainland.

However, there were also important differences between the organisms on the islands and those on the mainland. Large sea birds called cormorants, for example, lived in both places. The cormorants on the mainland were able to fly, while those on the Galapagos Islands were unable to fly. The iguanas on the Galapagos Islands had large claws that allowed them to keep their grip on slippery rocks, where they fed on seaweed. The iguanas on the mainland had smaller claws. Smaller claws allowed the mainland iguanas to climb trees, where they ate leaves.

From his observations, Darwin inferred that a small number of different plant and animal species had come to the Galapagos Islands from the mainland. They might have been blown out to sea during a storm or set adrift on a fallen log. Once the plants and animals reached the islands, they reproduced. Eventually, their offspring became different from their mainland relatives.

Darwin also noticed many differences among similar organisms as he traveled from one Galapagos island to the next. For example, the tortoises on one island had dome-shaped shells. Those on another island had saddle-shaped shells. The governor of one of the islands told Darwin that he could tell which island a tortoise came from just by looking at its shell.

✓ *Checkpoint* How did Darwin think plants and animals had originally come to the Galapagos Islands?

Figure 2 Darwin observed many differences between organisms in South America and similar organisms on the Galapagos Islands. For example, green iguanas (left) live in South America. Marine iguanas (right) live on the Galapagos Islands. *Comparing and Contrasting How are the two species similar? How are they different?*

Background

Facts and Figures Ever since Darwin's time, scientists have suggested that one way species can become dispersed around the world is on natural rafts of fallen trees blown out to sea during storms. However, until recently there was virtually no direct evidence to support this idea. Then, in 1995, two powerful hurricanes passed through the Caribbean Sea, and a large clump of trees was blown into the sea from the island of Guadeloupe. Storm winds blew the natural raft across more than 300 km of sea, and it eventually washed ashore on the island of Anguilla. On the raft were 15 green iguanas, native to Guadeloupe but, until that time, not found on Anguilla. Most of the iguanas survived the journey and within a few months started reproducing. Scientists speculate that green iguanas eventually will become established on Anguilla.

Figure 3 Darwin made these drawings of four species of Galapagos finches. The beak of each finch is adapted to the type of food it eats.

Adaptations

Like the tortoises, the finches on the Galapagos Islands were noticeably different from one island to another. The most obvious differences were the varied sizes and shapes of the birds' beaks. As Darwin studied the different finches, he noticed that each species was well suited to the life it led. Finches that ate insects had sharp, needlelike beaks. Finches that ate seeds had strong, wide beaks. Beak shape is an example of an **adaptation,** a trait that helps an organism survive and reproduce.

Evolution

After he returned home to England, Darwin continued to think about what he had seen during his voyage on the *Beagle*. Darwin spent the next 20 years consulting with many other scientists, gathering more information, and thinking through his ideas. He especially wanted to understand how the variety of organisms with different adaptations arose on the Galapagos Islands.

Darwin reasoned that plants or animals that arrived on one of the Galapagos Islands faced conditions that were different from those on the mainland. **Perhaps, Darwin thought, the species gradually changed over many generations and became better adapted to the new conditions.** The gradual change in a species over time is called **evolution.**

Darwin's ideas are often referred to as the theory of evolution. A **scientific theory** is a well-tested concept that explains a wide range of observations.

It was clear to Darwin that evolution had occurred on the Galapagos Islands. He did not know, however, how this process had occurred. Darwin had to draw on other examples of changes in living things to help him understand how evolution occurs.

Bird Beak Adaptations

Use this activity to explore adaptations in birds.

1. Scatter a small amount of bird seed on a paper plate. Scatter 20 raisins on the plate to represent insects.

2. Obtain a variety of objects such as tweezers, hair clips, clothes pins, and hairpins. Pick one object to use as a "beak."

3. See how many seeds you can pick up and drop into a cup in 10 seconds.

4. Now see how many "insects" you can pick up and drop into a cup in 10 seconds.

5. Use a different "beak" and repeat Steps 3 and 4.

Inferring What type of beak worked well for seeds? For insects? How are different-shaped beaks useful for eating different foods?

TRY THIS

Skills Focus inferring
Materials *bird seed, paper plate, 20 raisins, tweezers, hair clips, hairpins, clothes pins, stopwatch, paper cup*
Time 10 minutes
Tips Have students work with partners so one student can pick up the seeds or raisins while the partner watches the clock.
Expected Outcome Students will find that some objects are better for picking up seeds and others for picking up raisins. Students should infer that some bird beaks are better for picking up seeds and others for picking up insects.
Extend Ask: **Which species in Figure 3 appear to be adapted to a diet of seeds, and which to a diet of insects?** *(Species 1, 2, and possibly 3 appear to be adapted to a diet of seeds, and species 4 to a diet of insects.)* **learning modality: kinesthetic**

Evolution

Addressing Naive Conceptions

People often say, "It's only a theory," and this may lead students to believe that a theory is just any idea. Address this naive conception by asking: **What makes an idea a theory?** *(It is well-tested and explains many observations.)* **How is a theory different from a fact?** *(A fact is a specific observation, known to be true; a theory is a broad concept, thought to be true because it explains many facts.)* **Upon which facts did Darwin base his theory of evolution?** *(The similarities and differences he observed among living things)* **learning modality: verbal**

Answers to Self-Assessment

Caption Question

Figure 2 Both species have spines, claws, and scaly skin. Green iguanas are green, have smaller claws, and live in trees. Marine iguanas are gray, have larger claws, and live on rocks near the ocean.

 Checkpoint

Perhaps by being blown out to sea during a storm or set adrift on a fallen log

Ongoing Assessment

Oral Presentation Call on students at random to define each term in their own words: *species, adaptation, evolution,* and *scientific theory.*

Evolution, continued

Including All Students

Support students who need more help in understanding natural selection by relating it to selective breeding, which they learned about in Chapter 4. Create a simple compare/contrast table on the chalkboard and call on students to help you complete it. The table should have two rows, one for selective breeding and one for natural selection. It also should have columns such as: **Type of Traits Selected** (*Selective breeding: traits that benefit humans; natural selection: traits that benefit the organism*); **Examples of Traits Selected** (*Selective breeding: fine wool in sheep or many kernels in corn; natural selection: ability to escape predators or resist drought*); **How Traits Are Selected** (*Selective breeding: by humans, who allow only organisms with the traits to reproduce; natural selection: by natural events, which allow organisms with the traits to produce more offspring*) After the table is completed, ask: **Why would *artificial* selection be a good term for selective breeding?** (*Because, like natural selection, selective breeding leads to changes in a species' traits, but artificial human choices, not natural events, control the process*) **learning modality: logical/mathematical**

Natural Selection

Building Inquiry Skills: Communicating

Encourage students who need extra challenges to learn about and then communicate to the rest of the class how natural selection has resulted in the viceroy butterfly bearing a close but superficial resemblance to the monarch butterfly. Urge students to use diagrams and illustrations to communicate what they learn. After students have communicated their findings, ask: **Why is this type of natural selection called mimicry?** (*Because natural selection results in one species looking like, or mimicking, another species*) **learning modality: verbal**

Darwin knew that people used selective breeding to produce organisms with desired traits. For example, English farmers used selective breeding to produce sheep with fine wool. Darwin himself had bred pigeons with large, fan-shaped tails. By repeatedly allowing only those pigeons with many tail feathers to mate, Darwin produced pigeons with two or three times the usual number of tail feathers. Darwin thought that a process similar to selective breeding must happen in nature. But he wondered why certain traits were selected for, and how.

☑ *Checkpoint* *What observations led Darwin to propose his theory of evolution?*

Natural Selection

In 1858, Darwin and another British biologist, Alfred Russel Wallace, proposed an explanation for how evolution occurs. The next year, Darwin described this mechanism in a book entitled *The Origin of Species*. In his book, Darwin explained that evolution occurs by means of natural selection. **Natural selection** is the process by which individuals that are better adapted to their environment are more likely to survive and reproduce than other members of the same species. Darwin identified a number of factors that affect the process of natural selection: overproduction, competition, and variations.

Overproduction Most species produce far more offspring than can possibly survive. In many species, so many offspring are produced that there are not enough resources—food, water, and living space—for all of them. For example, each year a female sea turtle may lay more than 100 eggs. If all the young turtles survived, the sea would soon be full of turtles. Darwin knew that this doesn't happen. Why not?

Figure 4 Most newborn loggerhead sea turtles will not survive to adulthood. *Making Generalizations What factors limit the number of young that survive?*

144 ◆ C

Figure 5 The walruses lying on this rocky beach in Alaska must compete for resources. All organisms compete for limited resources such as food.

Competition Since food and other resources are limited, the offspring must compete with each other to survive. Competition does not usually involve direct physical fights between members of a species. Instead, competition is usually indirect. For example, some turtles may fail to find enough to eat. Others may not be able to escape from predators. Only a few turtles will survive long enough to reproduce.

Variations As you learned in your study of genetics, members of a species differ from one another in many of their traits. Any difference between individuals of the same species is called a **variation.** For example, some newly hatched turtles are able to swim faster than other turtles.

Selection Some variations make certain individuals better adapted to their environment. Those individuals are more likely to survive and reproduce. When those individuals reproduce, their offspring may inherit the allele for the helpful trait. The off-spring, in turn, will be more likely to survive and reproduce, and thus pass on the allele to their offspring. After many generations, more members of the species will have the helpful trait. In effect, the environment has "selected" organisms with helpful traits to be the parents of the next generation—hence the term "natural selection." **Over a long period of time, natural selection can lead to evolution. Helpful variations gradually accumulate in a species, while unfavorable ones disappear.**

For example, suppose a new fast-swimming predator moves into the turtles' habitat. Turtles that are able to swim faster would be more likely to escape from the new predator. The faster turtles would thus be more likely to survive and repro-duce. Over time, more and more turtles in the species would have the "fast-swimmer" trait.

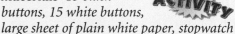

Inferring ACTIVITY

Scatter 15 black buttons and 15 white buttons on a sheet of white paper. Have a partner time you to see how many buttons you can pick up in 10 seconds. Pick up the buttons one at a time.

Did you collect more buttons of one color than the other? Why? How can a variation such as color affect the process of natural selection?

Program Resources

◆ **Integrated Science Laboratory Manual**
C-5, "Variation in a Population"

Answers to Self-Assessment

✓ Checkpoint
Darwin proposed his theory of evolution based on observations of similarities and differences among species in nature and observations of domestic animals selectively bred to have desired traits.

Caption Question
Figure 4 Factors include predators and limited resources.

Cultural Diversity
Point out to students that human beings are unusual among living things in the variation of their behavior. Explain that the ability of humans to adapt their behavior has allowed them to move into a wide range of environments without evolving specific physical adaptations. In very cold climates, for example, animals such as polar bears have evolved thick fur to stay warm. Humans, on the other hand, have been able to use behavioral means, such as making and wearing clothing, to stay warm. As a result, humans do not have any special physical adaptations to extreme cold. Ask: **What are some behavioral means that humans use to protect themselves from predators?** *(Possible ways might include making and using weapons and living in groups.)* **learning modality: verbal**

Sharpen your **Skills**

Inferring

Materials *15 black buttons, 15 white buttons, large sheet of plain white paper, stopwatch*
Time *10 minutes*
Tips Have students work in pairs so one student can focus on picking up buttons while the other keeps track of the time. All the buttons should be identical except for color.
Expected Outcome Students are likely to pick up more black buttons than white buttons. They should infer that a variation such as color can affect natural selection by making an organism more or less likely to be seen and captured by a predator.
Extend Ask: **Besides color, what are some other variations that might affect whether or not an organism is seen and captured by a predator?** *(Accept any reasonable responses, such as other physical traits, intelligence, and acuteness of senses.)* **learning modality: kinesthetic**

Ongoing Assessment

Writing Have students explain how overproduction, competition, and variations lead to natural selection.

Nature at Work

Preparing for Inquiry

Key Concept Natural selection can lead to changes in a species' traits over time.

Skills Objectives Students will be able to

◆ make a dynamic model of natural selection in mice;

◆ observe how selection changes a species;

◆ predict how changing environmental conditions will affect natural selection in the model.

Time 40 minutes

Advance Planning To save time, before class begins you can prepare enough mouse and event cards so there is a complete set of cards for each group of students.

Guiding Inquiry

Invitation Tell students that in this lab they will simulate natural selection in mice of two different colors. Ask: **How do you think variation of color in a species might affect natural selection?** *(Some colors might make individuals better able to hide from predators, making them more likely to survive and reproduce. Other colors might make it more difficult for individuals to hide from predators, making them less likely to survive and reproduce.)*

Introducing the Procedure

Make sure students understand the rationale behind each step of the procedure. It may not be obvious to them, for example, why they cannot simply use cards representing mice of each color, rather than cards representing alleles. Ask: **Why do the mouse cards represent alleles rather than phenotypes?** *(Because alleles are passed on to the next generation, not phenotypes)* Point out that choosing alleles to make up the next generation is a realistic way to model reproduction and the inheritance of traits while choosing phenotypes is not.

Nature at Work

In this lab, you will investigate how natural selection can lead to changes in a species over time. You'll explore how both genetic and environmental factors play a part in natural selection.

Problem

How do species change over time?

Materials

scissors
marking pen
construction paper, 2 colors

Procedure

1. Work on this lab with two other students. One student should choose construction paper of one color and make the team's 50 "mouse" cards, as described in Table 1. The second student should choose a different color construction paper and make the team's 25 "event" cards, as described in Table 2. The third student should copy the data table and record all the data.

Part 1 A White Sand Environment

2. Mix up the mouse cards.

3. Begin by using the cards to model what might happen to a group of mice in an environment of white sand dunes. Choose two mouse cards. Allele pairs *WW* and *Ww* produce a white mouse. Allele pair *ww* produces a brown mouse. Record the color of the mouse with a tally mark in the data table.

4. Choose an event card. An "S" card means the mouse survives. A "D" or a "P" card means the mouse dies. A "C" card means the mouse dies if its color contrasts with the white sand dunes. (Only brown mice will die when a "C" card is drawn.) Record each death with a tally mark in the data table.

5. If the mouse lives, put the two mouse cards in a "live mice" pile. If the mouse dies, put the cards in a "dead mice" pile. Put the event card at the bottom of its pack.

6. Repeat Steps 3 through 5 with the remaining mouse cards to study the first generation of mice. Record your results.

7. Leave the dead mice cards untouched. Mix up the cards from the live mice pile. Mix up the events cards.

8. Repeat Steps 3 through 7 for the second generation. Then repeat Steps 3 through 6 for the third generation.

Table 1: "Mouse" Cards

Number	Label	Meaning
25	W	Dominant allele for white fur
25	w	Recessive allele for brown fur

Table 2: "Event" Cards

Number	Label	Meaning
5	S	Mouse survives.
1	D	Disease kills mouse.
1	P	Predator kills mice of all colors.
18	C	Predator kills mice that contrast with the environment.

Troubleshooting the Experiment

◆ Divide students into groups of three before they start the lab, and make sure group members divide the tasks as specified in the text.

◆ Check that students are assigning the right phenotype to each genotype. Remind them that the *W* allele for white fur is dominant to the *w* allele for brown fur.

Expected Outcome

Groups should find that the number of mice declines each generation, with the number of brown mice declining faster than the number of white mice in Part 1, and the number of white mice declining faster than the number of brown mice in Part 2.

DATA TABLE				
Type of Environment:				
Generation	White Mice	Brown Mice	Deaths	
			White Mice	Brown Mice
1				
2				
3				

Part 2 A Forest Floor Environment

9. How would the data differ if the mice in this model lived on a dark brown forest floor? Record your prediction in your notebook.

10. Make a new copy of the data table. Then use the cards to test your prediction. Remember that a "C" card now means that any mouse with white fur will die.

Analyze and Conclude

1. In Part 1, how many white mice were there in each generation? How many brown mice? In each generation, which color mouse had the higher death rate? (*Hint:* To calculate the death rate for white mice, divide the number of white mice that died by the total number of white mice, then multiply by 100%.)

2. If the events in Part 1 occurred in nature, how would the group of mice change over time?

3. How did the results in Part 2 differ from those in Part 1?

4. What are some ways in which this investigation models natural selection? What are some ways in which natural selection differs from this model?

5. **Think About It** How would it affect your model if you increased the number of "C" cards? If you decreased the number?

Design an Experiment

Choose a different species with a trait that interests you. Make a set of cards similar to these cards to investigate how natural selection might bring about the evolution of that species.

Sample Data Table
Type of Environment: White Sand

Generation	White Mice	Brown Mice	Deaths of White Mice	Deaths of Brown Mice
1	18	7	2	5
2	16	2	2	1
3	14	1	1	1

Program Resources

◆ **Teaching Resources** Chapter 5 Skills Lab, pp. 135–137

Safety

Review the safety guidelines in Appendix A.

Analyze and Conclude

1. Answers will depend on the genotypes of the mice in each generation and the order in which the mouse and event cards are drawn. For the sample data, there were 18 white mice in the first generation, of which 2 died, yielding a death rate of 11% for the white mice. There were also 7 brown mice in the first generation, of which 5 died, yielding a death rate of 71% for the brown mice.

2. The population of mice would contain more and more mice with white fur.

3. In Part 2, the population contains more brown mice each generation because white mice are selected against, whereas in Part 1, the population contains more white mice each generation because the brown mice are selected against.

4. This investigation models natural selection in that an organism's chances of surviving and reproducing depend both on the organism's inherited traits and on the environment in which the organism lives. Natural selection differs from the model in that other environmental factors besides predators and disease, and other traits besides fur color, are likely to influence an organism's chances of surviving and reproducing.

5. If you increased the number of "C" cards, natural selection against mice that contrast with the environment would be stronger and contrasting-color mice would decrease in number more quickly. If you decreased the number of "C" cards, natural selection against mice that contrast with the environment would be weaker and contrasting-color mice would decrease in number more slowly.

Extending the Inquiry

Design an Experiment Urge students to select a trait that is controlled by a recessive allele so they can see how dominance affects the rate at which natural selection changes the genetic makeup of the population. The trait they choose to model may be real or hypothetical.

The Role of Genes in Evolution

Inquiry Challenge

Time 10 minutes

ACTIVITY

Divide the class into groups, and challenge students in each group to brainstorm an experiment to demonstrate that only inherited traits are affected by natural selection. You may wish to share the information on Lamarck in the Background below to stimulate students' thinking. *(One way is to change experimental organisms in some way, for example, by dyeing the hair of lab rats, and then observing whether the changed trait appears in their offspring.)* Have each group elect a spokesperson to describe its plan to the rest of the class, and urge the class to give the group feedback on its ideas. Then ask: **Why are only inherited traits affected by natural selection?** *(Because only genes are passed from parents to their offspring)*
cooperative learning

Evolution in Action

Social Studies
CONNECTION

Give students a context for the feature by explaining that the type of natural selection it describes is called *industrial melanism.* Explain that melanism refers to the pigment melanin, which gives many organisms—from peppered moths to humans—their color. The change in color of moths was documented in several unrelated species and in several different places, all of which were heavily industrialized. Point out that industrial melanism is one of the best analyzed examples of natural selection in action in the real world.

In Your Journal Students should (correctly) predict that strict pollution laws since the 1950s would lead to trees returning to their light gray color and natural selection favoring light-colored moths. This, in turn, would result in peppered moth populations becoming mostly light-colored again. **learning modality: logical/mathematical**

Social Studies
CONNECTION

An example of how human actions can influence natural selection occurred in England in the 1850s. Early in the 1800s, most English peppered moths were light gray in color. The light-colored moths had an advantage over black peppered moths because birds could not see them against the light-gray trees. Natural selection favored the light-colored moths over the black moths.

The Industrial Revolution began in England in the late 1700s. People built factories to make cloth and other goods. Over time, smoke from the factories blackened the trunks of the trees. Now the light-colored moths were easier to see than the black ones. As a result, birds caught more light-colored moths. Natural selection favored the black moths. In time, almost all the peppered moths were black.

In Your Journal

Since the 1950s, strict pollution laws have reduced the amount of smoke released into the air in England. Predict how this has affected the trees and the moths.

The Role of Genes in Evolution

Without variations, all the members of a species would have the same traits. Evolution by natural selection would not occur because all individuals would have an equal chance of surviving and reproducing. But where do variations come from? How are they passed on from parents to offspring? Darwin could not answer these questions.

Darwin did not know anything about genes or mutations. It is not surprising that he could not explain what caused variations or how they were passed on. As scientists later learned, variations can result from mutations in genes or from the shuffling of alleles during meiosis. Only genes are passed from parents to their offspring. Because of this, only traits that are inherited, or controlled by genes, can be acted upon by natural selection.

Evolution in Action

Since Darwin published his book, scientists have observed many examples of evolution in action. In a 1977 study of the finches on Daphne Major, one of the Galapagos Islands, scientists observed that beak size could change very quickly by natural selection. That year, little rain fell on the island—only 25 millimeters instead of the usual 130 millimeters or so. Because of the lack of rain, many plants died. Fewer of the seeds that the finches usually ate were available. Instead, the birds had to eat large seeds that were enclosed in tough, thorny seed pods.

Finches with larger and stronger beaks were better able to open the tough pods than were finches with smaller, weaker beaks. Many of the finches with smaller beaks did not survive the drought. The next year, more finches on the island had larger and stronger beaks. Evolution by natural selection had occurred in just one year.

Figure 6 The Industrial Revolution affected natural selection in peppered moths in England. As pollution blackened the tree trunks, black moths became more likely to survive and reproduce.

Background

History of Science Darwin was not the first person to propose a theory of evolution. In the early 1800s, a well-known French naturalist named Jean-Baptiste Lamarck also developed a theory of evolution to explain changes in a species' traits through time. Lamarck thought that changes in an organism during its lifetime could be passed on to its offspring. For example, dog breeders cut off parts of the ears of some breeds of dogs to make the ears stand up. According to Lamarck, the offspring of the dogs with cropped ears would also have cropped ears. This idea is often called "the inheritance of acquired characteristics," and it is now known to be incorrect. Changes in an organism cannot be passed on to its offspring unless they are controlled by genes.

How Do New Species Form?

Darwin's theory of evolution by natural selection explains how variations can lead to changes in a species. But how does an entirely new species evolve? Since Darwin's time, scientists have come to understand that geographic isolation is one of the main ways that new species form. Isolation, or complete separation, occurs when some members of a species become cut off from the rest of the species.

Sometimes a group is separated from the rest of its species by a river, volcano, or mountain range. Even an ocean wave can separate a few individuals from the rest of their species by sweeping them out to sea and later washing them ashore on an island. This may have happened on the Galapagos Islands. Once a group becomes isolated, members of the isolated group can no longer mate with members of the rest of the species.

A new species can form when a group of individuals remains separated from the rest of its species long enough to evolve different traits. The longer the group remains isolated from the rest of the species, the more likely it is to evolve into a new species. For example, the Abert squirrel and the Kaibab squirrel live in forests in the Southwest. About 10,000 years ago both types of squirrels were members of the same species. About that time, however, a small group of squirrels became isolated in a forest on the north side of the Grand Canyon in Arizona. Over time, this group evolved into the Kaibab squirrel, which has a distinctive black belly. Scientists are not sure whether the Kaibab squirrel has become different enough from the Abert squirrel to be considered a separate species.

✓ *Checkpoint* *How did geographic isolation affect the Kaibab squirrel?*

Figure 7 About 10,000 years ago, a group of squirrels became isolated from the rest of the species. As a result, the Kaibab squirrel (left) has evolved to become different from the Abert squirrel (right).
Interpreting Maps *What geographic feature separates the range of the Kaibab squirrel from that of the Abert squirrel?*

How Do New Species Form?

Inquiry Challenge

Divide the class into groups, and challenge each group to brainstorm a way that geographic isolation could arise and lead to the formation of a new species. (*A natural event such as an earthquake or a human activity such as the construction of a road could isolate some members of a species and keep them isolated long enough to evolve new traits.*) After groups have shared their ideas, ask: **Why must a group become isolated to develop into a new species?** (*Without isolation, matings could occur between the group and the rest of the species. As a result, any new traits would evolve not just in the group but throughout the entire species.*) **cooperative learning**

Using the Visuals: Figure 7

Use the figure to reinforce the information in the text for students who are still mastering English. First have students find the words *Arizona* and *Grand Canyon* on the map. Point out that the Grand Canyon is almost 30 km wide and 2 km deep. Stress how effectively a canyon of that size would isolate animals living on either side. Next have students carefully read the map key and the figure caption to locate the range of each type of squirrel on the map and identify which of the squirrels pictured above the map lives in each range. Finally, have students find the line in the text that answers the question: **What trait has the Kaibab squirrel evolved that makes it different from the Abert squirrel?** (*A black belly*) **limited English proficiency**

Ongoing Assessment

Writing Have students explain how species can change, using the finches on Daphne Major as an example. (*Students should explain how evolution by natural selection changed an isolated group of finches.*)

Continental Drift

Demonstration

Display a map of Pangaea. Point out that Australia broke away from Pangaea 250 million years ago, while other continents were still joined as recently as 50 million years ago. This isolated marsupials in Australia from competition with other mammals. Ask: **What are some other Australian marsupials?** *(kangaroo, koala, wombat)* **learning modality: visual**

3 Assess

Section 1 Review Answers

1. Evolution is the gradual change in a species over time. Darwin observed different adaptations among organisms.
2. Otherwise all individuals would be equally adapted to their environment and equally likely to survive and reproduce.
3. A new species can form when a group of individuals becomes isolated from the rest of its species and remains separated long enough to evolve different traits.
4. Insects that look like sticks are camouflaged among twigs and may be overlooked by predators. If the trait increases the insect's chances of surviving and reproducing, then insects with the trait would become more common than insects without it.

Check Your Progress

CHAPTER PROJECT 5

Review students' plans to make sure they have chosen workable models. Distribute Worksheet 1, and guide students through the procedure of making a scale model of their own life history to date. When students are comfortable with the process, let each group start its first time line.

Performance Assessment

Skills Check Have students explain how continental drift led to the evolution of many different marsupials in Australia.

Continental Drift

Geographic isolation has also occurred on a worldwide scale. For example, hundreds of millions of years ago all of Earth's landmasses were connected as one landmass. It formed a supercontinent called Pangaea. Organisms could migrate from one part of the supercontinent to another. Over millions of years, Pangaea gradually split apart in a process called continental drift. As the continents separated, species became isolated from one another and began to evolve independently.

Perhaps the most striking example of how continental drift affected the evolution of species is on the continent of Australia. The organisms living in Australia have been isolated from all other organisms on Earth for millions of years. Because of this, unique organisms have evolved in Australia. For example, most mammals in Australia belong to the group known as marsupials. Unlike other mammals, a marsupial gives birth to very small young that continue to develop in a pouch on the mother's body. Figure 8 shows two of the many marsupial species that exist in Australia. In contrast, few species of marsupials exist on other continents.

Figure 8 As a result of continental drift, many species of marsupials evolved in Australia. Australian marsupials include the numbat (top) and the spotted cuscus (bottom).

Section 1 Review

1. What is evolution? What did Darwin observe on the Galapagos Islands that he thought was the result of evolution?
2. Explain why variations are needed for natural selection to occur.
3. Describe how geographic isolation can result in the formation of a new species.
4. Thinking Critically Applying Concepts Some insects look just like sticks. How could this be an advantage to the insects? How could this trait have evolved through natural selection?

Check Your Progress

CHAPTER PROJECT 5

You should now be ready to submit your plans for your time lines to your teacher. Include a list of the major events you will include on your time lines. Remember, you want to emphasize the life forms that were present at each period. When your plans are approved, begin to construct your time lines. (*Hint:* You will need to divide your time lines into equal-sized intervals. For example, if you use a 12-month calendar to represent 5 billion years, calculate how many months will represent 1 billion years.)

Program Resources

 Science Explorer Series *Inside Earth,* Chapter 1, has more information about continental drift.
◆ **Teaching Resources** 5-1 Review and Reinforce, p. 125; 5-1 Enrich, p. 126

Media and Technology

Interactive Student Tutorial CD-ROM C-5

Exploring Life Science Videodisc Unit 5, Side 2, "The Drifters"

Chapter 6

SECTION 2 The Fossil Record

What Can You Learn From Fossils?

1. Look at the fossil in the photograph. Describe the fossil's characteristics in as much detail as you can.

2. From your description in Step 1, try to figure out how the organism lived. How did it move? Where did it live?

Think It Over

Inferring What type of present-day organism do you think is related to the fossil? Why?

A crime has been committed. You and another detective arrive at the crime scene after the burglar has fled. To piece together what happened, you begin searching for clues. First you notice a broken first-floor window. Leading up to the window are footprints in the mud. From the prints, you can infer the size and type of shoes the burglar wore. As you gather these and other clues, you slowly piece together a picture of what happened and who the burglar might be.

To understand events that occurred long ago, scientists act like detectives. Some of the most important clues to Earth's past arc fossils. A **fossil** is the preserved remains or traces of an organism that lived in the past. A fossil can be formed from a bone, tooth, shell, or other part of an organism. Other fossils can be traces of the organism, such as footprints or worm burrows left in mud that later turned to stone.

How Do Fossils Form?

Very few fossils are of complete organisms. Often when an animal dies, the soft parts of its body either decay or are eaten before a fossil can form. Usually only the hard parts of the animal, such as the bones or shells, remain. Plants also form fossils. The parts of plants that are most often preserved as fossils include leaves, stems, roots, and seeds.

The formation of any fossil is a rare event. The conditions must be just right for a fossil to form. **Most fossils form when organisms that die become buried in sediments.** Sediments are

GUIDE FOR READING

◆ How do most fossils form?

◆ How can scientists determine a fossil's age?

Reading Tip Before you read, preview *Exploring Life's History* on pages 156–157. Make a list of questions you have about geologic time and the evolution of life.

A fossilized shark tooth ▼

SECTION 2 The Fossil Record

Objectives

After completing the lesson, students will be able to
◆ describe how most fossils form;
◆ explain how a scientist determines a fossil's age;
◆ describe the main events of the Geologic Time Scale;
◆ describe two theories of how fast evolution occurs.

Key Terms fossil, sedimentary rock, petrified fossil, mold, cast, relative dating, absolute dating, radioactive element, half-life, fossil record, extinct, gradualism, punctuated equilibria

1 Engage/Explore

Activating Prior Knowledge

Most students are likely to know a lot about dinosaurs. Ask: **How do we know so much about dinosaurs if there are no longer any of them left alive?** *(From their remains, which have been preserved as fossils)* Tell students they will learn in this section how fossils are formed and how they are used by scientists to understand extinct organisms and their evolution.

DISCOVER

Skills Focus inferring
Time 5 minutes
Tips It may be helpful to provide a hand lens for any students with vision problems. After the activity, inform students that the fossil pictured is a trilobite, an ocean-bottom-dwelling animal that existed about 540 to 250 million years ago.
Expected Outcome Students are likely to describe the overall shape and obvious physical features of the fossil, including what appear to be a shell and numerous legs.
Think It Over Students may say the fossil is related to present-day insects or crabs, because it resembles them in its physical features.

Program Resources

◆ **Teaching Resources** 5-2 Lesson Plan, p. 127; 5-2 Section Summary, p. 128

Media and Technology

 Audiotapes English-Spanish Summary 5-2

 Transparencies "How Fossils Form," Transparency 17

READING STRATEGIES

Reading Tip If students write questions that are not answered in the text, challenge them to use encyclopedias or other sources to find the answers and to share them with the class.

Vocabulary Urge students who are having difficulty or are still mastering English to make and use flash cards for the key terms.

2 Facilitate

How Do Fossils Form?

Demonstration

Materials *clear plastic container, sand, soil, shells, other small objects*
Time 10 minutes

Demonstrate how most fossils form by gradually layering sand and soil in a clear container and scattering small shells or other objects throughout the layers to represent organic remains. As you add the layers of sediment, point out to students how the gradual accumulation of sediment buries and helps preserve the remains of organisms. Relate the demonstration to the actual formation of fossils by asking: **How would real animal remains become buried in this way?** *(By wind or water dropping sand and soil on them)* **How might the fossils become uncovered again?** *(Answers may vary. Usually erosion wears away layers of rock.)* **learning modality: visual**

Including All Students

Materials *baking sheet, modeling clay, prepared gelatin, shell or other small object*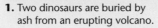
Time 5 minutes one day; 5 minutes the next day

Give hands-on learners an opportunity to experience how molds and casts are formed. Instruct students to lay a flat piece of clay on a baking sheet and make an impression in the clay with a small object such as a shell. Then have students pour a small amount of prepared gelatin into the depression and put the baking sheet in a refrigerator overnight. The next day, advise students to gently dislodge the hardened gelatin from the clay. The gelatin should have the same shape as the object that made the depression in the clay. Ask: **Which part of your model represents a mold? Which part represents a cast?** *(The depression in the clay represents a mold; the gelatin shape represents a cast.)* **learning modality: kinesthetic**

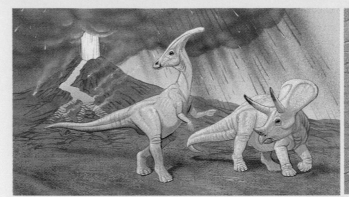

1. Two dinosaurs are buried by ash from an erupting volcano.

2. Minerals gradually replace the remains. Over millions of years, the fossils become buried by sediments.

Figure 9 Fossils are the preserved remains or traces of organisms that lived in the past. Fossils can form when organisms that die become buried in sediments.
Interpreting Diagrams What is one way in which a buried fossil can become uncovered?

particles of soil and rock. When a river flows into a lake or ocean, the sediments carried by the river settle to the bottom. Layers of sediments build up and cover the dead organisms. Over millions of years, the layers harden to become **sedimentary rock.**

Petrified Fossils Some remains that become buried in sediments are actually changed to rock. Minerals dissolved in the water soak into the buried remains. Gradually, the minerals replace the remains, changing them into rock. Fossils that form in this way are called **petrified fossils.**

Molds and Casts Sometimes shells or other hard parts buried by sediments are gradually dissolved. An empty space remains in the place the part once occupied. A hollow space in sediment in the shape of an organism or part of an organism is called a **mold.**

Sometimes a mold becomes filled in with hardened minerals, forming a **cast.** A cast is a copy of the shape of the organism that made the mold. If you have ever made a gelatin dessert in a plastic mold, then you can understand how a cast forms.

Preserved Remains Organisms can also be preserved in substances other than sediments. Entire organisms, such as the huge elephant-like mammoths that lived thousands of years ago, have been preserved in ice. The low temperatures preserved the mammoths' soft parts.

The bones and teeth of other ancient animals have been preserved in tar pits. Tar is a dark, sticky form of oil. Tar pits formed when tar seeped up from under the ground to the surface. The tar pits were often covered with water. Animals that came to drink the water became stuck in the tar.

Background

Facts and Figures Some of the most useful fossils for reconstructing the behavior of extinct animals are fossilized footprints. Fossilized footprints are relatively common because a single organism can leave a great many footprints and also because footprints tend to fossilize well if they are made in sand or mud. Fossilized footprints of dinosaurs, for example, have been found at more than 1,000 sites. Fossilized footprints can reveal a great deal about the animal that left them. For example, they provide evidence of the speed and length of the animal's stride, whether the animal walked on two or four legs, the bone structure of the animal's feet, and whether the animal traveled in a herd.

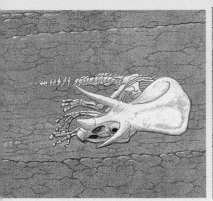

3. Running water cuts through the sedimentary rock layers, exposing the fossils.

Insects and some other organisms can become stuck in the sticky sap that some evergreen trees produce. The sap then hardens, forming amber. The amber protects the organism's body from decay.

Determining a Fossil's Age

To understand how living things have changed through time, scientists need to be able to determine the ages of fossils. They can then determine the sequence in which past events occurred. This information can be used to reconstruct the history of life on Earth. **Scientists can determine a fossil's age in two ways: relative dating and absolute dating.**

Relative Dating Scientists use **relative dating** to determine which of two fossils is older. To understand how relative dating works, imagine that a river has cut down through layers of sedimentary rock to form a canyon. If you look at the canyon walls, you can see the layers of sedimentary rock piled up one on top of another. The layers near the top of the canyon were formed most recently. These layers are the youngest rock layers. The lower down the canyon wall you go, the older the layers are. Therefore, fossils found in layers near the top of the canyon are younger than fossils found near the bottom of the canyon.

Relative dating can only be used when the rock layers have been preserved in their original sequence. Relative dating can help scientists determine whether one fossil is older than another. However, relative dating does not tell scientists the fossil's actual age.

☑ *Checkpoint* *Which rock layers contain younger fossils?*

Preservation in Ice

1. Place fresh fruit, such as apple slices, strawberries, and blueberries, in an open plastic container.
2. Completely cover the fruit with water. Put the container in a freezer.
3. Place the same type and amount of fresh fruit in another open container. Leave it somewhere where no one will disturb it.
4. After three days, observe the fruit in both containers.

Inferring Use your observations to explain why fossils preserved in ice are more likely to include soft, fleshy body parts.

Answers to Self-Assessment

Caption Question

Figure 9 A buried fossil can become uncovered when running water cuts through sedimentary rock layers.

☑ *Checkpoint*

The rock layers nearer the surface contain younger fossils.

TRY THIS

Skills Focus inferring
Materials *fresh fruit, two plastic containers, water*
Time 10 minutes
Tips Make sure students find a place to put the container of fruit that is left out so it will not be disturbed. Warn students not to eat the fruit that has been left out.
Expected Outcome The frozen fruit is well preserved, whereas the fruit that was left out is starting to spoil. Students should infer that freezing prevents the soft parts from drying out and/or rotting.
Extend Ask: **How do you think a mammoth or other animal might get preserved in this way?** (*Accept any reasonable response, such as an avalanche burying the animal or the animal falling into a crevasse in a glacier.*) **learning modality: kinesthetic**

Determining a Fossil's Age

Building Inquiry Skills: Problem Solving

Have students assume they are scientists who have excavated two fossil reptile skulls. Tell them that one skull was found 20 m below the surface and the other was found 30 m below the surface. Then ask: **Based on this information alone, what can you infer about the age of the two skulls?** (*The skull found nearer the surface is most likely younger than the skull found farther down in the ground.*) Urge students to draw a diagram to illustrate the problem and its solution. **learning modality: logical/mathematical**

Ongoing Assessment

Oral Presentation Call on students at random to describe how petrified fossils, molds, and casts form.

Determining a Fossil's Age, continued

Integrating Chemistry

Reinforce students' understanding of absolute dating by calling their attention to Figure 10 and asking: **If the sample contains one eighth of the original amount of potassium-40, how old is it?** *(Three half-lives, or 3.9 billion years, old)* **What proportion of the same sample would be argon-40?** *(seven eighths)* **learning modality: logical/mathematical**

What Do Fossils Reveal?

Addressing Naive Conceptions

Explain that of the millions of extinct species, only a fraction of one percent are likely to have been preserved as fossils. Ask: **Which organisms are most likely to be found as fossils: those that lived when much of Earth was covered by shallow seas or those that lived when Earth's mountain ranges were being formed?** *(Those that lived when much of Earth was covered by shallow seas)* **learning modality: verbal**

Figure 10 The half-life of potassium-40, a radioactive element, is 1.3 billion years. This means that half of the potassium-40 in a sample will break down into argon-40 every 1.3 billion years. *Interpreting Charts If a sample contains one fourth of the original amount of potassium-40, how old is the sample?*

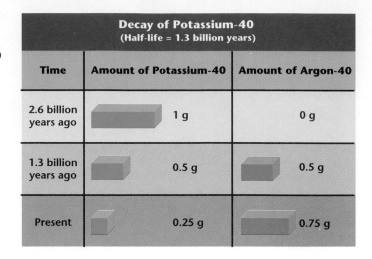

Decay of Potassium-40 (Half-life = 1.3 billion years)		
Time	**Amount of Potassium-40**	**Amount of Argon-40**
2.6 billion years ago	1 g	0 g
1.3 billion years ago	0.5 g	0.5 g
Present	0.25 g	0.75 g

Absolute Dating Another technique, called **absolute dating,** *INTEGRATING CHEMISTRY* allows scientists to determine the actual age of fossils. The rocks that fossils are found near contain **radioactive elements,** unstable elements that decay, or break down, into different elements. The **half-life** of a radioactive element is the time it takes for half of the atoms in a sample to decay. Figure 10 shows how a sample of potassium-40, a radioactive element, breaks down into argon-40 over time.

Scientists can compare the amount of a radioactive element in a sample to the amount of the element into which it breaks down. As you can see in Figure 10, this information can be used to calculate the age of the rock, and thus the age of the fossil.

☑ *Checkpoint* *What is a half-life?*

What Do Fossils Reveal?

Like pieces in a jigsaw puzzle, fossils help scientists piece together information about Earth's past. The millions of fossils that scientists have collected are called the **fossil record.** The fossil record, however, is incomplete. Many organisms die without leaving fossils behind. Despite gaps in the fossil record, it has given scientists a lot of important information about past life on Earth.

Almost all of the species preserved as fossils are now extinct. A species is **extinct** if no members of that species are still alive. Most of what scientists know about extinct species is based on the fossil record. Scientists use fossils of bones and teeth to build models of extinct animals. Fossil footprints provide clues about how fast an animal could move and how tall it was.

Background

Facts and Figures Another element used in absolute dating is carbon-14. All plants and animals contain some radioactive carbon-14. As plants and animals grow, carbon atoms are added to their tissues. After the organism dies, no more carbon-14 is added and the carbon-14 in the organism's body decays. To determine the absolute age of a sample, scientists measure the amount of carbon-14 that is left in the organism's remains.

Carbon-14 has been used to date frozen mammoths and the skeletons of prehistoric humans, as well as pieces of wood and bone.

Carbon-14 is very useful in dating materials from plants and animals that lived up to about 50,000 years ago. Since carbon-14 has a half-life of only 5,730 years, it can't be used to date really ancient fossils or rocks. The amount of carbon-14 left would be too small to measure accurately.

The fossil record also provides clues about how and when new groups of organisms evolved. The first animals appeared in the seas about 540 million years ago. These animals included worms, sponges, and other invertebrates—animals without backbones. About 500 million years ago, fishes evolved. These early fishes were the first vertebrates—animals with backbones.

The first land plants, which were similar to mosses, evolved around 410 million years ago. Land plants gradually evolved strong stems that held them upright. These plants were similar to modern ferns and cone-bearing trees. Look at *Exploring Life's History* on pages 156 and 157 to see when other groups of organisms evolved.

The Geologic Time Scale

Using absolute dating, scientists have calculated the ages of many different fossils and rocks. From this information, scientists have created a "calendar" of Earth's history that spans more than 4.6 billion years. Scientists have divided this large time period into smaller units called eras and periods. This calendar of Earth's history is sometimes called the Geologic Time Scale.

The largest span of time in the Geologic Time Scale is Precambrian Time, also called the Precambrian (pree KAM bree un). It covers the first 4 billion years of Earth's history. Scientists know very little about the Precambrian because there are few fossils from these ancient times. After the Precambrian, the Geologic Time Scale is divided into three major blocks of time, or eras. Each era is further divided into shorter periods. In *Exploring Life's History,* you can see the events that occurred during each time period.

Figure 11 Complete skeletons of animals that lived thousands of years ago have been found in the Rancho La Brea tar pits in Los Angeles, California. The photo shows a model of an elephant-like animal. Scientists created the model based on information learned from the fossils.

Students are referred in the text to the *Exploring Life's History* on pages 156 and 157. Check that they are interpreting the diagram correctly and extracting the most important information from the feature by asking them the following series of questions: **When did the first amphibians evolve?** (*During the Devonian Period, about 380 million years ago*) **When did the earliest reptiles appear on Earth?** (*During the Carboniferous Period, about 320 million years ago*) **When did the first dinosaurs and mammals evolve?** (*In the Triassic Period, about 220 million years ago*) **When did the first birds appear?** (*During the Jurassic Period, about 150 million years ago*) **When did the first primates appear?** (*During the Tertiary Period, about 66 million years ago*) **When did humans evolve?** (*During the Quaternary Period, about 1.5 million years ago*) **learning modality: verbal**

The Geologic Time Scale

Including All Students

Support students who need more help in learning the names of the eras in the Geologic Time Scale by explaining the words' roots. The combining form *-zoic* comes from the Greek word for "life," *paleo-* from the Greek word for "ancient," *meso-* from the Greek word for "middle," and *ceno-* from the Greek word for "recent." After students have learned the meanings of the combining forms, check their understanding by asking: **What do the terms *Paleozoic, Mesozoic,* and *Cenozoic* mean?** (*Ancient life, middle life, and recent life, respectively*) **learning modality: verbal**

Media and Technology

 Exploring Life Science Videodisc
Unit 5, Side 2,
"Extinction"

Chapter 7

 Exploring Life Science Videodisc
Unit 5, Side 2,
"Geologic Time"

Chapter 4

Answers to Self-Assessment

Caption Question

Figure 10 The sample is two half-lives, or 2.6 billion years, old.

 Checkpoint

A half-life is the time it takes for half the atoms in a sample of a radioactive element to break down, or decay.

Ongoing Assessment

Skills Check Have students create a table that compares and contrasts relative and absolute dating.

 Students can save their tables in their portfolios.

C ◆ 155

The Geologic Time Scale, continued

EXPLORING
Life's History

Call students' attention to the feature and stress that the captions at the bottom summarize the important evolutionary events in each time period. Make sure that students understand the time line that runs across the top of the feature. Explain that the Precambrian actually covers most of Earth's *total* history, but because there were few living things during the Precambrian, it makes up very little of Earth's *life* history. Add that almost one-quarter of Earth's history passed before the first life forms appeared around 3.5 billion years ago. Inform students that the earliest life forms on Earth were confined to the water. Then ask: **When did the first land plants and animals appear on Earth?** *(During the Silurian Period, about 430 million years ago)* The amount of detail in the feature may overwhelm some students, so make sure you are clear about how much detail you expect them to learn. **learning modality: visual**

Building Inquiry Skills: Communicating

Challenge students to imagine that they are in a machine traveling back in time from the present to another period in Earth's history. Then have them write an eyewitness report, modeled on a television or newspaper story, relaying what they might observe in their time travels. In their report, they should address such questions as: **What would it be like to live during another time period? What type of organisms would you see? What familiar species of today would you not see?** Encourage students who need extra challenges to use outside sources in addition to *Exploring Life's History* for more information, such as descriptions of climate or land forms. Ask volunteers to share their reports with the rest of the class, and challenge other students to identify each time period as it is described in the reports. **learning modality: verbal**

EXPLORING
Life's History
Take a trip through time to see how life on Earth has changed.

PRECAMBRIAN TIME The Precambrian covers about 87 percent of Earth's history.

4.6 billion years ago

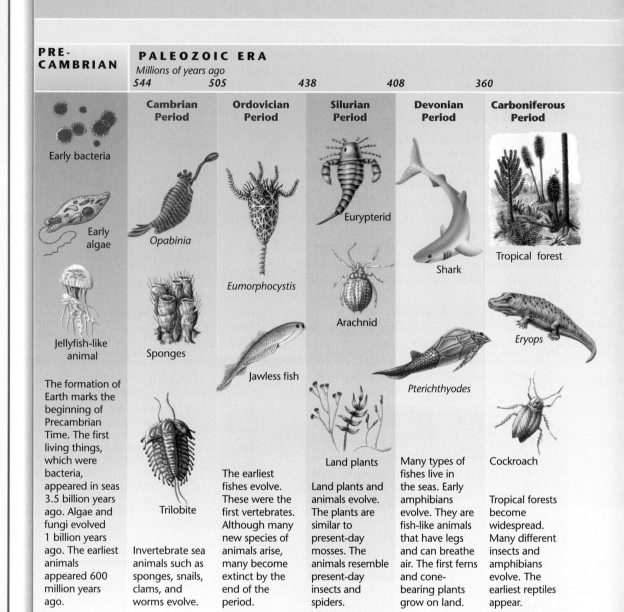

PRE-CAMBRIAN

PALEOZOIC ERA
Millions of years ago

| 544 | 505 | 438 | 408 | 360 |

Early bacteria

Early algae

Jellyfish-like animal

The formation of Earth marks the beginning of Precambrian Time. The first living things, which were bacteria, appeared in seas 3.5 billion years ago. Algae and fungi evolved 1 billion years ago. The earliest animals appeared 600 million years ago.

Cambrian Period

Opabinia

Sponges

Trilobite

Invertebrate sea animals such as sponges, snails, clams, and worms evolve.

Ordovician Period

Eumorphocystis

Jawless fish

The earliest fishes evolve. These were the first vertebrates. Although many new species of animals arise, many become extinct by the end of the period.

Silurian Period

Eurypterid

Arachnid

Land plants

Land plants and animals evolve. The plants are similar to present-day mosses. The animals resemble present-day insects and spiders.

Devonian Period

Shark

Pterichthyodes

Many types of fishes live in the seas. Early amphibians evolve. They are fish-like animals that have legs and can breathe air. The first ferns and cone-bearing plants grow on land.

Carboniferous Period

Tropical forest

Eryops

Cockroach

Tropical forests become widespread. Many different insects and amphibians evolve. The earliest reptiles appear.

156 ◆ C

Background

Facts and Figures Scientists have concluded that there were mass extinctions at the end of the Cretaceous Period, including the extinction of the dinosaurs, but there is still debate about the cause. Many theories have been proposed, ranging from climatic changes to predators. In the early 1980s, scientists at the University of California proposed another theory—that a giant asteroid or comet struck Earth and sent so much dust into the atmosphere that it blocked sunlight for more than two years. This event would have greatly reduced photosynthesis and led to the collapse of food chains and to mass extinctions. This theory is based on direct evidence of a collision crater in the Yucatan and the presence at Cretaceous sites of the element iridium, rare on Earth but plentiful in asteroids.

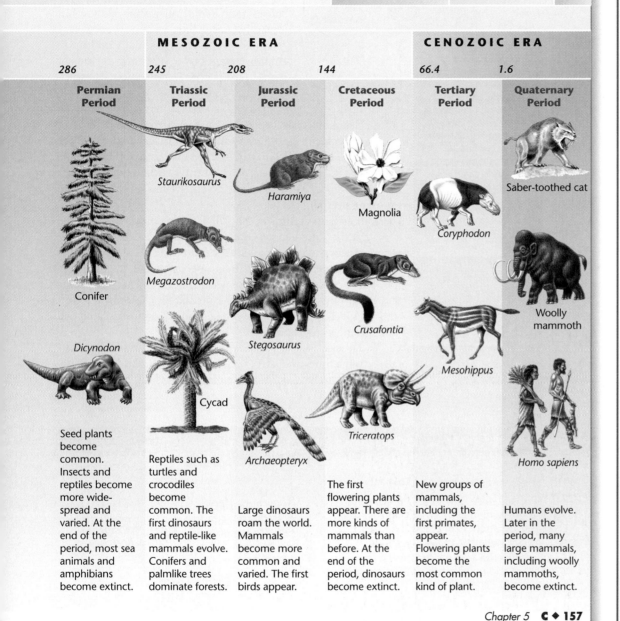

PALEOZOIC		**MESOZOIC**		**CENOZOIC**	
	544 million years ago	245 million years ago		66.4 million years ago	

MESOZOIC ERA				**CENOZOIC ERA**	
286	245	208	144	66.4	1.6
Permian Period	**Triassic Period**	**Jurassic Period**	**Cretaceous Period**	**Tertiary Period**	**Quaternary Period**

Staurikosaurus

Haramiya

Magnolia

Saber-toothed cat

Coryphodon

Conifer

Megazostrodon

Dicynodon

Stegosaurus

Crusafontia

Woolly mammoth

Cycad

Mesohippus

Archaeopteryx

Triceratops

Homo sapiens

Seed plants become common. Insects and reptiles become more wide-spread and varied. At the end of the period, most sea animals and amphibians become extinct.

Reptiles such as turtles and crocodiles become common. The first dinosaurs and reptile-like mammals evolve. Conifers and palmlike trees dominate forests.

Large dinosaurs roam the world. Mammals become more common and varied. The first birds appear.

The first flowering plants appear. There are more kinds of mammals than before. At the end of the period, dinosaurs become extinct.

New groups of mammals, including the first primates, appear. Flowering plants become the most common kind of plant.

Humans evolve. Later in the period, many large mammals, including woolly mammoths, become extinct.

Chapter 5 **C ◆ 157**

Inquiry Challenge

Materials *poster board, dice, index cards, markers, small toys or other items for game tokens*
Time 30 minutes

Divide the class into groups, and challenge each group to create a board game, called *A Trip Through Geologic Time,* to reinforce their knowledge of Earth's life history. The game board should start in the Precambrian and continue on to the present. To advance around the game board (and through time), players should be required to answer questions, perhaps written on chance cards, about each period. Escaping from carnivorous dinosaurs, skirting around treacherous tar pits, or avoiding similar relevant obstacles in particular time periods might be included on the game board to add excitement to the game and require students to apply more of the information from *Exploring Life's History.* After students have created their games, urge groups to exchange and play each other's games. **cooperative learning**

Including All Students

Materials *index cards*
Time 30 minutes

Pair students who are having difficulty or who are still mastering English with other students who have strong verbal skills. Then have the members of each pair work together to make flash cards for the periods of the Geologic Time Scale. On each card, they should include the dates for the period and the most important life history events. Challenge pairs to exchange flash cards and use them to quiz each other on the material. **limited English proficiency**

Ongoing Assessment

.Oral Presentation Call on students at random to each describe an event in the evolution of plants or animals, based on the information in *Exploring Life's History.*

How Fast Does Evolution Occur?

Building Inquiry Skills: Inferring

Ask students: **Why are fossils of intermediate life forms likely to be rare if the theory of punctuated equilibria explains how evolution occurs?** *(The theory proposes that new species evolve rapidly over a short period of time, so the chances of fossils of intermediate species forming are greatly reduced.)* **learning modality: logical/mathematical**

3 Assess

Section 2 Review Answers

1. Most fossils form when organisms that die become buried in layers of sediment and the layers harden to become sedimentary rock.

2. Scientists compare the amount of a radioactive element in a sample to the amount of the element into which it breaks down and then calculate the age of the fossil based on the element's constant rate of decay.

3. The fossil record refers to the millions of fossils scientists have collected. It reveals how extinct species looked, behaved, and evolved.

4. Both theories attempt to explain the fossil record. Gradualism proposes that evolution occurs slowly and steadily. Punctuated equilibria proposes that evolution occurs during short periods of rapid change separated by long periods of little or no change.

Science at Home

Tips Advise students to use mud that contains a lot of clay and enough water to make it the consistency of yogurt or pudding.

Performance Assessment

Skills Check Have students make a table to compare and contrast the theories of gradualism and punctuated equilibria.

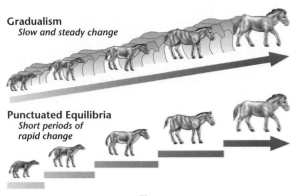

Gradualism
Slow and steady change

Punctuated Equilibria
Short periods of rapid change

⟶ *Time* ⟶

Figure 12 According to the theory of gradualism, new species of horses evolved slowly and continuously. Intermediate forms were common. According to punctuated equilibria, new species evolved rapidly during short periods of time. Intermediate forms were rare.

How Fast Does Evolution Occur?

Because the fossil record is incomplete, many questions about evolution remain unanswered. For example, scientists cannot always tell from the fossil record how quickly a particular species evolved.

One theory, called **gradualism,** proposes that evolution occurs slowly but steadily. According to this theory, tiny changes in a species gradually add up to major changes over very long periods of time. This is how Darwin thought evolution occurred.

If the theory of gradualism is correct, intermediate forms of all species should have existed. However, the fossil record often shows no intermediate forms for long periods of time. Then, quite suddenly, fossils appear that are distinctly different. One possible explanation for the lack of intermediate forms is that the fossil record is incomplete. Scientists may eventually find more fossils to fill the gaps.

Rather than assuming that the fossil record is incomplete, two scientists, Stephen Jay Gould and Niles Eldridge, have developed a theory that agrees with the fossil data. According to the theory of **punctuated equilibria,** species evolve during short periods of rapid change. These periods of rapid change are separated by long periods of little or no change. According to this theory, species evolve quickly when groups become isolated and adapt to new environments.

Today most scientists think that evolution can occur gradually at some times and fairly rapidly at others. Both forms of evolution seem to have occurred during Earth's long history.

Section 2 Review

1. Describe how fossils form in sedimentary rock.
2. Explain the process of absolute dating.
3. What is the fossil record? What does the fossil record reveal about extinct species?
4. **Thinking Critically** *Comparing and Contrasting* How are the theories of gradualism and punctuated equilibria similar? How are they different?

Science at Home

With an adult family member, spread some mud in a shallow flat-bottomed pan. Smooth the surface of the mud. Use your fingertips to make "footprints" across the mud. Let the mud dry and harden, so that the footprints become permanent. Explain to your family how this is similar to the way some fossils form.

Background

Facts and Figures Just how short are the periods of rapid change proposed by supporters of the punctuated equilibria theory? Generally, they are on the order of 50,000 to 100,000 years, which is very short indeed compared with the billions of years of the Geologic Time Scale. The best data in support of the theory come from the fossilized remains of invertebrates, or animals without backbones, such as snails.

Program Resources

◆ **Teaching Resources** 5-2 Review and Reinforce, p. 129; 5-2 Enrich, p. 130

Media and Technology

Interactive Student Tutorial CD-ROM C-5

3 Other Evidence for Evolution

DISCOVER

How Can You Classify Species?

1. Collect six to eight different pens. Each pen will represent a different species of similar organisms.

2. Choose a trait that varies among your pen species, such as size or ink color. Using this trait, try to divide the pen species into two groups.

3. Now choose another trait. Divide each group into two smaller groups.

Think It Over

Classifying Which of the pen species share the most characteristics? What might the similarities suggest about how the pen species evolved?

Do you know anyone who has had their appendix out? The appendix is a tiny organ attached to the small intestine. You might think that having a part of the body removed might cause a problem. After all, you need your heart, lungs, stomach and other body parts to live. However, this is not the case with the appendix. In humans, the appendix does not seem to have any function. In some other species of mammals, though, the appendix is much larger and plays an important role in digestion. To scientists, this is a clue that the ancestors of modern-day humans had a larger appendix that was important for digestion.

The appendix is just one example of how modern-day organisms can provide clues about evolution. By comparing organisms, scientists can infer how closely related the organisms are in an evolutionary sense. **Scientists compare body structures, development before birth, and DNA sequences to determine the evolutionary relationships among organisms.**

Similarities in Body Structure

Scientists long ago began to compare the body structures of living species to look for clues about evolution. In fact, this is how Darwin came to understand that evolution had occurred on the Galapagos Islands. An organism's body structure is its basic body plan, such as how its bones are arranged. Fishes, amphibians, reptiles, birds, and mammals, for example, all have a similar body

GUIDE FOR READING

◆ What evidence from modern-day organisms can help scientists determine evolutionary relationships among groups?

Reading Tip As you read, use the headings to make an outline about the different types of evidence for evolution.

Chapter 5 **C ◆ 159**

Program Resources

◆ **Teaching Resources** 5-3 Lesson Plan, p. 131; 5-3 Section Summary, p. 132

Media and Technology

 Audiotapes English-Spanish Summary 5-3

 Transparencies "Homologous Structures," Transparency 20

READING STRATEGIES

Reading Tip Suggest that students fill in their outline with details as they read the section. Advise students to save their completed outlines to use as study guides.

Study and Comprehension Have visual learners preview the section by studying the figures and reading the captions. Tell students they will understand and retain the material better if they focus on a real-life example of each type of similarity.

---

3 Other Evidence for Evolution

Objectives

After completing the lesson, students will be able to
◆ state evidence from modern-day organisms that scientists use to show evolutionary relationships among groups;
◆ describe how scientists classify organisms and place them on branching trees.

Key Terms homologous structure, branching tree

1 Engage/Explore

Activating Prior Knowledge

On the chalkboard write the following list: *horse, rabbit, zebra, squirrel, donkey, deer, chipmunk,* and *mouse.* Then ask: **Which animals would you group together based on their similarities?** (*Students are likely to place the horse, zebra, donkey, and deer in one group and the rabbit, squirrel, chipmunk, and mouse in another.*) Tell students that, in this section, they will see how scientists use similarities among living species to infer how the species evolved.

DISCOVER

Skills Focus classifying
Materials *6 to 8 pens*
Time 10 minutes
Tips Have extra pens to guarantee that each student has enough. Include pens that are somewhat different from each other.
Expected Outcome How students classify their pens will depend on their particular sample of pens and the traits they choose for classification.
Think It Over Students may say that the pen species that are most similar evolved from a common ancestor.

C ◆ 159

2 Facilitate

Similarities in Body Structure

Sharpen your Skills

Drawing Conclusions

Time 5 minutes

Tips If students have

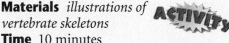

difficulty identifying similarities between the crocodile's leg and the legs of the animals shown in Figure 13, advise them to focus on the number and arrangement of bones.

Expected Outcome Students are likely to say that crocodiles share a common ancestor with birds, dolphins, and dogs because of the similar structure of the bones in their legs.

Extend Ask: **What other animals do you think would have forelimbs similar in structure to those of crocodiles, birds, dolphins, and dogs?** *(Possible answers include any reptile, bird, or mammal.)* **learning modality: logical/mathematical**

Building Inquiry Skills: Observing

Materials *illustrations of vertebrate skeletons*

Time 10 minutes

Show students illustrations of skeletons from a variety of vertebrates, such as fish, reptiles, birds, and mammals. (Illustrations can be found in zoology and anatomy textbooks, as well as in general reference books such as encyclopedias.) Challenge students to compare the skeletal structures, then ask: **What evidence suggests that all of these animals share a common ancestor?** *(Students should point out ways that the skeletal structures are similar in the number and arrangement of bones. They should also explain how such similarities are used to infer evolutionary relationships.)* **learning modality: visual**

Sharpen your Skills

Drawing Conclusions

Look at the drawing below of the bones in a crocodile's leg. Compare this drawing to Figure 13. Do you think that crocodiles share a common ancestor with birds, dolphins, and dogs? Support your answer with evidence.

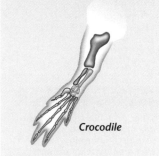

Crocodile

Figure 13 A bird's wing, dolphin's flipper, and dog's leg are all adapted to performing different tasks. However, the structure of the bones in each forelimb is very similar. These homologous structures provide evidence that these animals evolved from a common ancestor. *Observing What similarities in structure do the three forelimbs share?*

structure—an internal skeleton with a backbone. This is why scientists classify all five groups of animals together as vertebrates. Presumably, these groups all inherited these similarities in structure from an early vertebrate ancestor that they shared.

Look closely at the structure of the bones in the bird's wing, dolphin's flipper, and dog's leg shown in Figure 13. Notice that the bones in the forelimbs of these three animals are arranged in a similar way. These similarities provide evidence that these three organisms all evolved from a common ancestor. Similar structures that related species have inherited from a common ancestor are called **homologous structures** (hoh MAHL uh gus).

Sometimes scientists find fossil evidence that supports the evidence provided by homologous structures. For example, scientists have recently found fossils of ancient whale-like creatures. The fossils show that the ancestors of today's whales had legs and walked on land. This evidence supports other evidence that whales and humans share a common ancestor.

☑ *Checkpoint* *What information do homologous structures reveal?*

Similarities in Early Development

Scientists can also make inferences about evolutionary relationships by comparing the early development of different organisms. Suppose you were asked to compare an adult turtle, a chicken, and a rat. You would probably say they look quite different from each other. However, during early development, these three organisms go through similar stages, as you can see

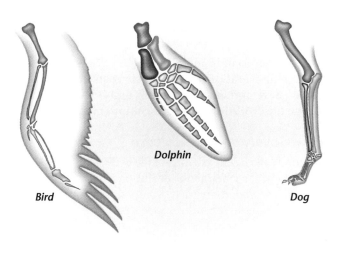

Bird

Dolphin

Dog

Background

Facts and Figures The system of classification based on homologous structures is believed to have been developed by Carolus Linnaeus, the eighteenth century Swedish botanist who developed the taxonomic system for classifying living things that is still in use today. Based on homologous structures, humans are classified as primates along with monkeys and apes, and lions are classified as cats

along with tigers and leopards.

Sometimes species have similar structures that reflect parallel adaptations but not a common ancestor. Such structures are called analogous structures. A good example is the wing of a bird and the wing of a butterfly. The wings of both animals perform the same function, but their internal structures are quite different because the animals evolved from different ancestors.

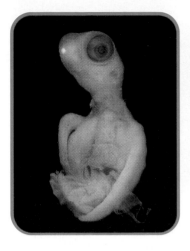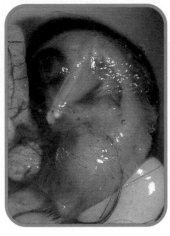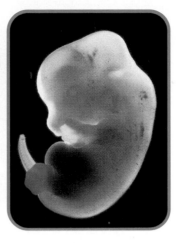

Figure 14 Turtles (left), chickens (center), and rats (right) look similar during the earliest stages of development. These similarities provide evidence that these three animals evolved from a common ancestor.

in Figure 14. For example, during the early stages of development all three organisms have a tail and tiny gill slits in their throats. These similarities suggest that these three vertebrate species are related and share a common ancestor.

When scientists study early development more closely, they notice that the turtle appears more similar to the chicken than it does to the rat. This evidence supports the conclusion that turtles are more closely related to chickens than they are to rats.

Similarities in DNA

Why do related species have similar body structures and development patterns? Scientists infer that the species inherited many of the same genes from a common ancestor. Recently, scientists have begun to compare the genes of different species to determine how closely related the species are.

Recall that genes are made of DNA. By comparing the sequence of nitrogen bases in the DNA of different species, scientists can infer how closely related the species are. The more similar the sequences, the more closely related the species are.

Recall also that the DNA bases along a gene specify what type of protein will be produced. Thus, scientists can also compare the order of amino acids in a protein to see how closely related two species are.

Sometimes DNA evidence does not confirm earlier conclusions about relationships between species. For example, aside from its long nose, the tiny elephant shrew looks very similar to rodents such as mice. Because of this, biologists used to think that the elephant shrew was closely related to rodents. But when scientists compared DNA from elephant shrews to that of both

---

Program Resources

🔵 **Science Explorer Series** *Animals,* Chapter 3, has more information about vertebrates and vertebrate evolution.

Answers to Self-Assessment

☑ *Checkpoint*
Homologous structures reveal that organisms share a common ancestor.

Caption Question
Figure 13 The three forelimbs share a similar number and arrangement of bones.

Similarities in Early Development

Using the Visuals: Figure 14
Challenge students to detect ways that the three embryos are similar and different. *(Similarities might include tails and gill slits; differences might include shape of head and body.)* Point out that scientists have concluded, on the basis of such similarities and differences, that turtles are more closely related to chickens than to rats. Then ask: **In what ways do the turtle and chicken appear to be more similar than the turtle and rat?** *(Students may say that the turtle and chicken both have large eyes and a pointed mouth.)* **learning modality: visual**

Similarities in DNA

Inquiry Challenge
Challenge pairs of students to draw short sections of DNA base sequences for three hypothetical related species to illustrate how DNA similarities can be used to infer evolutionary relationships. Remind students that there are four bases in DNA: adenine, thymine, guanine, and cytosine, which they can abbreviate as A, T, G, and C, respectively. After students have finished their drawings, urge volunteers to share their work with the class. Have other students try to infer from the DNA base sequences how the three species are related. *(They should infer that the more similar the DNA base sequences, the more closely related the species.)* Conclude by asking: **How do you think the amino acid sequences in the proteins of the three species would compare? Why?** *(Students should say that the amino acid sequences in the proteins would reflect the same evolutionary relationships as the DNA base sequences. This is because the amino acid sequences are encoded in the DNA.)* **learning modality: logical/mathematical**

Ongoing Assessment

Oral Presentation Call on students at random to describe the three kinds of similarities in living species that scientists use to reconstruct evolutionary relationships.

Similarities in DNA, continued

Encourage students to think about how recent advances in DNA technology may affect the way scientists study evolutionary relationships. Ask: **What can scientists learn from fossil DNA that they could not learn by studying the physical structure of the fossils?** *(DNA provides more direct evidence of genetic relationships.)* **Will the ability to extract DNA from fossils mean that scientists will no longer have to compare living species in order to reconstruct evolutionary relationships?** *(The fossil record is incomplete, so being able to extract DNA from fossils will not add any new information about many extinct species. Therefore, scientists will still have to compare living species to reconstruct evolutionary relationships.)* **learning modality: logical/mathematical**

Combining the Evidence

Building Inquiry Skills: Interpreting Data

Time 10 minutes

ACTIVITY

Have students interpret data to infer how three hypothetical species—A, B, and C—are related. First tell students that A and C appear to be more similar in body structure than A and B or B and C. Then tell students that A and B appear to be more similar in their early development than A and C or B and C. Finally, tell students that the DNA base sequences of A and B are more similar than the DNA base sequences of A and C or B and C. After providing students with this information, challenge them to combine and weigh the evidence. Then ask: **What are the evolutionary relationships among the three species?** *(Species A and B are more closely related to each other than either species is related to species C because of the similarities in their early development and DNA.)* Challenge students to draw a branching tree to illustrate the evolutionary relationships among the three species. **learning modality: logical/mathematical**

Figure 15 Because of its appearance, the tiny elephant shrew was thought to be closely related to mice and other rodents. Surprisingly, DNA comparisons showed that the elephant shrew is actually more closely related to elephants.

rodents and elephants, they got a surprise. The elephant shrew's DNA was more similar to the elephant's DNA than it was to the rodent's DNA. Scientists now think that elephant shrews are more closely related to elephants than to rodents.

INTEGRATING TECHNOLOGY Recently, scientists have developed techniques that allow them to extract, or remove, DNA from fossils. Using these techniques, scientists have now extracted DNA from fossils of bones, teeth, and plants, and from insects trapped in amber. The DNA from fossils has provided scientists with new evidence about evolution.

Combining the Evidence

Scientists have combined evidence from fossils, body structures, early development, and DNA and protein sequences to determine the evolutionary relationships among species. In most cases, DNA and protein sequences have confirmed conclusions based on earlier evidence. For example, recent DNA comparisons show that dogs are more similar to wolves than they are to coyotes. Scientists had already reached this conclusion based on similarities in the structure and development of these three species.

Another example of how scientists combined evidence from different sources is shown in the branching tree in Figure 16. A **branching tree** is a diagram that shows how scientists think different groups of organisms are related. Based on similar body structures, lesser pandas were thought to be closely related to giant pandas. The two panda species also resemble both bears and raccoons. Until recently, scientists were not sure how these four groups were related. DNA analysis and other methods have shown that giant pandas and lesser pandas are not closely related. Instead, giant pandas are more closely related to bears, while lesser pandas are more closely related to raccoons.

Background

Integrating Science Similarities and differences in DNA base sequences are assessed using a technique called DNA hybridization. In this technique, double strands of DNA from two different species are separated and then recombined into a new molecule called hybrid DNA. The genetic similarity of the two species is then measured by calculating the number of base pairs that do not match along the hybrid sequence, that is, pairs in which adenine is not matched with thymine or cytosine is not matched with guanine.

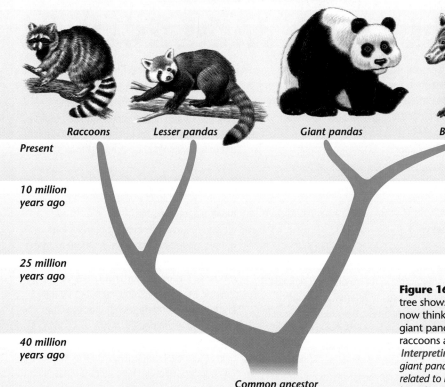

Raccoons   Lesser pandas   Giant pandas   Bears

Present

10 million years ago

25 million years ago

40 million years ago

Common ancestor

Figure 16 This branching tree shows how scientists now think that lesser pandas, giant pandas, bears, and raccoons are related. *Interpreting Diagrams Are giant pandas more closely related to lesser pandas or to bears?*

Section 3 Review

1. Name three types of evidence from modern-day organisms that scientists use to determine evolutionary relationships.
2. What are homologous structures?
3. What information did scientists learn by comparing the early developmental stages of turtles, chickens, and rats?
4. If two species are closely related, what would you expect a comparison of their DNA base sequences to reveal?
5. **Thinking Critically Making Judgments** Most scientists today consider similarities in DNA to be the best indicator of how closely two species are related. Why do you think this is the case?

Check Your Progress

CHAPTER PROJECT 5

You should be completing construction of the time line that covers 5 billion years. Now begin work on the time line showing 600 million years. This version is a magnified view of one part of the first time line. It will give you additional space to show what happened in the more recent years of Earth's history. (*Hint:* Prepare drawings to show how life forms on Earth were changing. Also, try to include three or more events not mentioned in the text.)

Chapter 5 **C ◆ 163**

Program Resources

◆ **Teaching Resources** 5-3 Review and Reinforce, p. 133; 5-3 Enrich, p. 134

Media and Technology

 Interactive Student Tutorial CD-ROM C-5

Answers to Self-Assessment

Caption Question

Figure 16 Giant pandas are more closely related to bears than to lesser pandas.

Using the Visuals: Figure 16

Reinforce students' understanding of branching trees and evolutionary relationships. Ask: **When did giant pandas and bears evolve from their common ancestor?** (*About 10 million years ago*) **When did raccoons and lesser pandas evolve from their common ancestor?** (*About 25 million years ago*) **Which are more closely related, raccoons and lesser pandas, or giant pandas and bears?** (*Giant pandas and bears*) **learning modality: visual**

3 Assess

Section 3 Review Answers

1. Similarities in body structure, similarities in early development, and similarities in DNA base sequences
2. Similar structures that related species have inherited from a common ancestor
3. Scientists learned that these animals evolved from a common ancestor.
4. You would expect the base sequences to be very similar.
5. DNA similarities are the most direct indicator that species inherited their genes from a common ancestor.

Check Your Progress

CHAPTER PROJECT 5

Review each group's first time line, and offer comments before the group starts its second time line. Make sure students understand that because the second time line is an enlargement of one section of the first time line, its scale will be different. Distribute Worksheet 2, which lists additional evolutionary events not in the text. Provide source materials for students to use.

Performance Assessment

Drawing Have students draw a branching tree that shows how dogs, wolves, and coyotes are related. (*Students' drawings should show that dogs and wolves shared a common ancestor more recently than either species did with coyotes.*)

Telltale Molecules

Preparing for Inquiry

Key Concept The more similar the amino acid sequence in proteins of different species, the more closely the species are related.

Skills Objectives Students will be able to

◆ interpret data on amino acid sequences in proteins;

◆ compare and contrast amino acid sequences in the same protein for different species;

◆ draw conclusions about how the species are related based on the amino acid comparisons.

Time 30 minutes

Advance Planning You may need to review with students what they learned about protein synthesis in Chapter 3.

Alternative Materials You may want to provide students with copies of tables comparing actual amino acid sequences from a genetics textbook to show how similar the data in the lab are to data scientists actually use to reconstruct evolutionary relationships.

Guiding Inquiry

Invitation Ask students: **What is a genetic code?** (*It is the order of the nitrogen bases along a gene.*) **How do cells use a genetic code to make proteins?** (*The nitrogen bases code for the production of specific amino acids, which are the building blocks of proteins.*) **What are genes made of?** (*DNA*)

Introducing the Procedure

◆ Have students read the entire lab, then ask: **What is the objective of this lab activity?** (*To use the amino acid sequence of a protein to determine the evolutionary relationship among several animals*) **What do the letters in the table represent?** (*Each letter represents a different amino acid.*)

◆ Suggest that students create a table to record the number of differences between the horse and each of the other animals.

TELLTALE MOLECULES

In this lab, you will compare the structure of one protein in a variety of animals. You'll use the data to draw conclusions about how closely related those animals are.

Problem

What information can protein structure reveal about evolutionary relationships among organisms?

Procedure

1. Examine the table below. It shows the sequence of amino acids in one region of a protein, cytochrome c, for six different animals. Each letter represents a different amino acid.
2. Predict which of the five other animals is most closely related to the horse. Which animal do you think is most distantly related?
3. Compare the amino acid sequence of the horse to that of the donkey. How many amino acids differ between the two species? Record that number in your notebook.
4. Compare the amino acid sequences of each of the other animals to that of the horse. Record the number of differences in your notebook.

Analyze and Conclude

1. Which animal's amino acid sequence was most similar to that of the horse? What similarities and difference(s) did you observe?
2. How did the amino acid sequences of each of the other animals compare with that of the horse?
3. Based on this data, which species is the most closely related to the horse? Which is the most distantly related?
4. For the entire cytochrome c protein, the horse's amino acid sequence differs from the other animals as follows: donkey, 1 difference; rabbit, 6; snake, 22; turtle, 11; and whale, 5. How do the relationships indicated by the entire protein compare with those for the region you examined?
5. **Think About It** Explain why data about amino acid sequences can provide information about evolutionary relationships among organisms.

More to Explore

Use the amino acid data to construct a branching tree that includes horses, donkeys, and snakes. The tree should show one way that the three species could have evolved from a common ancestor.

Section of Cytochrome c Protein in Animals															
Amino Acid Position															
Animal	**39**	**40**	**41**	**42**	**43**	**44**	**45**	**46**	**47**	**48**	**49**	**50**	**51**	**52**	**53**
Horse	A	B	C	D	E	F	G	H	I	J	K	L	M	N	O
Donkey	A	B	C	D	E	F	G	H	Z	J	K	L	M	N	O
Rabbit	A	B	C	D	E	Y	G	H	Z	J	K	L	M	N	O
Snake	A	B	C	D	E	Y	G	H	Z	J	K	W	M	N	O
Turtle	A	B	C	D	E	V	G	H	Z	J	K	U	M	N	O
Whale	A	B	C	D	E	Y	G	H	Z	J	K	L	M	N	O

Troubleshooting the Experiment

◆ Make sure students understand how to read the table correctly before they compare the different species.

Expected Outcome

Students should infer from the amino acid comparisons which species are most closely related and which are least closely related to the horse.

Program Resources

◆ **Teaching Resources** Chapter 5 Skills Lab, pp. 138–139

CHAPTER 5 REVIEW

SECTION 1 — Darwin's Voyage

Key Ideas

- Darwin thought that species gradually changed over many generations as they became better adapted to new conditions. This process is called evolution.
- Darwin's observations led him to propose that evolution occurs through natural selection. Natural selection occurs due to overproduction, competition, and variations.
- Only traits controlled by genes can change over time as a result of natural selection.
- If a group of individuals remains separated from the rest of its species long enough to evolve different traits, a new species can form.

Key Terms

species
adaptation
evolution

scientific theory
natural selection
variation

SECTION 2 — The Fossil Record

INTEGRATING EARTH SCIENCE

Key Ideas

- Most fossils form when organisms die and sediments bury them. The sediments harden, preserving parts of the organisms.
- Relative dating determines which of two fossils is older and which is younger. Absolute dating determines the actual age of a fossil.
- Fossils help scientists understand how extinct organisms looked and evolved.
- The Geologic Time Scale shows when during Earth's 4.6-billion-year history major groups of organisms evolved.
- Evolution has occurred gradually at some times and fairly rapidly at other times.

Key Terms

fossil
sedimentary rock
petrified fossil
mold
cast
relative dating
absolute dating

radioactive element
half-life
fossil record
extinct
gradualism
punctuated equilibria

SECTION 3 — Other Evidence for Evolution

Key Ideas

- By comparing modern-day organisms, scientists can infer how closely related they are in an evolutionary sense.
- Homologous structures can provide evidence of how species are related and of how they evolved from a common ancestor.
- Similarities in early developmental stages are evidence that species are related and shared a common ancestor.
- Scientists can compare DNA and protein sequences to determine more precisely how species are related.
- A branching tree is a diagram that shows how scientists think different groups of organisms are related.

Key Terms

homologous structure
branching tree

USING THE INTERNET
www.science-explorer.phschool.com

Chapter 5 **C ◆ 165**

Analyze and Conclude

1. The donkey's amino acid sequence was most similar to that of the horse, differing only in the amino acid in position 47.
2. The rabbit and whale differed from the horse in two amino acids. The snake and turtle differed from the horse in three amino acids.
3. Based on this data, the donkey is most closely related to the horse and the turtle and snake are least closely related to the horse.
4. The relationships indicated by the entire protein are similar to the relationships indicated by the region of the protein examined in the lab.
5. As two or more species evolve from a common ancestor, their DNA may undergo different mutations, causing changes in the amino acids making up common proteins. The fewer differences in the amino acids, the more closely the given species are related.

Extending the Inquiry

More to Explore Students' branching trees should show that the horse and donkey have the most recent common ancestor and that the horse and snake have the most distant common ancestor.

Reviewing Content:
Multiple Choice
1. b 2. b 3. b 4. c 5. c

True or False
6. true 7. true 8. true
9. absolute dating 10. true

Checking Concepts

11. The overproduction of offspring leads to competition in which only the better adapted organisms survive and reproduce.

12. Examples will vary. *Sample answer:* A large number of turtles are born every year but only a few will be able to swim fast enough to escape predators. Because being able to swim faster makes the turtles more likely to survive and reproduce, natural selection leads to an increase through time in the fast-swimming trait.

13. Fossils found in layers of rock nearer the surface are younger than fossils found in deeper layers.

14. According to the theory of punctuated equilibria, the fossil record includes very few intermediate forms because new species evolve so rapidly that there is very little chance that such intermediate forms will be preserved as fossils.

15. Related species inherit the same basic developmental plan from their common ancestor.

16. Students' questions and answers will vary, but they should demonstrate clearly that students understand Darwin's theory of evolution by natural selection.

Thinking Visually

17. *Sample title:* How Natural Selection Works

a. Since food and other resources are limited, the offspring must compete with each other to survive.

b. The offspring will have variations that make some of them better adapted to their environment.

c. Better adapted offspring are more likely to survive and reproduce, and after many generations more members of the species will have the adaptive variations.

Reviewing Content

 For more review of key concepts, see the Interactive Student Tutorial CD-ROM.

Multiple Choice
Choose the letter of the best answer.

1. Changes in a species over long periods of time are called
   a. relative dating.
   b. evolution.
   c. homologous structures.
   d. developmental stages.

2. A trait that helps an organism survive and reproduce is called a(n)
   a. variation.   **b.** adaptation.
   c. species.   **d.** selection.

3. The type of fossil formed when an organism dissolves and leaves an empty space in a rock is called a
   a. cast.   **b.** mold.
   c. trace.   **d.** petrified fossil.

4. The rate of decay of a radioactive element is measured by its
   a. year.   **b.** era.
   c. half-life.   **d.** period.

5. Which of these is *not* used as evidence for evolution?
   a. DNA sequences
   b. stages of development
   c. body size
   d. body structures

True or False
If the statement is true, write true. If it is false, change the underlined word or words to make the statement true.

6. Darwin's idea about how evolution occurs is called <u>natural selection</u>.

7. Most members of a species show differences, or <u>variations</u>.

8. A footprint of an extinct dinosaur is an example of a <u>fossil</u>.

9. The technique of <u>relative dating</u> can be used to determine the actual age of a fossil.

10. <u>Homologous structures</u> are similar structures in related organisms.

Checking Concepts

11. What role does the overproduction of offspring play in the process of natural selection?

12. Use an example to explain how natural selection can lead to evolution.

13. How are rock layers used to determine the relative ages of fossils?

14. According to the theory of punctuated equilibria, why does the fossil record include very few intermediate forms?

15. Explain why similarities in the early development of different species suggest that the species are related.

16. **Writing to Learn** You are a young reporter for a local newspaper near the home of Charles Darwin. You have been asked to interview Darwin about his theory of evolution. Write three questions that you would ask Darwin. Then choose one question and answer it as Darwin would have.

Thinking Visually

17. Flowchart Copy the flowchart about natural selection onto a separate sheet of paper. Complete the flowchart by writing a sentence describing each factor that leads to natural selection. Then add a title. (For more on flowcharts, see the Skills Handbook.)

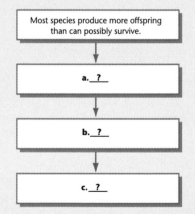

Applying Skills

18. Based on the positions of the fossils in the rock layers, B is the youngest, C is intermediate in age, and A is the oldest.

19. Based on the carbon-14 and nitrogen data, A is 17,190 years old, B is 5,730 years old, and C is 11,460 years old.

20. Students should say that the answers based on the two methods of dating are in agreement.

Thinking Critically

21. The islands were characterized by a great diversity of species that had developed different adaptations.

22. Geographic isolation prevents mating between members of the isolated population and the rest of the species. This, in turn, allows natural selection to lead to the evolution of different traits in the isolated population.

23. Relative dating determines which of two fossils is older and which is younger based on their relative positions in layers of sedimentary

Applying Skills

Radioactive carbon-14 decays to nitrogen with a half-life of 5,730 years. Use this information and the table below to answer Questions 18–20.

Fossil	Amount of Carbon-14 in Fossil	Amount of Nitrogen in Fossil	Position of Fossil in Rock Layers
A	1 gram	7 grams	bottom layer
B	4 grams	4 grams	top layer
C	2 grams	6 grams	middle layer

18. Inferring Use the positions of the fossils in the rock layers to put the fossils in order from youngest to oldest.

19. Calculating Calculate the age of each fossil using the data about carbon-14 and nitrogen.

20. Drawing Conclusions Do your answers to Questions 18 and 19 agree or disagree with each other? Explain.

Thinking Critically

21. Applying Concepts Why did Darwin's visit to the Galapagos Islands have such an important influence on his development of the theory of evolution by natural selection?

22. Relating Cause and Effect What is the role of geographic isolation in the formation of new species?

23. Comparing and Contrasting How does relative dating differ from absolute dating?

24. Applying Concepts A seal's flipper and a human arm have very different functions. What evidence might scientists look for to determine whether both structures evolved from the forelimb of a common ancestor?

25. Predicting Predict how an extreme change in climate might affect natural selection in a species.

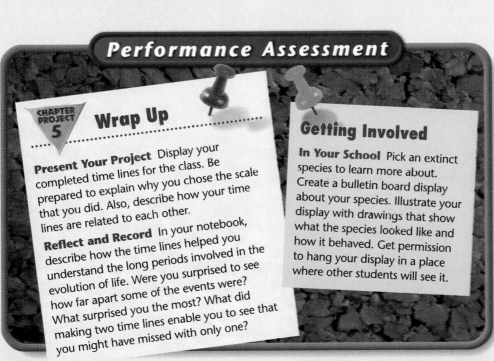

Performance Assessment

CHAPTER PROJECT 5

Wrap Up

Present Your Project Display your completed time lines for the class. Be prepared to explain why you chose the scale that you did. Also, describe how your time lines are related to each other.

Reflect and Record In your notebook, describe how the time lines helped you understand the long periods involved in the evolution of life. Were you surprised to see how far apart some of the events were? What surprised you the most? What did making two time lines enable you to see that you might have missed with only one?

Getting Involved

In Your School Pick an extinct species to learn more about. Create a bulletin board display about your species. Illustrate your display with drawings that show what the species looked like and how it behaved. Get permission to hang your display in a place where other students will see it.

---

rock. Absolute dating determines the actual age of fossils in years based on the amount of decay of radioactive elements in the fossils.

24. Scientists might look for evidence that the structures are homologous, for example, whether they have the same number and arrangement of bones.

25. Natural selection would favor members of the species that were better adapted to the new climate. For example, in a species of mammal, a colder climate might lead to natural selection for animals with thicker fur.

Program Resources

◆ **Inquiry Skills Activity Book** Provides teaching and review of all inquiry skills

---

Performance Assessment

CHAPTER PROJECT 5

Wrap Up
Present Your Project
Give each group an opportunity to show its two time lines to the rest of the class, describe how the models were made, and explain how the second time line relates to the first time line. Ask each group to point out any evolutionary events that were not included in the textbook's time line. Encourage the rest of the class to ask questions.
Reflect and Record Students' responses to these questions will vary, but students should realize that making a second time line for the past 600 millions years allowed them to see the time spans and placements of evolutionary events much more clearly. Let students share their ideas in a class discussion.

Getting Involved

In Your School You may want to divide students into groups to work on this project, especially if space to display their work is limited. Encourage each student or group to select a different species of extinct organism. For example, urge some students to select species that went extinct millions of years ago due to natural events and other students to select species that went extinct recently due to human actions. Suggest that students find out not only what the extinct species looked like and how it behaved, but also why scientists think the species became extinct. Provide a place for students to put up their bulletin board displays and encourage other students to examine them.

Dogs—Loyal Companions

This interdisciplinary feature presents the central theme of dogs and the traits of various breeds that make them similar and different by connecting four different disciplines: science, social studies, language arts, and mathematics. The four explorations are designed to capture students' interest and help them see how the content they are studying in science relates to other school subjects and to real-world events. The unit is particularly suitable for team teaching.

1 Engage/Explore

Activating Prior Knowledge

Help students recall what they learned in Chapter 3, Genetics: The Science of Heredity, by asking questions such as: **How are traits inherited from parent to offspring?** *(The alleles of genes are carried from parents to their offspring on chromosomes.)* **Why do offspring sometimes look different from parents?** *(Offspring inherit different combinations of alleles from parents so they might express a trait controlled by a recessive allele that is masked in the parents or inherit a trait controlled by a dominant allele that is expressed in one parent, but not the other.)*

Introducing the Unit

Invite students who own dogs to share the characteristics of their dogs with the class. Separately list on the board each dog's characteristics, and have students compare the characteristics of each dog. Ask: **How are these dogs different?** *(Differences might include size, temperament, length and color of fur, type of ears, and length of tail.)* **What causes these differences?** *(The combination of alleles that each dog inherited from its parents)*

DOGS
LOYAL COMPANIONS

WHAT'S YOUR IMAGE OF A DOG?

✦ A small, floppy-eared spaniel?

✦ A large, powerful Great Dane?

✦ A protective German shepherd guide dog?

✦ A shaggy sheepdog?

✦ A tiny, lively Chihuahua?

✦ A friendly, lovable mutt?

The gray wolf is the ancestor of most modern breeds of dogs.

More than 3,000 years ago, an artist in ancient Egypt drew three dogs chasing a hyena. ▼

Most dogs are descendants of the gray wolf, which was originally found throughout Europe, Asia, and North America. Dogs were the first animals to be domesticated, or tamed. As far back as 9,000 years ago, farmers who raised sheep, cattle, and goats tamed dogs to herd and guard the livestock.

After taming dogs, people began to breed them for traits that people valued. Early herding dogs helped shepherds. Speedy hunting dogs learned to chase deer and other game. Strong, sturdy working dogs pulled sleds and even rescued people. Small, quick terriers hunted animals, such as rats. "Toy" dogs were companions to people of wealth and leisure. More recently, sporting dogs were trained to flush out and retrieve birds. Still others were bred to be guard dogs. But perhaps the real reason people bred dogs was for their loyalty and companionship.

168 ◆ C

Program Resources

◆ **Teaching Resources** Interdisciplinary Exploration, Science, pp. 140–142; Social Studies, pp. 143–145; Language Arts, pp. 146–148; Mathematics, pp. 149–151

Program Resources

◆ **Teaching Resources** The following worksheets correlate with page 169: Developing a Classification System, page 140; Breeding Spinoni, page 141; Identifying Dog Adaptations, page 142.

From Wolf to Purebred

About ten thousand years ago, some wolves may have been attracted to human settlements. They may have found it easier to feed on food scraps than to hunt for themselves. Gradually the wolves came to depend on people for food. The wolves, in turn, kept the campsites clean and safe. They ate the garbage and barked to warn of approaching strangers. These wolves were the ancestors of the dogs you know today.

Over time dogs became more and more a part of human society. People began to breed dogs for the traits needed for tasks such as herding sheep and hunting. Large, aggressive dogs, for example, were bred to be herding dogs, while fast dogs with a keen sense of smell were bred to be hunting dogs. Today there are hundreds of breeds. They range from the tiny Chihuahua to the massive Saint Bernard, one of which can weigh as much as fifty Chihuahuas.

Today, people breed dogs mostly for their appearance and personality. Physical features such as long ears or a narrow snout are valued in particular breeds of dogs. To create "pure" breeds of dogs, breeders use a method known as inbreeding. Inbreeding involves mating dogs that are genetically very similar. Inbreeding is the surest way to produce dogs with a uniform physical appearance.

One undesirable result of inbreeding is an increase in genetic disorders. Experts estimate that 25 percent of all purebred dogs have a genetic disorder. Dalmatians, for example, often inherit deafness. German shepherds may develop severe hip problems. Mixed-breed dogs, in contrast, are less likely to inherit genetic disorders.

In Labrador retrievers, the allele for dark-colored fur is dominant over the allele for yellow fur.

Science Activity

Most traits that dogs are bred for are controlled by more than one gene. A few traits, however, show simpler inheritance patterns. For example, in Labrador retrievers, a single gene with one dominant and one recessive allele determines whether the dog's fur will be dark or yellow. The allele for dark fur (*D*) is dominant over the allele for yellow fur (*d*).

◆ Construct a Punnett square for a cross between 2 Labrador retrievers that are both heterozygous for dark fur (*Dd*).

◆ Suppose there were 8 puppies in the litter. Predict how many would have dark fur and how many would have yellow fur.

◆ Construct a second Punnett square for a cross between a Labrador retriever with yellow fur (*dd*) and one with dark fur (*Dd*). In a litter with 6 puppies, predict how many would have dark fur and how many would have yellow fur.

C ◆ 169

Background

Facts and Figures Some people still hand raise wild wolf puppies to keep in captivity. For example, Aleuts in Alaska and northern Canada often breed wolves with their own dogs to improve their stamina. They also use tamed wolves, as well as wolf-dog mixes, for their dog sled teams. A tamed wolf, however, can be very dangerous. Because they are still instinctively wild animals, they tend to react defensively in unfamiliar situations—being around new people or in a new place. When a wolf reacts defensively, it usually attacks whatever or whomever it feels is threatening it. It requires several generations of breeding in captivity, isolated from the wild species, to remove this defensive instinct.

---

2 Facilitate

◆ Point out the role of genetics in the development of dog breeds. Ask: **What are some traits that people select for when breeding dogs?** (*Size, sense of smell, aggressiveness, personality, speed, appearance*) Remind students that genes control these traits.

◆ Ask students: **Why does inbreeding cause an increase in genetic disorders?** (*Since inbred dogs are genetically similar, there is a greater chance that breeders will unknowingly cross two carriers to produce offspring with the disorder.*) **Why are mixed-breed dogs less likely to have genetic disorders?** (*Mixed breeds are hybrids. They usually have two different alleles for most traits, so an allele for a genetic disorder would probably be masked by the normal allele.*)

Science Activity

Have students complete the activity on their own. Suggest that students calculate the probability for each color of offspring before they calculate the number of puppies with a certain color.

3 Assess

Activity Assessment

Punnett square for $Dd \times Dd$ has offspring DD, Dd, Dd, dd. Out of 8 puppies, the ratio is 6 with dark fur (8×0.75) and 2 with yellow fur (8×0.25). Punnett square for $dd \times Dd$ has offspring Dd, dd, Dd, dd. Out of 6 puppies, the ratio is 3 with dark fur (6×0.5) and 3 with yellow fur (6×0.5).

2 Facilitate

◆ After students have read about each dog breed, discuss how people have developed each breed to fit a particular role. Ask: **Which breeds are hunters?** (*Golden retriever, chow chow, Akita, basset hound, dachshund, greyhound*) **Which were bred for herding?** (*Border collie, chow chow*) **Which were bred for guarding?** (*Chow chow, Akita, Lhaso apso*) **Which were bred for pulling sleds?** (*Siberian husky*) **Which were bred for companionship?** (*Pekingese*) Point out that each breed has certain traits that make it well suited for its role in people's lives. Some dogs are still used as working dogs, but most dogs now are simply companions.

◆ Invite students to locate on the map the places of origin for each breed shown. Explain that breeds have also originated in the United States, such as the Alaskan malamute and the bluetick coonhound, and in Australia, such as the silky terrier and the Australian kelpie. Point out that the origins of the older breeds coincide with the locations of ancient civilizations. **Which breed is the oldest?** (*greyhound*) **In which ancient civilization did it originate?** (*ancient Egypt*)

◆ Encourage students to identify working roles that dogs play in the lives of people today. (*Modern roles played by dogs include search and rescue; finding drugs, explosives, or weapons; assisting people with disabilities; tracking criminals; hunting game; herding livestock; and guarding property or people.*) As students identify roles, challenge them to identify traits that make the dogs well suited for their roles.

Golden Retriever
Great Britain, A.D. 1870s
Lord Tweedsmouth developed this breed to help hunters retrieve waterfowl and other small animals.

Border Collie
Great Britain, after A.D. 1100
This breed was developed in the counties near the border of England and Scotland for herding sheep. The Border collie's ancestors were cross-breeds of local sheepdogs and dogs brought to Scotland by the Vikings.

Dachshund
Germany, A.D. 1700s
These dogs were bred to catch badgers or rats. Their short legs and long body can fit into a badger's burrow. In fact, in German the word *Dachshund* means "badger dog."

Basset Hound
France, A.D. 1600s
Second only to the bloodhound at following a scent, the basset hound has short legs and a compact body that help it run through underbrush.

Greyhound
Egypt, 3500 B.C.
These speedy, slender hounds were bred for chasing prey. Today, greyhounds are famous as racers.

Background

Facts and Figures The American Kennel Club divides dog breeds into seven groups. These groups are sporting dogs, hounds, working dogs, terriers, toy dogs, nonsporting dogs, and herding dogs. Sporting dogs were bred to assist hunters who use guns. Hounds were bred to hunt for prey by catching it themselves or by cornering it until the hunter arrives. Working dogs were bred for specific jobs, such as guarding, hauling, pulling sleds, or rescuing people and other animals. Terriers were bred to dig into the ground in pursuit of prey, mostly rodents. Toy dogs are small dogs that are companions. Nonsporting dogs are large companion dogs. Herding dogs were bred to protect and herd livestock, such as sheep.

Dogs and People

Over thousands of years, people have developed many different breeds of dogs. Each of the dogs shown on the map was bred for a purpose—hunting, herding, guarding, pulling sleds—as well as companionship. Every breed has its own story.

Siberian Husky
Siberia, 1000 B.C.
The Chukchi people of northeastern Siberia used these strong working dogs to pull sleds long distances across the snow.

Pekingese
China, A.D. 700s
These lapdogs were bred as pets in ancient China. One Chinese name for a Pekingese means "lion dog," which refers to the dog's long, golden mane.

Chow Chow
China, 150 B.C.
Chow chows, the working dogs of ancient China, worked as hunters, herders, and guard dogs.

Akita
Japan, A.D. 1600s
This breed was developed in the cold mountains of northern Japan as a guard dog and hunting dog. The Akita is able to hunt in deep snow and is also a powerful swimmer.

Lhasa Apso
Tibet, A.D. 1100
This breed has a long, thick coat to protect it from the cold air of the high Tibetan plateau. In spite of its small size, the Lhasa apso guarded homes and temples.

Social Studies Activity

Draw a time line that shows the approximate date of origin of different breeds of domestic dogs from 7000 B.C. to the present. Use the information on the map to fill out your time line. Include information about where each breed was developed.

♦ Extend this exploration by encouraging interested students to find the place and time of origin for their favorite breed of dog. Students can find this kind of information in encyclopedias of dog breeds.

Social Studies Activity

Students can work individually or in small groups. Provide students with shelf paper or butcher's paper so that they have adequate space to draw and label the time lines. Encourage students to add drawings or pictures of the different dog breeds. Remind students to make the divisions in time equal in length on the time line. They can do this by first calculating the total number of years in the time line.

3 Assess

Activity Assessment

Display the time lines in the classroom and in the hallway. You might consider allowing class time for students to present their time lines. Each time line should be divided into equal increments with the origins of all dog breeds clearly and accurately labeled. Students should also include information about each dog breed as presented in the text, especially where each breed was developed. Excellent time lines will also be illustrated with the dog breeds.

Program Resources

♦ **Teaching Resources** The following worksheets correlate with pages 170–171: Reading a Data Table, page 143; Finding Your Way Around a Sheepdog Trial, page 144; The Responsibilities of Owning a Dog, page 145.

2 Facilitate

◆ Before students read this section, ask if they are familiar with James Herriot and have read any of his books or watched the television series based on his books. If so, let these students describe what the books are about.

◆ After students have read the excerpt, ask: **How does Herriot feel about getting a Border terrier?** *(He was happy, excited, and content.)* **What do you think Herriot meant when he wrote, "The wheel had indeed turned?"** *(He finally felt complete because he finally found the dog that he had wanted for so long.)*

Language Arts Activity

Before students begin writing their narratives, encourage them to think about their lives and choose one event that is particularly memorable to them. Instruct students to write down why this particular event was so memorable to them. Did they overcome a problem, for example, or were they recognized for their special efforts? Then encourage students to list the emotions they felt during this event and record why they felt those emotions.

3 Assess

Activity Assessment

Invite students to read their narratives aloud to the rest of the class. Evaluate students' narratives based on their use of first-person point of view, the use of dialog, and the clarity with which they expressed their emotions.

Picking a Puppy

People look for different traits in the dogs they choose. Here is how one expert selected his dog based on good breeding and personality.

James Herriot, a veterinarian in England, had owned several dogs during his lifetime. But he had always wanted a Border terrier. These small, sturdy dogs are descendants of working terrier breeds that lived on the border of England and Scotland. For centuries they were used to hunt foxes, rats, and other small animals. In this story, Herriot and his wife Helen follow up on an advertisement for Border terrier puppies.

Language Arts Activity

James Herriot describes this scene using dialog and first-person narrative. The narrative describes Herriot's feelings about a memorable event—finally finding the dog he had wanted for so long. Write a first-person narrative describing a memorable event in your life. You might choose a childhood memory or a personal achievement at school. What emotions did you feel? How did you make your decision? If possible, use dialog in your writing.

Border terrier ▶

She [Helen, his wife] turned to me and spoke agitatedly, "I've got Mrs. Mason on the line now. There's only one pup left out of the litter and there are people coming from as far as eighty miles away to see it. We'll have to hurry. What a long time you've been out there!"

We bolted our lunch and Helen, Rosie, granddaughter Emma and I drove out to Bedale. Mrs. Mason led us into the kitchen and pointed to a tiny brindle creature twisting and writhing under the table.

"That's him," she said.

I reached down and lifted the puppy as he curled his little body round, apparently trying to touch his tail with his nose. But that tail wagged furiously and the pink tongue was busy at my hand. I knew he was ours before my quick examination for hernia and overshot jaw.

The deal was quickly struck and we went outside to inspect the puppy's relations. His mother and grandmother were out there. They lived in little barrels which served as kennels and both of them darted out and stood up at our legs, tails lashing, mouths panting in delight. I felt vastly reassured. With happy, healthy ancestors like those I knew we had every chance of a first rate dog.

As we drove home with the puppy in Emma's arms, the warm thought came to me. The wheel had indeed turned. After nearly fifty years I had my Border terrier.

James Herriot was a country veterinarian in Yorkshire, England. In several popular books published in the 1970s and 1980s, he wrote warm, humorous stories about the animals he cared for. His book *All Creatures Great and Small* was the basis for a television series.

Background

Facts and Figures James Herriot was the pen name of James Alfred Wight, a British veterinarian and writer. Herriot began practicing veterinary medicine in North Yorkshire, England, after he graduated from veterinary school in 1937. In his practice, he cared for cows, horses, and sheep, as well as dogs and cats. He began writing about his experiences with people and animals in his practice when he was 50 years old. His first book, *All Creatures Great and Small*, was published in 1972. He published three other books *All Things Bright and Beautiful, All Things Wise and Wonderful,* and *The Lord God Made Them All,* as well as children's stories and a book of photographs describing the Yorkshire countryside. James Herriot died in 1995 at the age of 78.

Breed	1970	1980	1990	1997
Poodle	265,879	92,250	71,757	54,773
Labrador Retriever	25,667	52,398	99,776	158,366
Cocker Spaniel	21,811	76,113	105,642	41,439

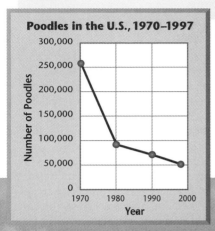

Poodles in the U.S., 1970–1997

Math Activity

The popularity of different breeds of dogs changes over time. For example, the line graph shows how the number of poodles registered with the American Kennel Club changed between 1970 and 1997. Use the table to create your own line graph for Labrador retrievers and cocker spaniels.

Which breed was more popular in 1980, Labrador retrievers or cocker spaniels? How has the number of Labrador retrievers changed from 1970 to 1997? How has the number of cocker spaniels changed over the same time?

Tie It Together

Best of Breed Show

In many places proud dog owners of all ages bring their animals to compete in dog shows. Organize your own dog show. With a partner, choose one specific breed of dog. Pick a breed shown on the map on pages 170–171, or use library resources to research another breed.

◆ Find out what the breed looks like, the time and place where it originated, and what traits it was first bred for.

◆ List your breed's characteristics, height, weight, and coloring.

◆ Research the breed's personality and behavior.

◆ Find out your breed's strengths. Learn what weakness may develop as a result of inbreeding.

◆ Make a poster for your breed. Include a drawing or photo and the information that you researched.

◆ With your class, organize the dog displays into categories of breeds, such as hunting dogs, herding dogs, and toy dogs.

C ◆ 173

2 Facilitate

◆ To assess students' understanding of the data, ask questions such as: **What breed was most popular in 1980?** *(poodle)* **Which breed is most popular now?** *(Labrador retriever)*

◆ Ask students questions about the graph, such as: **How has the number of poodles changed from 1970 to 1997?** *(There has been a sharp decrease.)*

Mathematics Activity

Have students complete the activity on their own. Provide them with graph paper. Students may draw separate graphs for each breed or combine the breeds on one graph. Encourage students to use the graph on this page as a guide for their own graphs.

3 Assess

Activity Assessment

Students' graphs should look similar to the graph for poodles on this page. In 1980, cocker spaniels were more popular. Labrador retrievers have increased steadily in popularity from 1970 to 1997. Cocker spaniel popularity increased steadily until 1990, when it began to decrease sharply.

Tie It Together

Time 1 week (2 days for research, 2 days for the poster, 1 day for the show)

Tips Students can learn about specific dog breeds on the Internet. They can use the breed name as the search word. Have the class vote for their favorite breed to determine "Best of Show."

Program Resources

◆ **Teaching Resources** The following worksheets correlate with page 172: Developing Dialog, page 146; Practicing Point of View, page 147; Researching for the Right Dog, page 148.

Program Resources

◆ **Teaching Resources** The following Worksheets correlate with page 173: Making a Bar Graph, page 149; The Cost of Owning a Dog, page 150; Calculating Points in an Obedience Trial, page 151.

Developing scientific thinking in students is important for a solid science education. To learn how to think scientifically, students need frequent opportunities to practice science process skills, critical thinking skills, as well as other skills that support scientific inquiry. The *Science Explorer* Skills Handbook introduces the following key science skills:

◆ Science Process Skills
◆ SI Measuring Skills
◆ Skills for Conducting a Scientific Investigation
◆ Critical Thinking Skills
◆ Information Organizing Skills
◆ Data Table and Graphing Skills

The Skills Handbook is designed as a reference for students to use whenever they need to review a science skill. You can use the activities provided in the Skills Handbook to teach or reinforce the skills.

Think Like a Scientist

Observing

ACTIVITY

Before students look at the photograph, remind them that an observation is only what they can see, hear, smell, taste, or feel. Ask: **Which senses will you use to make observations from this photograph?** *(Sight is the only sense that can be used to make observations from the photograph.)* **What are some observations you can make from the photograph?** *(Answers may vary. Sample answers: The boy is wearing sneakers, sport socks, shorts, and a tee shirt; the boy is sitting in the grass holding something blue against his knee; the boy is looking at his knee; there is a soccer ball laying beside the boy.)* List the observations on the chalkboard. If students make any inferences or predictions about the boy at this point, ask: **Can you be sure your statement is factual and accurate from just observing the photograph?** Help students understand how observations differ from inferences and predictions.

Inferring

ACTIVITY

Review students' observations from the photograph. Then ask: **What inferences can you make from your observations?** *(Students may say that the boy hurt his knee playing soccer and is holding a coldpack against his injured knee.)* **What experience or knowledge helped you make this inference?** *(Students may have experienced knee injuries from playing soccer, and they may be familiar with coldpacks like the one the boy is using.)* **Can anyone suggest another possible explanation for these observations?** *(Answers may vary. Sample answer: The boy hurt his knee jogging, and he just happened to sit beside a soccer ball his sister*

Think Like a Scientist

Although you may not know it, you think like a scientist every day. Whenever you ask a question and explore possible answers, you use many of the same skills that scientists do. Some of these skills are described on this page.

Observing

When you use one or more of your five senses to gather information about the world, you are **observing.** Hearing a dog bark, counting twelve green seeds, and smelling smoke are all observations. To increase the power of their senses, scientists sometimes use microscopes, telescopes, or other instruments that help them make more detailed observations.

An observation must be factual and accurate—an exact report of what your senses detect. It is important to keep careful records of your observations in science class by writing or drawing in a notebook. The information collected through observations is called evidence, or data.

Inferring

When you explain or interpret an observation, you are **inferring,** or making an inference. For example, if you hear your dog barking, you may infer that someone is at your front door. To make this inference, you combine the evidence—the barking dog—and your experience or knowledge—you know that your dog barks when strangers approach—to reach a logical conclusion.

Notice that an inference is not a fact; it is only one of many possible explanations for an observation. For example, your dog may be barking because it wants to go for a walk. An inference may turn out to be incorrect even if it is based on accurate observations and logical reasoning. The only way to find out if an inference is correct is to investigate further.

Predicting

When you listen to the weather forecast, you hear many predictions about the next day's weather—what the temperature will be, whether it will rain, and how windy it will be. Weather forecasters use observations and knowledge of weather patterns to predict the weather. The skill of **predicting** involves making an inference about a future event based on current evidence or past experience.

Because a prediction is an inference, it may prove to be false. In science class, you can test some of your predictions by doing experiments. For example, suppose you predict that larger paper airplanes can fly farther than smaller airplanes. How could you test your prediction?

 Use the photograph to answer the questions below.

Observing Look closely at the photograph. List at least three observations.

Inferring Use your observations to make an inference about what has happened. What experience or knowledge did you use to make the inference?

Predicting Predict what will happen next. On what evidence or experience do you base your prediction?

left in the yard.) **How can you find out whether an inference is correct?** *(by further investigation)*

Predicting

ACTIVITY

After coming to some consensus about the inference that the boy hurt his knee, encourage students to make predictions about what will happen next. *(Students' predictions may vary. Sample answers: The boy will go to the doctor. A friend will help the boy home. The boy will get up and continue playing soccer.)*

Classifying

Could you imagine searching for a book in the library if the books were shelved in no particular order? Your trip to the library would be an all-day event! Luckily, librarians group together books on similar topics or by the same author. Grouping together items that are alike in some way is called **classifying.** You can classify items in many ways: by size, by shape, by use, and by other important characteristics.

Like librarians, scientists use the skill of classifying to organize information and objects. When things are sorted into groups, the relationships among them become easier to understand.

Classify the objects in the photograph into two groups based on any characteristic you choose. Then use another characteristic to classify the objects into three groups.

ACTIVITY

Making Models

Have you ever drawn a picture to help someone understand what you were saying? Such a drawing is one type of model. A model is a picture, diagram, computer image, or other representation of a complex object or process. **Making models** helps people understand things that they cannot observe directly.

Scientists often use models to represent things that are either very large or very small, such as the planets in the solar system, or the parts of a cell. Such models are physical models—drawings or three-dimensional structures that look like the real thing. Other models are mental models—mathematical equations or words that describe how something works.

This student is using a model to demonstrate what causes day and night on Earth. What do the flashlight and the tennis ball in the model represent?

ACTIVITY

Communicating

Whenever you talk on the phone, write a letter, or listen to your teacher at school, you are communicating. **Communicating** is the process of sharing ideas and information with other people. Communicating effectively requires many skills, including writing, reading, speaking, listening, and making models.

Scientists communicate to share results, information, and opinions. Scientists often communicate about their work in journals, over the telephone, in letters, and on the Internet. They also attend scientific meetings where they share their ideas with one another in person.

On a sheet of paper, write out clear, detailed directions for tying your shoe. Then exchange directions with a partner. Follow your partner's directions exactly. How successful were you at tying your shoe? How could your partner have communicated more clearly?

ACTIVITY

C ◆ 175

On what did you base your prediction? *(Scientific predictions are based on knowledge and experience.)* Point out that in science, predictions can often be tested with experiments.

Classifying

ACTIVITY

Encourage students to think of other common things that are classified. Then ask: **What things at home are classified?** *(Clothing might be classified by placing it in different dresser drawers; glasses, plates, and silverware are grouped in different parts of the kitchen; screws, nuts, bolts, washers, and nails might be separated into small containers.)* **What are some things that scientists classify?** *(Scientists classify many things they study, including organisms, geological features and processes, and kinds of machines.)* After students have classified the different fruits in the photograph, have them share their criteria for classifying them. *(Some characteristics students might use include shape, color, size, and where they are grown.)*

Making Models

ACTIVITY

Ask students: **What are some models you have used to study science?** *(Students may have used human anatomical models, solar system models, maps, stream tables.)* **How did these models help you?** *(Models can help you learn about things that are difficult to study, either because they are too big, too small, or complex.)* Be sure students understand that a model does not have to be three-dimensional. For example, a map in a textbook is a model. Ask: **What do the flashlight and tennis ball represent?** *(The flashlight represents the sun, and the ball represents Earth.)* **What quality of each item makes this a good model?** *(The flashlight gives off light, and the ball is round and can be rotated by the student.)*

Communicating

ACTIVITY

Challenge students to identify the methods of communication they've used today. Then ask: **How is the way you communicate with a friend similar to and different from the way scientists communicate about their work to other scientists?** *(Both may communicate using various methods, but scientists must be very detailed and precise, whereas communication between friends may be less detailed and precise.)* Encourage students to communicate like a scientist as they carry out the activity. *(Students' directions should be detailed and precise enough for another person to successfully follow.)*

Making Measurements

Measuring in SI

Review SI units in class with students. Begin by providing metric rulers, graduated cylinders, balances, and Celsius thermometers. Use these tools to reinforce that the meter is the unit of length, the liter is the unit of volume, the gram is the unit of mass, and the degree Celsius is the unit for temperature. Ask: **If you want to measure the length and width of your classroom, which SI unit would you use?** *(meter)* **Which unit would you use to measure the amount of matter in your textbook?** *(gram)* **Which would you use to measure how much water a drinking glass holds?** *(liter)* **When would you use the Celsius scale?** *(To measure the temperature of something)* Then use the measuring equipment to review SI prefixes. For example, ask: **What are the smallest units on the metric ruler?** *(millimeters)* **How many millimeters are there in 1 cm?** *(10 mm)* **How many in 10 cm?** *(100 mm)* **How many centimeters are there in 1 m?** *(100 cm)* **What does 1,000 m equal?** *(1 km)*

Length *(Students should state that the shell is 4.6 centimeters, or 46 millimeters, long.)* If students need more practice measuring length, have them use meter sticks and metric rulers to measure various objects in the classroom.

Liquid Volume *(Students should state that the volume of water in the graduated cylinder is 62 milliliters.)* If students need more practice measuring liquid volume, have them use a graduated cylinder to measure different volumes of water.

Making Measurements

When scientists make observations, it is not sufficient to say that something is "big" or "heavy." Instead, scientists use instruments to measure just how big or heavy an object is. By measuring, scientists can express their observations more precisely and communicate more information about what they observe.

Measuring in SI

The standard system of measurement used by scientists around the world is known as the International System of Units, which is abbreviated as SI (in French, *Système International d'Unités*). SI units are easy to use because they are based on multiples of 10. Each unit is ten times larger than the next smallest unit and one tenth the size of the next largest unit. The table lists the prefixes used to name the most common SI units.

Common SI Prefixes		
Prefix	**Symbol**	**Meaning**
kilo-	k	1,000
hecto-	h	100
deka-	da	10
deci-	d	0.1 (one tenth)
centi-	c	0.01 (one hundredth)
milli-	m	0.001 (one thousandth)

Length To measure length, or the distance between two points, the unit of measure is the **meter (m).** One meter is the approximate distance from the floor to a doorknob. Long distances, such as the distance between two cities, are measured in kilometers (km). Small lengths are measured in centimeters (cm) or millimeters (mm). Scientists use metric rulers and meter sticks to measure length.

Common Conversions
1 km = 1,000 m
1 m = 100 cm
1 m = 1,000 mm
1 cm = 10 mm

The larger lines on the metric ruler in the picture show centimeter divisions, while the smaller, unnumbered lines show millimeter divisions. How many centimeters long is the shell? How many millimeters long is it? **ACTIVITY**

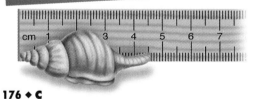

Liquid Volume To measure the volume of a liquid, or the amount of space it takes up, you will use a unit of measure known as the **liter (L).** One liter is the approximate volume of a medium-sized carton of milk. Smaller volumes are measured in milliliters (mL). Scientists use graduated cylinders to measure liquid volume.

Common Conversion
1 L = 1,000 mL

The graduated cylinder in the picture is marked in milliliter divisions. Notice that the water in the cylinder has a curved surface. This curved surface is called the *meniscus.* To measure the volume, you must read the level at the lowest point of the meniscus. What is the volume of water in this graduated cylinder? **ACTIVITY**

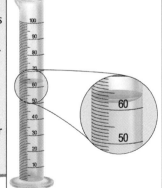

Mass

Mass To measure mass, or the amount of matter in an object, you will use a unit of measure known as the **gram (g)**. One gram is approximately the mass of a paper clip. Larger masses are measured in kilograms (kg). Scientists use a balance to find the mass of an object.

Common Conversion

1 kg = 1,000 g

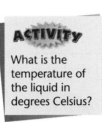

The electronic balance displays the mass of an apple in kilograms. What is the mass of the apple? Suppose a recipe for applesauce called for one kilogram of apples. About how many apples would you need?

ACTIVITY

Temperature

To measure the temperature of a substance, you will use the **Celsius scale**. Temperature is measured in degrees Celsius (°C) using a Celsius thermometer. Water freezes at 0°C and boils at 100°C.

ACTIVITY

What is the temperature of the liquid in degrees Celsius?

Mass *(Students should state that the mass of the apple is 0.1 kilograms. They would need 10 apples to make 1 kilogram.)* If students need practice determining mass, have them use a balance to determine the mass of various common objects, such as coins, paper clips, and books.

ACTIVITY

Temperature *(Students should state that the temperature of the liquid is 35°C.)* If students need practice measuring temperature, have them use a Celsius thermometer to measure the temperature of various water samples.

ACTIVITY

Converting SI Units

ACTIVITY

Review the steps for converting SI units and work through the example with students. Then ask: **How many millimeters are in 80 centimeters?** *(Students should follow the steps to calculate that 80 centimeters is equal to 800 millimeters.)*

Have students do the conversion problems in the activity. *(1. 600 millimeters = 0.6 meters; 2. 0.35 liters = 350 milliliters; 3. 1,050 grams = 1.05 kilograms)* If students need more practice converting SI units, have students make up conversion problems and trade with a partner.

Converting SI Units

To use the SI system, you must know how to convert between units. Converting from one unit to another involves the skill of **calculating**, or using mathematical operations. Converting between SI units is similar to converting between dollars and dimes because both systems are based on multiples of ten.

Suppose you want to convert a length of 80 centimeters to meters. Follow these steps to convert between units.

1. Begin by writing down the measurement you want to convert—in this example, 80 centimeters.

2. Write a conversion factor that represents the relationship between the two units you are converting. In this example, the relationship is *1 meter = 100 centimeters.* Write this conversion factor as a fraction, making sure to place the units you are converting from (centimeters, in this example) in the denominator.

3. Multiply the measurement you want to convert by the fraction. When you do this, the units in the first measurement will cancel out with the units in the denominator. Your answer will be in the units you are converting to (meters, in this example).

Example

80 centimeters = _____?_____ meters

$$80 \text{ centimeters} \times \frac{1 \text{ meter}}{100 \text{ centimeters}} = \frac{80 \text{ meters}}{100}$$

$$= 0.8 \text{ meters}$$

Convert between the following units.
1. 600 millimeters = _?_ meters
2. 0.35 liters = _?_ milliliters
3. 1,050 grams = _?_ kilograms

ACTIVITY

Conducting a Scientific Investigation

Posing Questions

Before students do the activity on the next page, walk them through the steps of a typical scientific investigation. Begin by asking: **Why is a scientific question important to a scientific investigation?** *(It is the reason for conducting a scientific investigation and how every investigation begins.)* **What is the scientific question in the activity at the bottom of the next page?** *(Is a ball's bounce affected by the height from which it is dropped?)*

Developing a Hypothesis

Emphasize that a hypothesis is a prediction about the outcome of a scientific investigation, but it is *not* a guess. Ask: **On what information do scientists base their hypotheses?** *(Their observations and previous knowledge or experience)* Point out that a hypothesis does not always turn out to be correct. Ask: **In that case, do you think the scientist wasted his or her time? Explain your answer.** *(No, because the scientist probably learned from the investigation and maybe could develop another hypothesis that could be supported.)*

Designing an Experiment

Have a volunteer read the Experimental Procedure in the box. Then call on students to identify the manipulated variable *(amount of salt added to water)*, the variables that are kept constant *(amount and starting temperature of water, placing containers in freezer)*, the responding variable *(time it takes water to freeze)*, and the control *(Container 3)*.

Ask: **How might the experiment be affected if Container 1 had only 100 mL of water?** *(It wouldn't be a fair comparison with the containers that have more water.)* **What if Container 3 was not included in the experiment?** *(You wouldn't have anything to compare the other two containers to know if their freezing times were faster or slower than normal.)* Help students understand the importance of

Conducting a Scientific Investigation

In some ways, scientists are like detectives, piecing together clues to learn about a process or event. One way that scientists gather clues is by carrying out experiments. An experiment tests an idea in a careful, orderly manner. Although all experiments do not follow the same steps in the same order, many follow a pattern similar to the one described here.

Posing Questions

Experiments begin by asking a scientific question. A scientific question is one that can be answered by gathering evidence. For example, the question "Which freezes faster—fresh water or salt water?" is a scientific question because you can carry out an investigation and gather information to answer the question.

Developing a Hypothesis

The next step is to form a hypothesis. A **hypothesis** is a prediction about the outcome of the experiment. Like all predictions, hypotheses are based on your observations and previous knowledge or experience. But, unlike many predictions, a hypothesis must be something that can be tested. A properly worded hypothesis should take the form of an *If… then…* statement. For example, a hypothesis might be *"If I add salt to fresh water, then the water will take longer to freeze."* A hypothesis worded this way serves as a rough outline of the experiment you should perform.

178 ◆ C

keeping all variables constant except the manipulated variable. Also be sure they understand the role of the control. Then ask: **What operational definition is used in this experiment?** *("Frozen" means the time at which a wooden stick can no longer move in a container.)*

Designing an Experiment

Next you need to plan a way to test your hypothesis. Your plan should be written out as a step-by-step procedure and should describe the observations or measurements you will make.

Two important steps involved in designing an experiment are controlling variables and forming operational definitions.

Controlling Variables In a well-designed experiment, you need to keep all variables the same except for one. A **variable** is any factor that can change in an experiment. The factor that you change is called the **manipulated variable.** In this experiment, the manipulated variable is the amount of salt added to the water. Other factors, such as the amount of water or the starting temperature, are kept constant.

The factor that changes as a result of the manipulated variable is called the responding variable. The **responding variable** is what you measure or observe to obtain your results. In this experiment, the responding variable is how long the water takes to freeze.

An experiment in which all factors except one are kept constant is a **controlled experiment.** Most controlled experiments include a test called the control. In this experiment, Container 3 is the control. Because no salt is added to Container 3, you can compare the results from the other containers to it. Any difference in results must be due to the addition of salt alone.

Forming Operational Definitions

Another important aspect of a well-designed experiment is having clear operational definitions. An **operational definition** is a statement that describes how a particular variable is to be measured or how a term is to be defined. For example, in this experiment, how will you determine if the water has frozen? You might decide to insert a stick in each container at the start of the experiment. Your operational definition of "frozen" would be the time at which the stick can no longer move.

EXPERIMENTAL PROCEDURE

1. Fill 3 containers with 300 milliliters of cold tap water.

2. Add 10 grams of salt to Container 1; stir. Add 20 grams of salt to Container 2; stir. Add no salt to Container 3.

3. Place the 3 containers in a freezer.

4. Check the containers every 15 minutes. Record your observations.

Interpreting Data

The observations and measurements you make in an experiment are called data. At the end of an experiment, you need to analyze the data to look for any patterns or trends. Patterns often become clear if you organize your data in a data table or graph. Then think through what the data reveal. Do they support your hypothesis? Do they point out a flaw in your experiment? Do you need to collect more data?

Drawing Conclusions

A conclusion is a statement that sums up what you have learned from an experiment. When you draw a conclusion, you need to decide whether the data you collected support your hypothesis or not. You may need to repeat an experiment several times before you can draw any conclusions from it. Conclusions often lead you to pose new questions and plan new experiments to answer them.

> Is a ball's bounce affected by the height from which it is dropped? Using the steps just described, plan a controlled experiment to investigate this problem. **ACTIVITY**

C ◆ 179

Interpreting Data

Emphasize the importance of collecting accurate and detailed data in a scientific investigation. Ask: **What if the students forgot to record the times that they made their observations in the experiment?** (*They wouldn't be able to completely analyze their data to draw valid conclusions.*) Then ask: **Why are data tables and graphs a good way to organize data?** (*They often make it easier to compare and analyze data.*) You may wish to have students review the Skills Handbook pages on Creating Data Tables and Graphs at this point.

Drawing Conclusions

Help students understand that a conclusion is not necessarily the end of a scientific investigation. A conclusion about one experiment may lead right into another experiment. Point out that in scientific investigations, a conclusion is a summary and explanation of the results of an experiment.

Tell students to suppose that for the Experimental Procedure described on this page, they obtained the following results: Container 1 froze in 45 minutes, Container 2 in 80 minutes, and Container 3 in 25 minutes. Ask: **What conclusions can you draw about this experiment?** (*Students might conclude that the more salt that is added to fresh water, the longer it takes the water to freeze. The hypothesis is supported, and the question of which freezes faster is answered—fresh water.*)

You might wish to have students work in pairs to plan the controlled experiment. **ACTIVITY** (*Students should develop a hypothesis, such as "If I increase the height from which a ball is dropped, then the height of its bounce will increase." They can test the hypothesis by dropping balls from varying heights (the manipulated variable). All trials should be done with the same kind of ball and on the same surface (constant variables). For each trial, they should measure the height of the bounce (responding variable).*) After students have designed the experiment, provide rubber balls and invite them to carry out the experiment so they can collect and interpret data and draw conclusions.

C ◆ 179

Thinking Critically

Comparing and Contrasting

Emphasize that the skill of comparing and contrasting often relies on good observation skills, as in this activity. *(Students' answers may vary. Sample answer: Similarities—both are dogs and have four legs, two eyes, two ears, brown and white fur, black noses, pink tongues; Differences—smooth coat vs. rough coat, more white fur vs. more brown fur, shorter vs. taller, long ears vs. short ears.)*

Applying Concepts

Point out to students that they apply concepts that they learn in school in their daily lives. For example, they learn to add, subtract, multiply, and divide in school. If they get a paper route or some other part-time job, they can apply those concepts. Challenge students to practice applying concepts by doing the activity. *(Antifreeze lowers the temperature at which the solution will freeze, and thus keeps the water in the radiator from freezing.)*

Interpreting Illustrations

Again, point out the need for good observation skills. Ask: **What is the difference between "interpreting illustrations" and "looking at the pictures"?** *("Interpreting illustrations" requires thorough examination of the illustration, caption, and labels, while "looking at the pictures" implies less thorough examination.)* Encourage students to thoroughly examine the diagram as they do the activity. *(Students' paragraphs may vary, but should describe the internal anatomy of an earthworm, including some of the organs in the earthworm.)*

Thinking Critically

Has a friend ever asked for your advice about a problem? If so, you may have helped your friend think through the problem in a logical way. Without knowing it, you used critical-thinking skills to help your friend. Critical thinking involves the use of reasoning and logic to solve problems or make decisions. Some critical-thinking skills are described below.

Comparing and Contrasting

When you examine two objects for similarities and differences, you are using the skill of **comparing and contrasting.** Comparing involves identifying similarities, or common characteristics. Contrasting involves identifying differences. Analyzing objects in this way can help you discover details that you might otherwise overlook.

> **ACTIVITY**
> Compare and contrast the two animals in the photo. First list all the similarities that you see. Then list all the differences.

Applying Concepts

When you use your knowledge about one situation to make sense of a similar situation, you are using the skill of **applying concepts.** Being able to transfer your knowledge from one situation to another shows that you truly understand a concept. You may use this skill in answering test questions that present different problems from the ones you've reviewed in class.

> **ACTIVITY**
> You have just learned that water takes longer to freeze when other substances are mixed into it. Use this knowledge to explain why people need a substance called antifreeze in their car's radiator in the winter.

Interpreting Illustrations

Diagrams, photographs, and maps are included in textbooks to help clarify what you read. These illustrations show processes, places, and ideas in a visual manner. The skill called **interpreting illustrations** can help you learn from these visual elements. To understand an illustration, take the time to study the illustration along with all the written information that accompanies it. Captions identify the key concepts shown in the illustration. Labels point out the important parts of a diagram or map, while keys identify the symbols used in a map.

Blood vessels
Reproductive organs
Hearts
Brain
Mouth
Bristles
Digestive tract
Nerve cord
Waste-removal organs
Intestine

▲ Internal anatomy of an earthworm

> **ACTIVITY**
> Study the diagram above. Then write a short paragraph explaining what you have learned.

Relating Cause and Effect

If one event causes another event to occur, the two events are said to have a cause-and-effect relationship. When you determine that such a relationship exists between two events, you use a skill called **relating cause and effect.** For example, if you notice an itchy, red bump on your skin, you might infer that a mosquito bit you. The mosquito bite is the cause, and the bump is the effect.

It is important to note that two events do not necessarily have a cause-and-effect relationship just because they occur together. Scientists carry out experiments or use past experience to determine whether a cause-and-effect relationship exists.

> **ACTIVITY**
> You are on a camping trip and your flashlight has stopped working. List some possible causes for the flashlight malfunction. How could you determine which cause-and-effect relationship has left you in the dark?

Making Generalizations

When you draw a conclusion about an entire group based on information about only some of the group's members, you are using a skill called **making generalizations.** For a generalization to be valid, the sample you choose must be large enough and representative of the entire group. You might, for example, put this skill to work at a farm stand if you see a sign that says, "Sample some grapes before you buy." If you sample a few sweet grapes, you may conclude that all the grapes are sweet—and purchase a large bunch.

> **ACTIVITY**
> A team of scientists needs to determine whether the water in a large reservoir is safe to drink. How could they use the skill of making generalizations to help them? What should they do?

Making Judgments

When you evaluate something to decide whether it is good or bad, or right or wrong, you are using a skill called **making judgments.** For example, you make judgments when you decide to eat healthful foods or to pick up litter in a park. Before you make a judgment, you need to think through the pros and cons of a situation, and identify the values or standards that you hold.

> **ACTIVITY**
> Should children and teens be required to wear helmets when bicycling? Explain why you feel the way you do.

Problem Solving

When you use critical-thinking skills to resolve an issue or decide on a course of action, you are using a skill called **problem solving.** Some problems, such as how to convert a fraction into a decimal, are straightforward. Other problems, such as figuring out why your computer has stopped working, are complex. Some complex problems can be solved using the trial and error method—try out one solution first, and if that doesn't work, try another. Other useful problem-solving strategies include making models and brainstorming possible solutions with a partner.

C ◆ 181

Emphasize that not all events that occur together have a cause-and-effect relationship. For example, tell students that you went to the grocery and your car stalled. Ask: **Is there a cause-and-effect relationship in this situation? Explain your answer.** *(No, because going to the grocery could not cause a car to stall. There must be another cause to make the car stall.)* Have students do the activity to practice relating cause and effect. *(Students should identify that the flashlight not working is the effect. Some possible causes include dead batteries, a burned-out light bulb, or a loose part.)*

Making Generalizations

Point out the importance of having a large, representative sample before making a generalization. Ask: **If you went fishing at a lake and caught three catfish, could you make the generalization that all fish in the lake are catfish? Why or why not?** *(No, because there might be other kinds of fish you didn't catch because they didn't like the bait or they may be in other parts of the lake.)* **How could you make a generalization about the kinds of fish in the lake?** *(By having a larger sample)* Have students do the activity to practice making generalizations. *(The scientists should collect and test water samples from a number of different parts of the reservoir.)*

Making Judgments

Remind students that they make a judgment almost every time they make a decision. Ask: **What steps should you follow to make a judgment?** *(Gather information, list pros and cons, analyze values, make judgment)* Invite students to do the activity, and then to share and discuss the judgments they made. *(Students' judgments will vary, but should be supported by valid reasoning. Sample answer: Children and teens should be required to wear helmets when bicycling because helmets have been proven to save lives and reduce head injuries.)*

Problem Solving **ACTIVITY**

Challenge student pairs to solve a problem about a soapbox derby. Explain that their younger brother is building a car to enter in the race. The brother wants to know how to make his soapbox car go faster. After student pairs have considered the problem, have them share their ideas about solutions with the class. *(Most will probably suggest using trial and error by making small changes to the car and testing the car after each change. Some students may suggest making and manipulating a model.)*

C ◆ 181

Organizing Information

Concept Maps

Challenge students to make a concept map with at least three levels of concepts to organize information about types of transportation. All students should start with the phrase *types of transportation* at the top of the concept map. After that point, their concept maps may vary. *(For example, some students might place* private transportation *and* public transportation *at the next level, while other students might have* human-powered *and* gas-powered. *Make sure students connect the concepts with linking words. Challenge students to include cross-linkages as well.)*

Compare/ Contrast Tables

Have students make their own compare/contrast tables using two or more different sports or other activities, such as playing musical instruments. Emphasize that students should select characteristics that highlight the similarities and differences between the activities. *(Students' compare/contrast tables should include several appropriate characteristics and list information about each activity for every characteristic.)*

Organizing Information

As you read this textbook, how can you make sense of all the information it contains? Some useful tools to help you organize information are shown on this page. These tools are called *graphic organizers* because they give you a visual picture of a topic, showing at a glance how key concepts are related.

Concept Maps

Concept maps are useful tools for organizing information on broad topics. A concept map begins with a general concept and shows how it can be broken down into more specific concepts. In that way, relationships between concepts become easier to understand.

A concept map is constructed by placing concept words (usually nouns) in ovals and connecting them with linking words. Often, the most general concept word is placed at the top, and the words become more specific as you move downward. Often the linking words, which are written on a line extending between two ovals, describe the relationship between the two concepts they connect. If you follow any string of concepts and linking words down the map, it should read like a sentence.

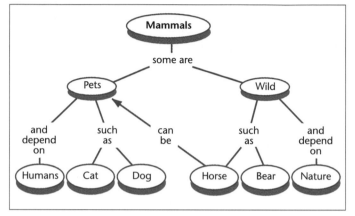

Some concept maps include linking words that connect a concept on one branch of the map to a concept on another branch. These linking words, called cross-linkages, show more complex interrelationships among concepts.

Compare/Contrast Tables

Compare/contrast tables are useful tools for sorting out the similarities and differences between two or more items. A table provides an organized framework in which to compare items based on specific characteristics that you identify.

To create a compare/contrast table, list the items to be compared across the top of a table. Then list the characteristics that will form the basis of your comparison in the left-hand

Characteristic	Baseball	Basketball
Number of Players	9	5
Playing Field	Baseball diamond	Basketball court
Equipment	Bat, baseball, mitts	Basket, basketball

column. Complete the table by filling in information about each characteristic, first for one item and then for the other.

Venn Diagrams

Another way to show similarities and differences between items is with a Venn diagram. A Venn diagram consists of two or more circles that partially overlap. Each circle represents a particular concept or idea. Common characteristics, or similarities, are written within the area of overlap between the two circles. Unique characteristics, or differences, are written in the parts of the circles outside the area of overlap.

To create a Venn diagram, draw two overlapping circles. Label the circles with the names of the items being compared. Write the

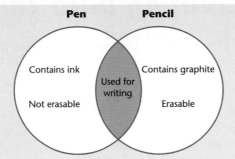

unique characteristics in each circle outside the area of overlap. Then write the shared characteristics within the area of overlap.

Flowcharts

A flowchart can help you understand the order in which certain events have occurred or should occur. Flowcharts are useful for outlining the stages in a process or the steps in a procedure.

To make a flowchart, write a brief description of each event in a box. Place the first event at the top of the page, followed by the second event, the third event, and so on. Then draw an arrow to connect each event to the one that occurs next.

Preparing Pasta

Boil water
↓
Cook pasta
↓
Drain water
↓
Add sauce

Cycle Diagrams

A cycle diagram can be used to show a sequence of events that is continuous, or cyclical. A continuous sequence does not have an end because, when the final event is over, the first event begins again. Like a flowchart, a cycle diagram can help you understand the order of events.

To create a cycle diagram, write a brief description of each event in a box. Place one event at the top of the page in the center. Then, moving in a clockwise direction around an imaginary circle, write each event in its proper sequence. Draw arrows that connect each event to the one that occurs next, forming a continuous circle.

Steps in a Science Experiment

Pose a question → Develop a hypothesis → Design an experiment → Interpret data → Draw conclusions → (back to Pose a question)

C ◆ 183

Venn Diagrams · ACTIVITY

Students can use the same information from their compare/contrast tables to create a Venn diagram. Make sure students understand that the overlapping area of the circles is used to list similarities and the parts of the circles outside the overlap area are used to show differences. If students want to list similarities and differences among three activities, show them how to add a third circle that overlaps each of the other two circles and has an area of overlap for all three circles. (*Students' Venn diagrams will vary. Make sure they have accurately listed similarities in the overlap area and differences in the parts of the circles that do not overlap.*)

Flowcharts · ACTIVITY

Encourage students to create a flowchart to show the things they did this morning as they got ready for school. Remind students that a flowchart should show the correct order in which events occurred or should occur. (*Students' flowcharts will vary somewhat. A typical flowchart might include: got up → ate breakfast → took a shower → brushed teeth → got dressed → gathered books and homework → put on jacket.*)

Cycle Diagrams · ACTIVITY

Review that a cycle diagram shows a sequence of events that is continuous. Then challenge students to create a cycle diagram that shows how the weather changes with the seasons where they live. (*Students' cycle diagrams may vary, though most will include four steps, one for each season.*)

Creating Data Tables and Graphs

Data Tables

Have students create a data table to show how much time they spend on different activities during one week. Suggest that students first list the main activities they do every week. Then they should determine the amount of time they spend on each activity each day. Remind students to give this data table a title. *(Students' data tables will vary. A sample data table is shown below.)*

Bar Graphs

Students can use the data from their data table above to make a bar graph showing how much time they spend on different activities during a week. The vertical axis should be divided into units of time, such as hours. Remind students to label both axes and give their graph a title. *(Students' bar graphs will vary. A sample bar graph is shown below.)*

Creating Data Tables and Graphs

How can you make sense of the data in a science experiment? The first step is to organize the data to help you understand them. Data tables and graphs are helpful tools for organizing data.

Data Tables

You have gathered your materials and set up your experiment. But before you start, you need to plan a way to record what happens during the experiment. By creating a data table, you can record your observations and measurements in an orderly way.

Suppose, for example, that a scientist conducted an experiment to find out how many Calories people of different body masses burn while doing various activities. The data table shows the results.

Notice in this data table that the manipulated variable (body mass) is the heading of one column. The responding variable (for Experiment 1, the number of Calories burned while bicycling) is the heading of the next column. Additional columns were added for related experiments.

CALORIES BURNED IN 30 MINUTES OF ACTIVITY			
Body Mass	Experiment 1 Bicycling	Experiment 2 Playing Basketball	Experiment 3 Watching Television
30 kg	60 Calories	120 Calories	21 Calories
40 kg	77 Calories	164 Calories	27 Calories
50 kg	95 Calories	206 Calories	33 Calories
60 kg	114 Calories	248 Calories	38 Calories

Bar Graphs

To compare how many Calories a person burns doing various activities, you could create a bar graph. A bar graph is used to display data in a number of separate, or distinct, categories. In this example, bicycling, playing basketball, and watching television are three separate categories.

To create a bar graph, follow these steps.

1. On graph paper, draw a horizontal, or *x*-, axis and a vertical, or *y*-, axis.
2. Write the names of the categories to be graphed along the horizontal axis. Include an overall label for the axis as well.
3. Label the vertical axis with the name of the responding variable. Include units of measurement. Then create a scale along the axis by marking off equally spaced numbers that cover the range of the data collected.
4. For each category, draw a solid bar using the scale on the vertical axis to determine the

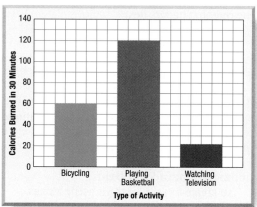

Calories Burned by a 30-kilogram Person in Various Activities

appropriate height. For example, for bicycling, draw the bar as high as the 60 mark on the vertical axis. Make all the bars the same width and leave equal spaces between them.
5. Add a title that describes the graph.

Time Spent on Different Activities in a Week

	Going to Classes	Eating Meals	Playing Soccer	Watching Television
Monday	6	2	2	0.5
Tuesday	6	1.5	1.5	1.5
Wednesday	6	2	1	2
Thursday	6	2	2	1.5
Friday	6	2	2	0.5
Saturday	0	2.5	2.5	1
Sunday	0	3	1	2

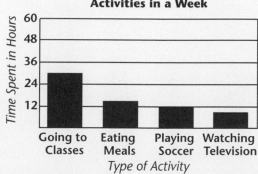

Time Spent on Different Activities in a Week

Line Graphs

To see whether a relationship exists between body mass and the number of Calories burned while bicycling, you could create a line graph. A line graph is used to display data that show how one variable (the responding variable) changes in response to another variable (the manipulated variable). You can use a line graph when your manipulated variable is *continuous*, that is, when there are other points between the ones that you tested. In this example, body mass is a continuous variable because there are other body masses between 30 and 40 kilograms (for example, 31 kilograms). Time is another example of a continuous variable.

Line graphs are powerful tools because they allow you to estimate values for conditions that you did not test in the experiment. For example, you can use the line graph to estimate that a 35-kilogram person would burn 68 Calories while bicycling.

To create a line graph, follow these steps.

1. On graph paper, draw a horizontal, or *x-*, axis and a vertical, or *y-*, axis.
2. Label the horizontal axis with the name of the manipulated variable. Label the vertical axis with the name of the responding variable. Include units of measurement.
3. Create a scale on each axis by marking off equally spaced numbers that cover the range of the data collected.
4. Plot a point on the graph for each piece of data. In the line graph above, the dotted lines show how to plot the first data point (30 kilograms and 60 Calories). Draw an imaginary vertical line extending up from the horizontal axis at the 30-kilogram mark. Then draw an imaginary horizontal line extending across from the vertical axis at the 60-Calorie mark. Plot the point where the two lines intersect.

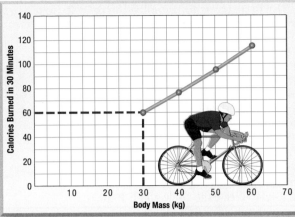

Effect of Body Mass on Calories Burned While Bicycling

5. Connect the plotted points with a solid line. (In some cases, it may be more appropriate to draw a line that shows the general trend of the plotted points. In those cases, some of the points may fall above or below the line.)
6. Add a title that identifies the variables or relationship in the graph.

ACTIVITY
Create line graphs to display the data from Experiment 2 and Experiment 3 in the data table.

ACTIVITY
You read in the newspaper that a total of 4 centimeters of rain fell in your area in June, 2.5 centimeters fell in July, and 1.5 centimeters fell in August. What type of graph would you use to display these data? Use graph paper to create the graph.

Line Graphs

Walk students through the steps involved in creating a line graph using the example illustrated on the page. For example, ask: **What is the label on the horizontal axis? On the vertical axis?** *(Body Mass (kg); Calories Burned in 30 Minutes)* **What scales are used on each axis?** *(3 squares per 10 kg on the x-axis and 2 squares per 20 Calories on the y-axis)* **What does the second data point represent?** *(77 Calories burned for a body mass of 40 kg)* **What trend or pattern does the graph show?** *(The number of Calories burned in 30 minutes of cycling increases with body mass.)*

Have students follow the steps to carry out the first **ACTIVITY** activity. *(Students should make a different graph for each experiment with different y-axis scales to practice making scales appropriate for data. See sample graphs below.)*

Have students carry out the second activity. **ACTIVITY** *(Students should conclude that a bar graph would be best to display the data. A sample bar graph for these data is shown below.)*

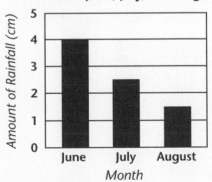

Rainfall in June, July, and August

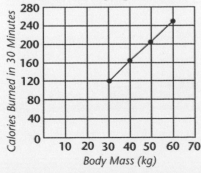

Effect of Body Mass on Calories Burned While Playing Basketball

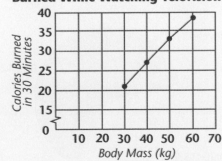

Effect of Body Mass on Calories Burned While Watching Television

Circle Graphs

Emphasize that a circle graph has to include 100 percent of the categories for the topic being graphed. For example, ask: **Could the data in the bar graph titled "Calories Burned by a 30-kilogram Person in Various Activities" (on the previous page) be shown in a circle graph? Why or why not?** (*No, because it does not include all the possible ways a 30-kilogram person can burn Calories.*) Then walk students through the steps for making a circle graph. Help students to use a compass and a protractor. Use the protractor to illustrate that a circle has 360 degrees. Make sure students understand the mathematical calculations involved in making a circle graph.

You might wish to have students work in pairs to **ACTIVITY** complete the activity. (*Students' circle graphs should look like the graph below.*)

Circle Graphs

Like bar graphs, circle graphs can be used to display data in a number of separate categories. Unlike bar graphs, however, circle graphs can only be used when you have data for *all* the categories that make up a given topic. A circle graph is sometimes called a pie chart because it resembles a pie cut into slices. The pie represents the entire topic, while the slices represent the individual categories. The size of a slice indicates what percentage of the whole a particular category makes up.

The data table below shows the results of a survey in which 24 teenagers were asked to identify their favorite sport. The data were then used to create the circle graph at the right.

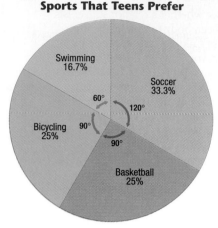

Sports That Teens Prefer

Swimming 16.7%
Soccer 33.3%
60°
120°
Bicycling 25%
90°
90°
Basketball 25%

FAVORITE SPORTS

Sport	Number of Students
Soccer	8
Basketball	6
Bicycling	6
Swimming	4

To create a circle graph, follow these steps.

1. Use a compass to draw a circle. Mark the center of the circle with a point. Then draw a line from the center point to the top of the circle.

2. Determine the size of each "slice" by setting up a proportion where *x* equals the number of degrees in a slice. (NOTE: A circle contains 360 degrees.) For example, to find the number of degrees in the "soccer" slice, set up the following proportion:

$$\frac{\text{students who prefer soccer}}{\text{total number of students}} = \frac{x}{\text{total number of degrees in a circle}}$$

$$\frac{8}{24} = \frac{x}{360}$$

Cross-multiply and solve for *x*.

$$24x = 8 \times 360$$
$$x = 120$$

The "soccer" slice should contain 120 degrees.

3. Use a protractor to measure the angle of the first slice, using the line you drew to the top of the circle as the 0° line. Draw a line from the center of the circle to the edge for the angle you measured.

4. Continue around the circle by measuring the size of each slice with the protractor. Start measuring from the edge of the previous slice so the wedges do not overlap. When you are done, the entire circle should be filled in.

5. Determine the percentage of the whole circle that each slice represents. To do this, divide the number of degrees in a slice by the total number of degrees in a circle (360), and multiply by 100%. For the "soccer" slice, you can find the percentage as follows:

$$\frac{120}{360} \times 100\% = 33.3\%$$

6. Use a different color to shade in each slice. Label each slice with the name of the category and with the percentage of the whole it represents.

7. Add a title to the circle graph.

In a class of 28 students, 12 students **ACTIVITY** take the bus to school, 10 students walk, and 6 students ride their bicycles. Create a circle graph to display these data.

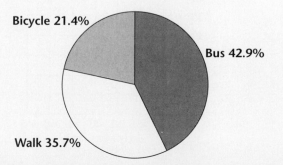

Ways Students Get to School

Bicycle 21.4%
Bus 42.9%
Walk 35.7%

Laboratory Safety

Safety Symbols

These symbols alert you to possible dangers in the laboratory and remind you to work carefully.

Safety Goggles Always wear safety goggles to protect your eyes in any activity involving chemicals, flames or heating, or the possibility of broken glassware.

Lab Apron Wear a laboratory apron to protect your skin and clothing from damage.

Breakage You are working with materials that may be breakable, such as glass containers, glass tubing, thermometers, or funnels. Handle breakable materials with care. Do not touch broken glassware.

Heat-resistant Gloves Use an oven mitt or other hand protection when handling hot materials. Hot plates, hot glassware, or hot water can cause burns. Do not touch hot objects with your bare hands.

Heating Use a clamp or tongs to pick up hot glassware. Do not touch hot objects with your bare hands.

Sharp Object Pointed-tip scissors, scalpels, knives, needles, pins, or tacks are sharp. They can cut or puncture your skin. Always direct a sharp edge or point away from yourself and others. Use sharp instruments only as instructed.

Electric Shock Avoid the possibility of electric shock. Never use electrical equipment around water, or when the equipment is wet or your hands are wet. Be sure cords are untangled and cannot trip anyone. Disconnect the equipment when it is not in use.

Corrosive Chemical You are working with an acid or another corrosive chemical. Avoid getting it on your skin or clothing, or in your eyes. Do not inhale the vapors. Wash your hands when you are finished with the activity.

Poison Do not let any poisonous chemical come in contact with your skin, and do not inhale its vapors. Wash your hands when you are finished with the activity.

Physical Safety When an experiment involves physical activity, take precautions to avoid injuring yourself or others. Follow instructions from your teacher. Alert your teacher if there is any reason you should not participate in the activity.

Animal Safety Treat live animals with care to avoid harming the animals or yourself. Working with animal parts or preserved animals also may require caution. Wash your hands when you are finished with the activity.

Plant Safety Handle plants in the laboratory or during field work only as directed by your teacher. If you are allergic to certain plants, tell your teacher before doing an activity in which those plants are used. Avoid touching harmful plants such as poison ivy, poison oak, or poison sumac, or plants with thorns. Wash your hands when you are finished with the activity.

Flames You may be working with flames from a lab burner, candle, or matches. Tie back loose hair and clothing. Follow instructions from your teacher about lighting and extinguishing flames.

No Flames Flammable materials may be present. Make sure there are no flames, sparks, or other exposed heat sources present.

Fumes When poisonous or unpleasant vapors may be involved, work in a ventilated area. Avoid inhaling vapors directly. Only test an odor when directed to do so by your teacher, and use a wafting motion to direct the vapor toward your nose.

Disposal Chemicals and other laboratory materials used in the activity must be disposed of safely. Follow the instructions from your teacher.

Hand Washing Wash your hands thoroughly when finished with the activity. Use antibacterial soap and warm water. Lather both sides of your hands and between your fingers. Rinse well.

General Safety Awareness You may see this symbol when none of the symbols described earlier appears. In this case, follow the specific instructions provided. You may also see this symbol when you are asked to develop your own procedure in a lab. Have your teacher approve your plan before you go further.

Laboratory Safety

Laboratory safety is an essential element of a successful science class. It is important for you to emphasize laboratory safety to students. Students need to understand exactly what is safe and unsafe behavior, and what the rationale is behind each safety rule.

Review with students the Safety Symbols and Science Safety Rules listed on this and the next two pages. Then follow the safety guidelines below to ensure that your classroom will be a safe place for students to learn science.

◆ Post safety rules in the classroom and review them regularly with students.

◆ Familiarize yourself with the safety procedures for each activity before introducing it to your students.

◆ Review specific safety precautions with students before beginning every science activity.

◆ Always act as an exemplary role model by displaying safe behavior.

◆ Know how to use safety equipment, such as fire extinguishers and fire blankets, and always have it accessible.

◆ Have students practice leaving the classroom quickly and orderly to prepare them for emergencies.

◆ Explain to students how to use the intercom or other available means of communication to get help during an emergency.

◆ Never leave students unattended while they are engaged in science activities.

◆ Provide enough space for students to safely carry out science activities.

◆ Keep your classroom and all science materials in proper condition. Replace worn or broken items.

◆ Instruct students to report all accidents and injuries to you immediately.

Laboratory Safety

Additional tips are listed below for the Science Safety Rules discussed on these two pages. Please keep these tips in mind when you carry out science activities in your classroom.

General Precautions

◆ For open-ended activities like Chapter Projects, go over general safety guidelines with students. Have students submit their procedures or design plans in writing and check them for safety considerations.

◆ In an activity where students are directed to taste something, be sure to store the material in clean, *nonscience* containers. Distribute the material to students in *new* plastic or paper dispensables, which should be discarded after the tasting. Tasting or eating should never be done in a lab classroom.

◆ During physical activity, make sure students do not overexert themselves.

◆ Remind students to handle microscopes and telescopes with care to avoid breakage.

Heating and Fire Safety

◆ No flammable substances should be in use around hot plates, light bulbs, or open flames.

◆ Test tubes should be heated only in water baths.

◆ Students should be permitted to strike matches to light candles or burners *only* with strict supervision. When possible, you should light the flames, especially when working with sixth graders.

◆ Be sure to have proper ventilation when fumes are produced during a procedure.

◆ All electrical equipment used in the lab should have GFI switches.

Using Chemicals Safely

◆ When students use both chemicals and microscopes in one activity, microscopes should be in a separate part of the room from the chemicals so that when students remove their goggles to use the microscopes, their eyes are not at risk.

Science Safety Rules

To prepare yourself to work safely in the laboratory, read over the following safety rules. Then read them a second time. Make sure you understand and follow each rule. Ask your teacher to explain any rules you do not understand.

Dress Code

1. To protect yourself from injuring your eyes, wear safety goggles whenever you work with chemicals, burners, glassware, or any substance that might get into your eyes. If you wear contact lenses, notify your teacher.
2. Wear a lab apron or coat whenever you work with corrosive chemicals or substances that can stain.
3. Tie back long hair to keep it away from any chemicals, flames, or equipment.
4. Remove or tie back any article of clothing or jewelry that can hang down and touch chemicals, flames, or equipment. Roll up or secure long sleeves.
5. Never wear open shoes or sandals.

General Precautions

6. Read all directions for an experiment several times before beginning the activity. Carefully follow all written and oral instructions. If you are in doubt about any part of the experiment, ask your teacher for assistance.
7. Never perform activities that are not assigned or authorized by your teacher. Obtain permission before "experimenting" on your own. Never handle any equipment unless you have specific permission.
8. Never perform lab activities without direct supervision.
9. Never eat or drink in the laboratory.
10. Keep work areas clean and tidy at all times. Bring only notebooks and lab manuals or written lab procedures to the work area. All other items, such as purses and backpacks, should be left in a designated area.
11. Do not engage in horseplay.

First Aid

12. Always report all accidents or injuries to your teacher, no matter how minor. Notify your teacher immediately about any fires.
13. Learn what to do in case of specific accidents, such as getting acid in your eyes or on your skin. (Rinse acids from your body with lots of water.)
14. Be aware of the location of the first-aid kit, but do not use it unless instructed by your teacher. In case of injury, your teacher should administer first aid. Your teacher may also send you to the school nurse or call a physician.
15. Know the location of emergency equipment, such as the fire extinguisher and fire blanket, and know how to use it.
16. Know the location of the nearest telephone and whom to contact in an emergency.

Heating and Fire Safety

17. Never use a heat source, such as a candle, burner, or hot plate, without wearing safety goggles.
18. Never heat anything unless instructed to do so. A chemical that is harmless when cool may be dangerous when heated.
19. Keep all combustible materials away from flames. Never use a flame or spark near a combustible chemical.
20. Never reach across a flame.
21. Before using a laboratory burner, make sure you know proper procedures for lighting and adjusting the burner, as demonstrated by your teacher. Do not touch the burner. It may be hot. And never leave a lighted burner unattended!
22. Chemicals can splash or boil out of a heated test tube. When heating a substance in a test tube, make sure that the mouth of the tube is not pointed at you or anyone else.
23. Never heat a liquid in a closed container. The expanding gases produced may blow the container apart.
24. Before picking up a container that has been heated, hold the back of your hand near it. If you can feel heat on the back of your hand, the container is too hot to handle. Use an oven mitt to pick up a container that has been heated.

Using Glassware Safely

◆ Use plastic containers, graduated cylinders, and beakers whenever possible. If using glass, students should wear safety goggles.

◆ Use only nonmercury thermometers with anti-roll protectors.

◆ Check all glassware periodically for chips and scratches, which can cause cuts and breakage.

Using Chemicals Safely

25. Never mix chemicals "for the fun of it." You might produce a dangerous, possibly explosive substance.

26. Never put your face near the mouth of a container that holds chemicals. Never touch, taste, or smell a chemical unless you are instructed by your teacher to do so. Many chemicals are poisonous.

27. Use only those chemicals needed in the activity. Read and double-check labels on supply bottles before removing any chemicals. Take only as much as you need. Keep all containers closed when chemicals are not being used.

28. Dispose of all chemicals as instructed by your teacher. To avoid contamination, never return chemicals to their original containers. Never simply pour chemicals or other substances into the sink or trash containers.

29. Be extra careful when working with acids or bases. Pour all chemicals over the sink or a container, not over your work surface.

30. If you are instructed to test for odors, use a wafting motion to direct the odors to your nose. Do not inhale the fumes directly from the container.

31. When mixing an acid and water, always pour the water into the container first and then add the acid to the water. Never pour water into an acid.

32. Take extreme care not to spill any material in the laboratory. Wash chemical spills and splashes immediately with plenty of water. Immediately begin rinsing with water any acids that get on your skin or clothing, and notify your teacher of any acid spill at the same time.

Using Glassware Safely

33. Never force glass tubing or thermometers into a rubber stopper or rubber tubing. Have your teacher insert the glass tubing or thermometer if required for an activity.

34. If you are using a laboratory burner, use a wire screen to protect glassware from any flame. Never heat glassware that is not thoroughly dry on the outside.

35. Keep in mind that hot glassware looks cool. Never pick up glassware without first checking to see if it is hot. Use an oven mitt. See rule 24.

36. Never use broken or chipped glassware. If glassware breaks, notify your teacher and dispose of the glassware in the proper broken-glassware container. Never handle broken glass with your bare hands.

37. Never eat or drink from lab glassware.

38. Thoroughly clean glassware before putting it away.

Using Sharp Instruments

39. Handle scalpels or other sharp instruments with extreme care. Never cut material toward you; cut away from you.

40. Immediately notify your teacher if you cut your skin when working in the laboratory.

Animal and Plant Safety

41. Never perform experiments that cause pain, discomfort, or harm to mammals, birds, reptiles, fishes, or amphibians. This rule applies at home as well as in the classroom.

42. Animals should be handled only if absolutely necessary. Your teacher will instruct you as to how to handle each animal species brought into the classroom.

43. If you know that you are allergic to certain plants, molds, or animals, tell your teacher before doing an activity in which these are used.

44. During field work, protect your skin by wearing long pants, long sleeves, socks, and closed shoes. Know how to recognize the poisonous plants and fungi in your area, as well as plants with thorns, and avoid contact with them.

45. Never eat any part of an unidentified plant or fungus.

46. Wash your hands thoroughly after handling animals or the cage containing animals. Wash your hands when you are finished with any activity involving animal parts, plants, or soil.

End-of-Experiment Rules

47. After an experiment has been completed, clean up your work area and return all equipment to its proper place.

48. Dispose of waste materials as instructed by your teacher.

49. Wash your hands after every experiment.

50. Always turn off all burners or hot plates when they are not in use. Unplug hot plates and other electrical equipment. If you used a burner, check that the gas-line valve to the burner is off as well.

Using Sharp Instruments

◆ Always use blunt-tip safety scissors, except when pointed-tip scissors are required.

Animal and Plant Safety

◆ When working with live animals or plants, check ahead of time for students who may have allergies to the specimens.

◆ When growing bacteria cultures, use only disposable petri dishes. After streaking, the dishes should be sealed and not opened again by students. After the lab, students should return the unopened dishes to you. Students should wash their hands with antibacterial soap.

◆ Two methods are recommended for the safe disposal of bacteria cultures. *First method:* Autoclave the petri dishes and discard without opening. *Second method*: If no autoclave is available, carefully open the dishes (never have a student do this) and pour full-strength bleach into the dishes and let stand for a day. Then pour the bleach from the petri dishes down a drain and flush the drain with lots of water. Tape the petri dishes back together and place in a sealed plastic bag. Wrap the plastic bag with a brown paper bag or newspaper and tape securely. Throw the sealed package in the trash. Thoroughly disinfect the work area with bleach.

◆ To grow mold, use a new, sealable plastic bag that is two to three times larger than the material to be placed inside. Seal the bag and tape it shut. After the bag is sealed, students should not open it. To dispose of the bag and mold culture, make a small cut near an edge of the bag and cook in a microwave oven on high setting for at least 1 minute. Discard the bag according to local ordinance, usually in the trash.

◆ Students should wear disposable nitrile, latex, or food-handling gloves when handling live animals or nonliving specimens.

End-of Experiment Rules

◆ Always have students use antibacterial soap for washing their hands.

Using the Microscope

The microscope is an essential tool in the study of life science. It allows you to see things that are too small to be seen with the unaided eye.

You will probably use a compound microscope like the one you see here. The compound microscope has more than one lens that magnifies the object you view.

Typically, a compound microscope has one lens in the eyepiece, the part you look through. The eyepiece lens usually magnifies 10 ×. Any object you view through this lens would appear 10 times larger than it is.

The compound microscope may contain one or two other lenses called objective lenses. If there are two objective lenses, they are called the low-power and high-power objective lenses. The low-power objective lens usually magnifies 10 ×. The high-power objective lens usually magnifies 40 ×.

To calculate the total magnification with which you are viewing an object, multiply the magnification of the eyepiece lens by the magnification of the objective lens you are using. For example, the eyepiece's magnification of 10 × multiplied by the low-power objective's magnification of 10 × equals a total magnification of 100 ×.

Use the photo of the compound microscope to become familiar with the parts of the microscope and their functions.

The Parts of the Compound Microscope

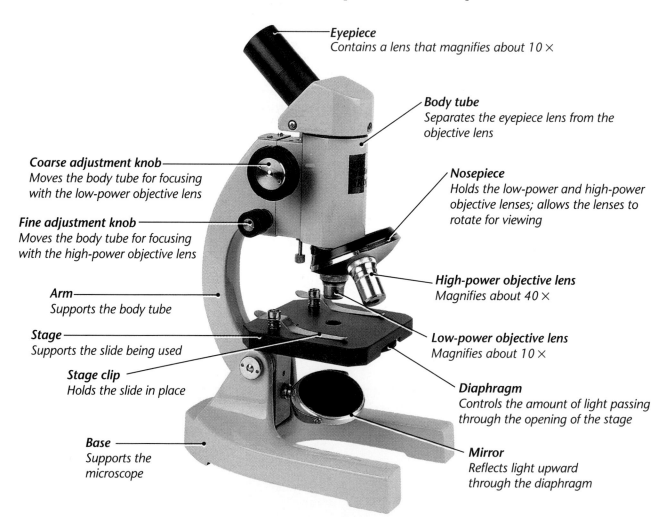

Eyepiece
Contains a lens that magnifies about 10 ×

Body tube
Separates the eyepiece lens from the objective lens

Coarse adjustment knob
Moves the body tube for focusing with the low-power objective lens

Nosepiece
Holds the low-power and high-power objective lenses; allows the lenses to rotate for viewing

Fine adjustment knob
Moves the body tube for focusing with the high-power objective lens

High-power objective lens
Magnifies about 40 ×

Arm
Supports the body tube

Stage
Supports the slide being used

Low-power objective lens
Magnifies about 10 ×

Stage clip
Holds the slide in place

Diaphragm
Controls the amount of light passing through the opening of the stage

Base
Supports the microscope

Mirror
Reflects light upward through the diaphragm

Using the Microscope

Use the following procedures when you are working with a microscope.

1. To carry the microscope grasp the microscope's arm with one hand. Place your other hand under the base.
2. Place the microscope on a table with the arm toward you.
3. Turn the coarse adjustment knob to raise the body tube.
4. Revolve the nosepiece until the low-power objective lens clicks into place.
5. Adjust the diaphragm. While looking through the eyepiece, also adjust the mirror until you see a bright white circle of light. **CAUTION:** *Never use direct sunlight as a light source.*
6. Place a slide on the stage. Center the specimen over the opening on the stage. Use the stage clips to hold the slide in place. **CAUTION:** *Glass slides are fragile.*
7. Look at the stage from the side. Carefully turn the coarse adjustment knob to lower the body tube until the low-power objective almost touches the slide.
8. Looking through the eyepiece, very slowly turn the coarse adjustment knob until the specimen comes into focus.
9. To switch to the high-power objective lens, look at the microscope from the side. Carefully revolve the nosepiece until the high-power objective lens clicks into place. Make sure the lens does not hit the slide.
10. Looking through the eyepiece, turn the fine adjustment knob until the specimen comes into focus.

Making a Wet-Mount Slide

Use the following procedures to make a wet-mount slide of a specimen.

1. Obtain a clean microscope slide and a coverslip. **CAUTION:** *Glass slides and coverslips are fragile.*
2. Place the specimen on the slide. The specimen must be thin enough for light to pass through it.
3. Using a plastic dropper, place a drop of water on the specimen.
4. Gently place one edge of the coverslip against the slide so that it touches the edge of the water drop at a 45° angle. Slowly lower the coverslip over the specimen. If air bubbles are trapped beneath the coverslip, tap the coverslip gently with the eraser end of a pencil.
5. Remove any excess water at the edge of the coverslip with a paper towel.

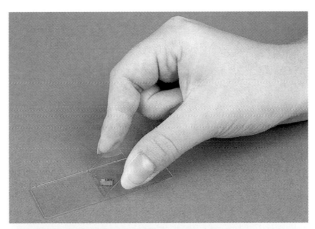

A

absolute dating A technique used to determine the actual age of a fossil. (p. 154)

active transport The movement of materials through a cell membrane using energy. (p. 43)

adaptation A trait that helps an organism survive and reproduce. (p. 143)

alleles The different forms of a gene. (p. 83)

amino acids Small molecules that are linked together chemically to form proteins. (p. 35)

amniocentesis A technique by which a small amount of the fluid that surrounds a developing baby is removed; the fluid is analyzed to determine whether the baby will have a genetic disorder. (p. 122)

atom The smallest unit of an element. (p. 33)

autotroph An organism that makes its own food. (p. 54)

B

branching tree A diagram that shows how scientists think different groups of organisms are related. (p. 162)

C

cancer A disease in which some body cells grow and divide uncontrollably, damaging the parts of the body around them. (p. 71)

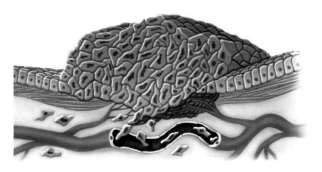

carbohydrates Energy-rich organic compounds, such as sugars and starches, that are made of the elements carbon, hydrogen, and oxygen. (p. 34)

carrier A person who has one recessive allele for a trait and one dominant allele, but does not have the trait. (p. 116)

cast A type of fossil that forms when a mold becomes filled in with minerals that then harden. (p. 152)

cell The basic unit of structure and function in living things. (p. 16)

cell cycle The regular sequence of growth and division that cells undergo. (p. 62)

cell membrane A cell structure that controls which substances can enter or leave the cell. (p. 24)

cell theory A widely accepted explanation of the relationship between cells and living things. (p. 20)

cell wall A rigid layer of nonliving material that surrounds the cells of plants and some other organisms. (p. 24)

chemotherapy The use of drugs to kill cancer cells. (p. 72)

chlorophyll A green pigment found in the chloroplasts of plants, algae, and some bacteria. (p. 52)

chloroplast A structure in the cells of plants and some other organisms that captures energy from sunlight and uses it to produce food. (p. 29)

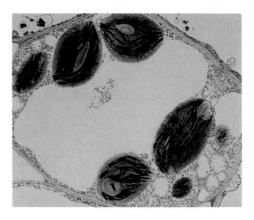

chromatid One of the identical rods of a chromosome. (p. 63)

chromatin Material in cells that contains DNA and carries genetic information. (p. 28)

chromosome A doubled rod of condensed chromatin; contains DNA that carries genetic information. (p. 63)

clone An organism that is genetically identical to the organism from which it was produced. (p. 128)

codominance A condition in which neither of two alleles of a gene is dominant or recessive. (p. 92)

compound Two or more elements that are chemically combined. (p. 33)

compound microscope A light microscope that has more than one lens. (p. 17)

controlled experiment An experiment in which all factors except one are kept constant. (p. 179)

convex lens A curved lens in which the center is thicker than the edges. (p. 21)

cytokinesis The final stage of the cell cycle, in which the cell's cytoplasm divides, distributing the organelles into each of the two new cells. (p. 66)

cytoplasm The region between the cell membrane and the nucleus; in organisms without a nucleus, the region located inside the cell membrane. (p. 28)

D

diffusion The process by which molecules move from an area of higher concentration to an area of lower concentration. (p. 41)

DNA Deoxyribonucleic acid; the genetic material that carries information about an organism and is passed from parent to offspring. (p. 36)

dominant allele An allele whose trait always shows up in the organism when the allele is present. (p. 83)

E

element Any substance that cannot be broken down into simpler substances. (p. 33)

endoplasmic reticulum A cell structure that forms a maze of passageways in which proteins and other materials are carried from one part of the cell to another. (p. 29)

enzyme A type of protein that speeds up a chemical reaction in a living thing. (p. 35)

evolution The gradual change in a species over time. (p. 143)

extinct A species that does not have any living members. (p. 154)

F

fermentation The process by which cells break down molecules to release energy without using oxygen. (p. 58)

fossil The preserved remains or traces of an organism that lived in the past. (p. 151)

fossil record The millions of fossils that scientists have collected. (p. 154)

G

gene therapy The insertion of working copies of a gene into the cells of a person with a genetic disorder in an attempt to correct the disorder. (p. 130)

gene A segment of DNA on a chromosome that codes for a specific trait. (p. 83)

genetic disorder An abnormal condition that a person inherits through genes or chromosomes. (p. 119)

genetic engineering The transfer of a gene from the DNA of one organism into another organism, in order to produce an organism with desired traits. (p. 128)

genetics The scientific study of heredity. (p. 80)

genome All of the DNA in one cell of an organism. (p. 132)

genotype An organism's genetic makeup, or allele combinations. (p. 92)

Golgi body A structure in a cell that receives proteins and other newly formed materials from the endoplasmic reticulum, packages them, and distributes them to other parts of the cell. (p. 29)

gradualism The theory that evolution occurs slowly but steadily. (p. 158)

H

half-life The time it takes for half of the atoms in a radioactive element to break down. (p. 154)

heredity The passing of traits from parents to offspring. (p. 80)

heterotroph An organism that cannot make its own food. (p. 54)

heterozygous Having two different alleles for a trait. (p. 92)

homologous structures Body parts that are structurally similar in related species; provide evidence that the structures were inherited from a common ancestor. (p. 160)

homozygous Having two identical alleles for a trait. (p. 92)

hybrid An organism that has two different alleles for a trait; an organism that is heterozygous for a particular trait. (p. 84)

hybridization A selective breeding method in which two genetically different individuals are crossed. (p. 127)

hypothesis A prediction about the outcome of an experiment. (p. 178)

I

inbreeding A selective breeding method in which two individuals with identical or similar sets of alleles are crossed. (p. 127)

inorganic compound A compound that does not contain carbon. (p. 34)

interphase The stage of the cell cycle that takes place before cell division occurs; during this stage, the cell grows, copies its DNA, and prepares to divide. (p. 62)

karyotype A picture of all the chromosomes in a cell arranged in pairs. (p. 123)

lipids Energy-rich organic compounds, such as fats, oils, and waxes, that are made of carbon, hydrogen, and oxygen. (p. 36)

lysosome A small round cell structure that contains chemicals that break down large food particles into smaller ones. (p. 30)

magnification The ability to make things look larger than they are. (p. 21)

manipulated variable The one factor that a scientist changes during an experiment. (p. 179)

meiosis The process that occurs in sex cells (sperm and egg) by which the number of chromosomes is reduced by half. (p. 98)

messenger RNA RNA that copies the coded message from DNA in the nucleus and carries the message into the cytoplasm. (p. 103)

microscope An instrument that makes small objects look larger. (p. 17)

mitochondria Rod-shaped cell structures that produce most of the energy needed to carry out the cell's functions. (p. 28)

mitosis The stage of the cell cycle during which the cell's nucleus divides into two new nuclei and one copy of the DNA is distributed into each daughter cell. (p. 63)

mold A type of fossil formed when a shell or other hard part of an organism dissolves, leaving an empty space in the shape of the part. (p. 152)

molecule The smallest unit of most compounds. (p. 33)

multiple alleles Three or more forms of a gene that code for a single trait. (p. 113)

mutation A change in a gene or chromosome. (p. 71)

natural selection The process by which individuals that are better adapted to their environment are more likely to survive and reproduce than other members of the same species. (p. 144)

nucleic acid A very large organic molecule made of carbon, oxygen, hydrogen, nitrogen, and phosphorus, that contains instructions that cells need to carry out all the functions of life. (p. 36)

nucleus A cell structure that contains nucleic acids, the chemical instructions that direct all the cell's activities. (p. 25)

operational definition A statement that describes how a particular variable is to be measured or a term is to be defined. (p. 179)

organelle A tiny cell structure that carries out a specific function within the cell. (p. 24)

organic compound A compound that contains carbon. (p. 34)

osmosis The diffusion of water molecules through a selectively permeable membrane. (p. 42)

passive transport The movement of materials through a cell membrane without using energy. (p. 43)

pedigree A chart or "family tree" that tracks which members of a family have a particular trait. (p. 117)

petrified fossil A fossil formed when minerals replace all or part of an organism. (p. 152)

phenotype An organism's physical appearance, or visible traits. (p. 92)

photosynthesis The process by which plants and some other organisms capture the energy in sunlight and use it to make food. (p. 51)

pigment A colored chemical compound that absorbs light. (p. 52)

probability The likelihood that a particular event will occur. (p. 88)

proteins Large organic molecules made of carbon, hydrogen, oxygen, nitrogen, and sometimes sulfur. (p. 35)

punctuated equilibria The theory that species evolve during short periods of rapid change. (p. 158)

Punnett square A chart that shows all the possible combinations of alleles that can result from a genetic cross. (p. 90)

purebred An organism that always produces offspring with the same form of a trait as the parent. (p. 81)

radioactive element An unstable particle that breaks down into a different element. (p. 154)

recessive allele An allele that is masked when a dominant allele is present. (p. 83)

relative dating A technique used to determine which of two fossils is older. (p. 153)

replication The process by which a cell makes a copy of the DNA in its nucleus. (p. 62)

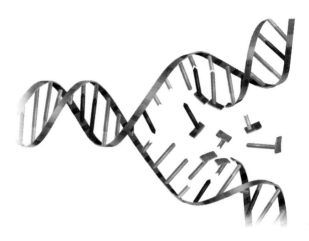

resolution The ability to clearly distinguish the individual parts of an object. (p. 22)

respiration The process by which cells break down simple food molecules to release the energy they contain. (p. 56)

responding variable The factor that changes as a result of changes to the manipulated variable in an experiment. (p. 179)

ribosome A small grain-like structure in the cytoplasm of a cell where proteins are made. (p. 29)

RNA Ribonucleic acid; a nucleic acid that plays an important role in the production of proteins. (p. 37)

scientific theory A well-tested concept that explains a wide range of observations. (p. 143)

sedimentary rock Rock formed when layers of sediments harden over millions of years. (p. 152)

selective breeding The process of selecting a few organisms with desired traits to serve as parents of the next generation. (p. 126)

selectively permeable A property of cell membranes that allows some substances to pass through, while others cannot. (p. 40)

sex-linked gene A gene that is carried on the X or Y chromosome. (p. 116)

species A group of similar organisms that can mate with each other and produce fertile offspring. (p. 141)

stomata Small openings on the underside of a leaf through which oxygen and carbon dioxide can move. (p. 52)

trait A characteristic that an organism can pass on to its offspring through its genes. (p. 80)

transfer RNA RNA in the cytoplasm that carries an amino acid to the ribosome and adds it to the growing protein chain. (p. 103)

tumor A mass of abnormal cells that develops when cancerous cells divide and grow uncontrollably. (p. 71)

vacuole A water-filled sac inside a cell that acts as a storage area. (p. 30)

variable Any factor that can change in an experiment. (p. 179)

variation Any difference between individuals of the same species. (p. 145)

inheritance, genetics and 112–118
inorganic compounds 34
insulin, genetic engineering of 11, 12–13, 129
insurance companies, access to genetic testing by 133
interphase 62–63, 64
interpreting data, skill of 179
interpreting illustrations, skill of 180
invertebrates 155
isolation, species formation and geographic 149–150

Jurassic Period 157

Kaibab squirrel 149
karyotype 123
Katahdin potato 106
kimchee 58

laboratory safety 187–189
Labrador retrievers 169
lactic-acid fermentation 58, 59
Leeuwenhoek, Anton van 18–19, 22
length, measuring 176
lenses of microscopes 17, 21
lesser pandas 162, 163
leukemia 74
Lhasa apso 171
light microscope 21–22
lipids 36
lung cancer 73
lysosomes 27, 30

magnification 21
making generalizations, skill of 181
making judgments, skill of 181
making models, skill of 175
manipulated variable 183
marsupials 150
mass, measuring 177
measuring, skill of 176
medicines, genetic engineering to produce 130
meiosis 98–99
    defined 98
    error during 122
    mutation during 105
    Punnett squares and 98
Mendel, Gregor 80–85, 92, 96, 127
    contribution of 85
    dominant and recessive alleles 83–85
    experiments of 81–82
    other traits studied by 82–83
    pea plant studies of 80–84
    probability and 90, 91
    understanding genetic crosses of 84
Mesozoic Era 157
messenger RNA 103, 104
    attachment of transfer RNA to 105
metaphase 63, 65
microscope
    compound 17, 18, 19, 21
    defined 17
    electron 22

invention of 17
light 21–22
magnification by 21
resolution of 22
scanning electron (SEM) 19
scanning tunneling (STM) 19
transmission electron (TEM) 19
mitochondria 28
    animal cell 27
    plant cell 26
    respiration in 57
mitosis 63, 64–65, 99
    defined 63
    phases of 63, 64–65
molds 152
molecular biologist 11
molecule, defined 33
Moore, John 74
multiple alleles 113
mutations 71, 104–106, 119, 148
    effects of 105–106
    types of 104–105

natural selection
    defined 144
    experiment on 146–147
    factors affecting process of 144–145
    of traits controlled by genes 148
nerve cells 31
Nicholas II, Czar 121
nitrogen bases 67, 103
    DNA replication and pairing of 68
    order of 102
nuclear membrane 25
nucleic acids 36–37
nucleolus 25, 28
nucleus of cell 25–28
    animal cell 27
    plant cell 26
numbat 150

observing, skill of 174
operational definitions 179
Ordovician Period 156
organelles 24
    in cytoplasm 28–30
organic compounds 34
Origin of Species, The (Darwin) 144
osmosis 42
overproduction, natural selection and 144
oxygen
    in Earth's atmosphere 54
    in photosynthesis 52, 53
    in respiration 57

Paleozoic Era 156
pandas 162, 163
Pangaea 150
parental generation (P generation) 81
passive transport 43
pedigree 111, 117, 118
Pekingese 171
percent, calculating 89
Permian Period 157
petrified fossils 152

phenotype 92, 112
    for height 114
    mutations affecting 106
phosphates 67
photosynthesis 49, 50–54
    comparing respiration and 58, 60
    defined 51
    equation for 53
    life and 54
    storing energy during 56
    two-stage process 51–52
pigments 52, 53
pistil 81
plant cells 20
    cell wall of 24, 26
    cytokinesis in 66
    structure of 26
plants
    cloning 128
    fossil record of 155
    fossils of 151
    genetic engineering in 130
    photosynthesis in 49, 50–54
    pigments in 52
    selective breeding of 126, 127
pollen 81
pores
    in cell membrane 25
    in nuclear membrane 25
posing questions 178
potassium-40, half-life of 154
Precambrian Time 155, 156–157
predicting, skill of 174
preserved remains, fossils as 152–153
probability 88
    of genetic disorders 123, 124–125
    genetics and 88–95
    Mendel and 90, 91
    predicting 91
    principles of 89
    Punnett squares 90–91, 93, 98
problem solving, skill of 181
prophase 65
proteins 35
    as building blocks of cells 12
    produced in genetically engineered bacteria 130
    ribosomes and production of 29
    structure of 35, 164
    transport 43
protein synthesis 102–105
    role of RNA in 103
    translating genetic code in 103
punctuated equilibria, theory of 158
Punnett square 90–91, 93, 98
    for red-green colorblindness 117
    for sex 115
    for widow's peaks 112, 113
purebred 81

Quaternary Period 157

radiation, treating cancer with 72
radioactive elements 154
Rancho La Brea tar pits 155

Acknowledgments

Illustration

Robert Fuller: 140–141
GeoSystems Global Corporation: 149, 170–171
Keith Kasnot: 26, 27, 28, 29, 63
Martucci Design: 66, 184, 185, 186
Matt Mayerchak: 46, 76, 136, 166, 182, 183,
Morgan Cain & Associates: 12–13, 20, 21, 33, 41, 43, 57, 64–65, 67, 68, 99, 102–103, 104–105, 154, 176, 177
J/B Woolsey Associates: 47, 53, 72–73, 87, 91, 93, 98, 113, 115, 118, 129, 156–157, 158, 160, 163, 180

Photography

Photo Research by Sharon Donahue
Cover image Tom Pantages/Phototake

Nature of Science
Page 10,11, Courtesy of Lydia Villa-Komaroff; **12t**, Biophoto Associates/ Science Source/Photo Researchers; **12b**, Howard Sochurek/The Stock Market; **13**, Will & Deni McIntyre/Photo Researchers.

Chapter 1
Pages 14–15, Julie Habel/Westlight; **16t**, Richard Haynes; **16bl**, Joseph Nettis/Photo Researchers; **16br**, John Coletti/Stock Boston; **17**, **18t**The Granger Collection, NY; **18b**, Corbis-Bettmann; **19t**, H.R. Bramaz/Peter Arnold; **19bl**, Corbis-Bettmann; **19br**, Lawrence Migdale/Stock Boston; **20**, Anup Shah/Masterfile; **22**, CNRI/Science Photo Library/Photo Researchers; **23t**, Runk/Schoenberger/Grant Heilman Photography; **23b**, Doug Wilson/Westlight; **24t**, M. Abbey/Visuals Unlimited; **24b**, Runk/Schoenberger/Grant Heilman Photography; **25**, Dr. Dennis Kunkel/Phototake; **28**, Bill Longcore/Photo Researchers; **29**, K.G. Murtis/Visuals Unlimited; **30**, A.B. Dowsett/Photo Researchers; **31l**, Dr. David Scott/CNRI/Phototake; **31r**, Dr. Dennis Kunkel/Phototake; **32**, Runk/Schoenberger/Grant Heilman Photography; **33**, Russ Lappa; **34**, Okapia-Frankfurt/Photo Researchers; **34 inset**, Andrew Syred/ Science Photo Library/Photo Researchers; **35**, Gary Bell/Masterfile; **36t**, Barry L. Runk/Grant Heilman Photography & Michael Mahovlich/Masterfile; **36l**, Lou Lainey; **36r** Barry L. Runk/Grant Heilman Photography; **36 inset**, Michael Mahovlich/ Masterfile; **37**, Hans Blohm/Masterfile; **38**, James Holmes/Farmer Giles Foods/ Science Photo Library/ Photo Researchers; **40**, NASA; **42l**, Stanley Flegler/Visuals Unlimited; **42m,r**, David M. Phillips/Visuals Unlimited; **44**, M. Abbey/Visuals Unlimited; **45**, CNRI/Science Photo Library/Photo Researchers.

Chapter 2
Pages 48–49, Carr Clifton/Minden Pictures; **50t**, Russ Lappa; **50b**, Paul Barton/The Stock Market; **51r**, Cosmo Condina; **51 inset**, Biophoto Associates/Photo Researchers; **52t**, Russ Lappa; **52bl**, **br** , Dr. Jeremy Burgess/Science Photo Library/Photo Researchers; **54t**, Frans Lanting/Minden Pictures; **54b**, Tom J. Ulrich/Visuals Unlimited; **55**, William Johnson/Stock Boston; **56l**, Stephen Dalton/Photo Researchers; **56r**, Phil Dotson/ Photo Researchers; **58**, Mark Newman/Visuals Unlimited; **59**, Terje Rakke/The Image Bank; **61t**, David Scharf/Peter Arnold; **61b**, Larry Lefever/Grant Heilman Photography; **62**, Art Wolfe/TSI; **63**, Biophoto Associates/Science Source/Photo Researchers; **64–65 all**, M. Abbey/Photo Researchers; **69**, Robert Knauft/Biology Media; **70t**, Richard Haynes; **70b**, Myrleen Ferguson/Photo Edit; **71**, National Cancer Institute/Science Photo Library/Photo Researchers; **74**, Joseph Sohm/Stock Boston; **75**, Frans Lanting/Minden Pictures.

Chapter 3
Pages 78–79, Ron Kimball; **80t**, Jane Burton/Bruce Coleman; **80b**, Corbis-Bettmann; **81**, Barry Runk/Grant Heilman Photography; **84 both**, Meinrad Faltner/The Stock Market; **85**, Inga Spence/The Picture Cube; **88-89**, Image Stop/Phototake; **92**, Hans Reinhard/Bruce Coleman; **95**, Richard Haynes; **96l**, David M. Phillips/Photo Researchers; **96r**, University "La Sapienza," Rome/Science Photo Library/Photo Researchers; **97l**, Jonathan D. Speer/Visuals Unlimited; **97r**, M. Abbey/Photo Researchers; **101**, AP/Wide World Photos; **106**, William E. Ferguson; **107t**, Jane Burton/Bruce Coleman; **107b**, Hans Reinhard/Bruce Coleman.

Chapter 4
Pages 110–111, Herb Snitzer/Stock Boston; **112**, Richard Haynes; **114**, Camille Tokerud/TSI; **115t**,**b**, Biophoto Associates/Science Source/Photo Researchers; **116**, Andrew McClenaghan/Science Photo Library/Photo Researchers; **118**, Superstock; **119t**, CNRI/Science Photo Library/Photo Researchers; **119b**, Lawrence Migdale/TSI; **120t**, Simon Fraser/RVI, Newcastle-upon-TYNE/Science Photo Library/Photo Researchers; **120b**, Stanley Flegler/Visuals Unlimited; **121**, Corbis-Bettmann; **122l**, CNRI/Science Photo Library/Photo Researchers; **122r**, Mugshots/The Stock Market; **123**, Will and Deni McIntyre/Photo Researchers Inc.; **124**, Richard Haynes; **126**, AP/Wide World Photos; **127**, Tim Barnwell/Stock Boston; **128**, Patricia J. Bruno/ Positive Images; **129**, LeLand Bobbe/TSI; **130**, Gary Wagner/Stock Boston; **131**, AP/Wide World Photos; **132**, U.S. Department of Energy/Human Genome Management Information System, Oak Ridge National Laboratory; **133**, David Parker/Science Photo Library/Photo Researchers; **134**, Michael Newman/PhotoEdit; **135**, Lawrence Migdale/TSI.

Chapter 5
Pages 138–139, Bill Varie/Westlight; **140t**, Portrait by George Richmond/Down House, Downe/The Bridgeman Art Library; **140b**, Corbis-Bettmann; **141t,b**, Tui De Roy/Minden Pictures; **141m**, Frans Lanting/Minden Pictures; **142l**, Zig Leszczynski/ Animals Animals; **142r**, Tui De Roy/Minden Pictures; **143**, Dr. Jeremy Burgess/ Science Photo Library/Photo Researchers; **144**, Mitsuaki Iwago/Minden Pictures; **145**, Jeff Gnass Photography/The Stock Market; **147**, Richard Haynes; **148l,r**, Breck P. Kent; **149l,r**, Pat & Tom Leeson/Photo Researchers; **150t**, John Cancalosi/Tom Stack & Associates; **150b**, Tom McHugh/Photo Researchers; **151t**, James L. Amos/Photo Researchers; **151b** Sinclair Stammers/Science Photo Library/Photo Researchers; **155**, Robert Landau/Westlight; **159**, Richard Haynes; **161l**, Keith Gillett/Animals Animals; **161m**, George Whiteley/Photo Researchers; **161r**, David Spears Ltd./ Science Photo Library/Photo Researchers; **162l**, Gary Milburn/Tom Stack & Associates; **162r**, Daryl Balfour/TSI; **165**, Tui De Roy/Minden Pictures.

Interdisciplinary Exploration
Page 168t, Tim Fitzharris/Minden Pictures; **168b**, Bridgeman Art Library; **169**, Ron Kimball; **170tr**, Charles Philip/Westlight; **170b**, Jack Daniels/TSI; **170tl**, **ml**, **mr**, Corel Corp.; **170ml**, C. Jeanne White/Photo Researchers; **171 all others**, Corel Corp.; **172t**, Peter Cade/TSI; **172b**, AP/ Wide World Photos; **172–173**, Nick Meers/ Panoramic Images.

Skills Handbook
Page 174, Mike Moreland/Photo Network; **175t**, Foodpix; **175m**, Richard Haynes; **175b**, Russ Lappa; **178**, Richard Haynes; **180**, Ron Kimball; **181**, Renee Lynn/Photo Researchers.

Appendix B
Page 190, Russ Lappa; **191 both**, Russ Lappa.